APPLE® II USER'S GUIDE

THIRD EDITION

By
Lon Poole
with
Martin McNiff
and
Steven Cook

Osborne **McGraw-Hill**
Berkeley, California

APPLE® II USER'S GUIDE

ASIAN EDITION

FIRST IMPRESSION MARCH 1986

ISBN 0-07-099152-9

Printed and Bound by KIN KEONG PRINTING CO. PTE. LTD. – Republic of Singapore

Contents

Preface

In the two years since I last revised this book, Apple has made some important changes to the Apple II computer, introduced some new accessories for it, and switched to a new operating system program. The Apple IIc was introduced in April 1984, and is the subject of another book, *Apple IIc User's Guide*. The improvements built into it were added to the Apple IIe about a year later and are covered in this book.

The mouse and Imagewriter printer, both made popular by the Apple Macintosh computer, now can also be used on an Apple II. This edition shows how to use them in BASIC programs.

This book also now describes both the ProDOS and DOS 3.3 operating systems. ProDOS replaced DOS 3.3 in January 1984 as the preferred operating system for BASIC programming on the Apple II.

In addition to covering the new Apple II developments, I have once again reorganized parts of the book. Disk and cassette commands now appear in their own chapter. The examples in the screen output and keyboard entry chapter have been reworked to incorporate more up-to-date programming methods.

All the authors thank Robert Thomson, who did the original research for much of the material now covered in Appendix A.

I wish to thank my wife Karin for her unflagging support and encouragement.

L. P.

Introduction

The *Apple II User's Guide, Third Edition* is your guide to the Apple II computer. It describes the Apple II itself along with the common accessories such as disk drives and printers. For those who aren't interested in programming the computer themselves, the book explains how to use programs that can be bought off the shelf. For those who do want to learn how to write their own programs, the book provides detailed lessons with lots of examples.

This book covers all models of the Apple II except the Apple IIc, which is covered in the companion *Apple IIc User's Guide*. This book puts special emphasis on the Apple IIe, both in the original version first delivered in 1983, and in the enhanced version first delivered in 1985. If you have an Apple II Plus or a standard Apple II, much of the material here still applies, although the part that pertains strictly to the Apple IIe will be superfluous.

The first four chapters answer two important questions: "What is an Apple II personal computer?" and "How do you make it work?" Chapter 1 tells you what the various components of the Apple II are and what they do. Chapter 2 explains how to get a program started and how to use the printer. Chapters 3 and 4 tell you how to get the most from disks. The information in the first four chapters prepares you to use any of the ready-to-run programs that are widely available for word processing, design, planning, information management, problem solving, financial analysis, bookkeeping, education, and entertainment.

The next nine chapters teach you how to write your own programs using the BASIC programming language. Chapter 5 begins with a tutorial approach to the fundamentals of both versions of BASIC available on the Apple II, Applesoft and Integer BASIC. Chapter 6 explains how to use disks and cassettes for storing the programs you write, whether you use the ProDOS operating system or the DOS 3.3 operating system.

Chapter 7 discusses the role that character strings and numbers play in programs. It explains how to store them in variables and arrays, manipulate them with expressions and functions, enter them from the keyboard, and display them on the screen.

In Chapter 8, you learn how to control the order in which program instructions are executed. Topics include branching, loops, subroutines, decision-making, and halting and resuming execution. You'll also learn how to access the Apple II memory directly and thereby control some special Apple II features.

Chapter 9 explains how to control where things appear and what they look like on the display screen. The chapter discusses how a carefully designed screen display can keep keyboard entry errors down. You'll also learn how to program the mouse.

Chapter 10 tells you how to switch output from the display screen to the printer and how to format printed output. The chapter explains how you can activate the alternate type styles and other features available on many printers.

In Chapter 11, you learn how to store and retrieve data on disk files. The chapter explains file structure and the different methods of accessing files. It illustrates these with two versions of a working mailing-list program.

Chapter 12 covers graphics. You'll learn about graphics modes, color selection, point plotting, line drawing, circle drawing, shape drawing, and shape manipulation. Program examples show how to draw scatter graphs, line graphs, bar graphs, pie charts, and graphics designs.

Chapter 13 explains how to program the built-in speaker to produce sounds and play music. It includes a program that plays a minuet by J.S. Bach and another program that lets you compose your own music.

The last chapter in the book, Chapter 14, tells you how to use the built-in Machine Language Monitor program to directly view and change the contents of memory locations. It also describes how to use the Mini-Assembler to write short programs in assembly language.

Appendix A contains a complete description of every command, statement, and function available in both versions of BASIC and in both operating systems. Along with appendixes B through H, it will serve as a handy reference once you know how to program in BASIC on the Apple II.

Presenting The Apple II 1

A complete Apple II computer system includes several separate pieces of equipment. Figure 1-1 shows a typical system, centered around an Apple IIe. Your system may not look exactly like the one pictured, because system components come from a long list of optional equipment. But there are three components that every system has in common: the Apple II computer itself, the built-in keyboard, and a television or monitor. Let's take a closer look at each of these and at some of the more common pieces of optional equipment. This chapter does not explain how to hook up any of these components to the Apple II. For complete installation instructions, refer to the owner's manual supplied with each individual piece of equipment.

There are five models of the Apple II computer. The standard Apple II, produced from 1977 to 1979, looks identical to the Apple II Plus, produced from 1979 to 1983 (refer to Figure 1-2). The Apple II Plus has a redefined key (the RESET key, described in Chapter 2) and some additional features that were once available only as add-on accessories. The Apple IIe, which was introduced in 1983, is outwardly similar to the earlier Apple II models (see Figure 1-3). The Apple IIe has an improved keyboard, a redesigned back panel, and even more built-in features that were previously available only as add-on accessories. The Apple IIc (shown in Figure 1-4), which first appeared in 1984, has a new look but works very much like a specially equipped Apple IIe. The enhanced Apple IIe, introduced in 1985, adds to the IIe some features formerly available only on the IIc. For a comparison of Apple II models, see Appendix D.

This book covers the standard Apple II, the Apple II Plus, and

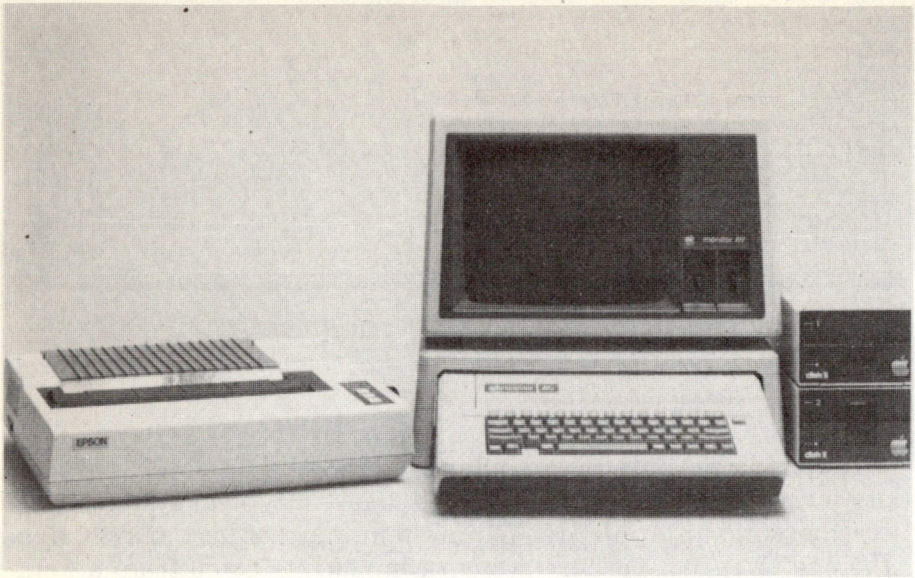

Figure 1-1. A typical Apple II computer system

Figure 1-2. The Apple II and Apple II Plus

Figure 1-3. The Apple IIe

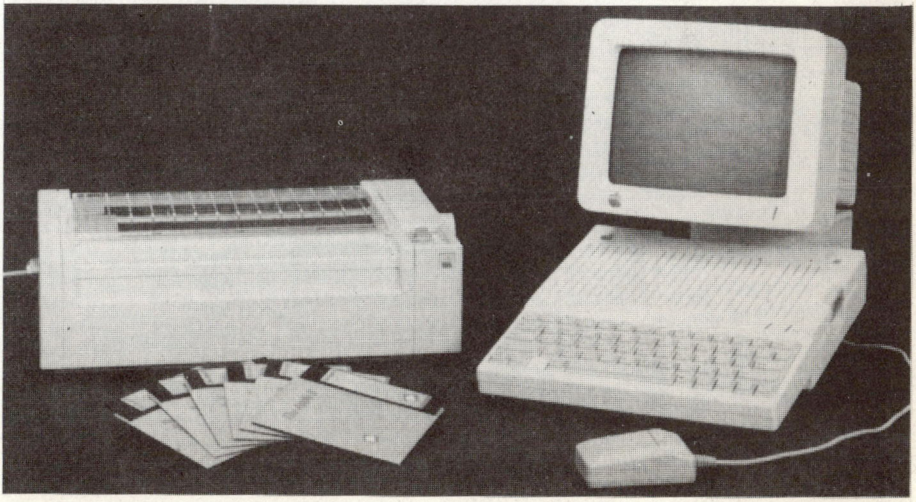

Figure 1-4. The Apple IIc

especially the Apple IIe (both original and enhanced models). It refers to all these models collectively as the Apple II, unless there is a reason to distinguish among them. The Apple IIc model is covered in a separate book, the *Apple IIc User's Guide* by Lon Poole (Berkeley: Osborne/McGraw-Hill, 1984).

THE APPLE II CONSOLE

The Apple II console houses the part of the computer that controls the rest of the system—under your guidance, of course. Lurking behind the keyboard are the main Apple II memory banks, the microprocessor, the connection points for all the accessory components, and much more. You would expect the Apple II to be a complex device, and one look inside the console confirms that it is (refer to Figure 1-5).

The exact interior arrangement of any particular Apple II depends on which model it is and which options are installed. The basic layout will be the same: a large flat circuit board with dozens of small black *integrated circuits* (also called *ICs* or *chips*)

Figure 1-5. Inside the Apple IIe

in orderly rows and some small circuit boards mounted vertically at the back of the main circuit board. The number of chips and the number and placement of the vertical circuit boards vary from one Apple II system to the next.

Memory

Computer memory is typically measured in units called *bytes.* One byte of computer memory—one memory cell—can hold one character, so you can think of bytes as characters, although computer memory also stores other information, including numeric values and programs. Because of certain facts about computer circuitry architecture, memory capacity is expressed as a multiple of 1024 bytes. That much memory is called one *kilobyte* (abbreviated *1K*). An Apple II has anywhere from 4K (4096 bytes) to 128K (131,072 bytes) of memory; the Apple IIe has at least 64K (65,532 bytes) of memory.

The Apple II actually has two kinds of memory. One is called *read-only memory (ROM).* The contents of ROM never change, even when you turn the computer's power off. ROM contains the programs that give the Apple II its unique identity and enable it to understand and respond appropriately to the commands you type in at the keyboard. The other kind of memory is called *read/write memory* (also called *random-access memory* or *RAM*). The contents of read/write memory do change. In fact, the program in read/write memory determines what task the Apple II is currently performing. Read/write memory works only as long as the power remains on. As soon as you turn the Apple II off, everything disappears from read/write memory.

Accessory Cards

At the back of the main Apple II circuit board are seven sockets, called *expansion slots,* into which you can plug additional electronic circuit cards, called *accessory cards* or *interface cards* (see Figure 1-6). The Apple IIe has an eighth expansion slot located near the center of the main circuit board, away from the standard seven slots. Apple II and Apple II Plus models have an eighth slot in the back alongside the other seven.

Some accessory cards let you use disk drives, printers, special video monitors, or other external equipment. Others add memory

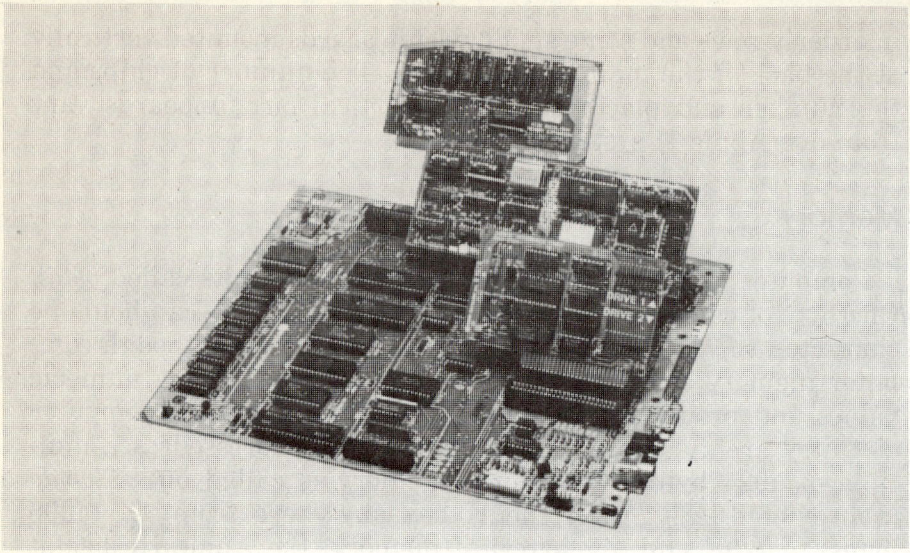

Figure 1-6. Some accessory cards and the expansion slots

or increase the number of characters allowed on a single display screen line. Most accessory cards can be installed in any of the seven expansion slots, but there is an established convention for locating some of the more common cards. Table 1-1 has the details.

THE KEYBOARD

You will probably use the keyboard more than any other part of your Apple II. The keyboard is the chief means of entering information and instructions into the computer.

To accommodate those who touch-type, the Apple II keyboard is arranged the same as a standard typewriter keyboard, although some of the punctuation and symbols may be in different locations. In fact, the Apple IIe keyboard places punctuation symbols in different locations from earlier models.

The keyboard also has some keys you won't find on a typewriter. These include the ESC, TAB, CONTROL (or CTRL), SHIFT LOCK,

Table 1-1. Accessory Card/Expansion Slot Conventions

Accessory card[a]	Slot[b]	Purpose
Super Serial	1	Printer
Super Serial	3	Communications
Parallel Interface	1 or 2	Printer; general use
80-column text[c]	A	Longer display lines
80-column plus memory[c]	A	Longer display lines; memory expansion
Language system[d]	0	Memory and programming language expansion
Integer BASIC firmware	0	BASIC interpreter
Applesoft firmware[d]	0	BASIC interpreter
Disk II controller	6	First pair of Disk II drives
Disk II controller	5	Second pair of Disk II drives
Disk II controller	4	Third pair of Disk II drives
Graphics Tablet controller	7	Graphics tablet

[a] Cards listed are from Apple Computer, Inc. Others are available.
[b] Slots are numbered 0 at the left to 7 at the right. Slot A is the unmarked Apple IIe auxiliary slot.
[c] Only for the Apple IIe.
[d] Built into the Apple IIe.

DELETE, RESET, RETURN, OPEN APPLE, SOLID APPLE, ←, →, ↓, and ↑ keys. The Apple IIe keyboard has all of these keys, but earlier models have only some of them. Earlier models also have a REPT key, which the Apple IIe does not have or need. Chapter 2 describes the use of these keys.

THE DISPLAY SCREEN

The Apple II "speaks" to you with written words and pictures displayed on the screen. The screen echoes your typing so you can see if it is correct, and the screen displays the computer's responses to what you type. The screen can show up to 24 lines of text, and the lines can have a maximum width of either 40 or 80 characters (including blank spaces). Both 40- and 80-character lines measure the same length; they reach all the way across the screen. But the characters on a 40-character line are twice as wide as the characters on an 80-character line. Naturally, the larger characters are easier to read.

The Apple II can use any one of several components as a display screen. The Apple Monitor IIe and Monitor ///, for example, display text and graphics (pictures) in green on a black background. Video monitors manufactured by other companies also work with the Apple II. Some of them display white letters, some display green letters, and others display orange letters. Because single-color, or monochrome, monitors typically display sharp, clear images, they are the best choice for displaying text on 80-character lines. Figure 1-7 shows how to attach a monochrome monitor to the Apple II console.

The Apple II can also display text and graphics in color, but this requires a different type of display screen. A television set handles most color graphics well and is adequate for the larger characters of 40-character text lines. Connecting the Apple II to a TV set requires a special part, called an *RF modulator*, that converts the computer's video signal to one the television can tune in. One kind of RF modulator has two pieces. There is a switch

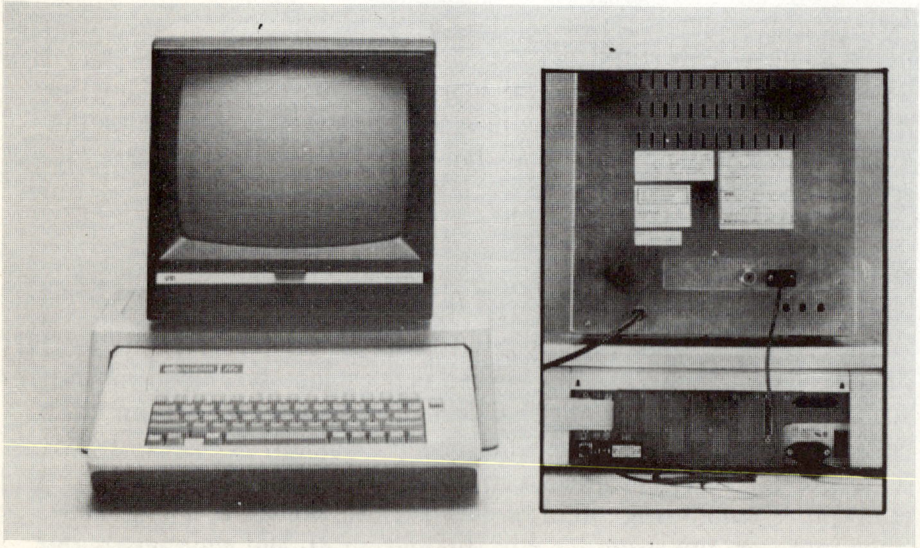

Figure 1-7. Attaching a monochrome or composite monitor

box that attaches to the TV antenna terminal and allows you to switch the reception between the Apple II and your regular TV antenna or cable. A cable runs from the switch box to a small converter box that attaches inside the Apple II. Another kind of RF modulator combines the switch and the converter in a single box that hangs from the TV antenna terminal. A cable connects it directly to the back of the Apple II. The second kind of RF modulator also uses a small power transformer that plugs into a wall socket. Figure 1-8 shows how to connect a television to the Apple II.

Because home television sets are engineered for broadcast shows and not computers, they cannot match the Apple II's optical resolution. Even the best sets lose detail and are inadequate for 80-character text lines or critical graphics displays. Fortunately, high-quality color monitors are available.

There are two types of color monitors, and they differ in price and picture quality. The less expensive ones, called *composite monitors,* offer better optical resolution than the best home TV

Figure 1-8. Attaching a television set

sets. They plug directly into the back of the Apple II without an RF modulator, just like a monochrome monitor.

The more expensive color monitors, called *RGB monitors*, approach the resolution of monochrome monitors. An RGB (Red-Green-Blue) monitor is the choice for those who must have the sharpest color display and must read the small characters on an 80-character text line. RGB monitors require a special adapter that plugs in between the Apple II and the monitor, as shown in Figure 1-9.

DISKS AND DISK DRIVES

A disk is an auxiliary storage device, a kind of memory extension. Even with 128K of memory in an Apple IIe, the computer cannot hold all the information it will be working with. Fortunately, anything in memory can be recorded on a disk. The information saved on disk can later be put back into memory so the computer can work with it directly. Disk drives come in all shapes and sizes with different storage capacities.

Figure 1-9. Attaching an RGB monitor

The entire disk setup consists of three parts: a disk controller card, a disk drive, and several disks (see Figure 1-10). The controller card fits in one of the expansion slots inside the Apple II and coordinates the transfer of information between memory and the disk drive. The drive is a machine that reads and writes information on a disk using technology similar to sound or video tape recording. The disk itself is a platter that spins inside the drive and stores information magnetically.

Diskettes

The Apple Disk II and Duodisk drives both use removable flexible disks, sometimes called *diskettes* or *floppy disks*, that measure 5 1/4 inches across. Most other disk drives used on Apple II computers also use removable 5 1/4-inch disks. Each removable disk has a protective plastic jacket enclosing a round piece of flexible plastic that is coated with a magnetic film.

The disk fits into a slot in the front of the Disk II or Duodisk.

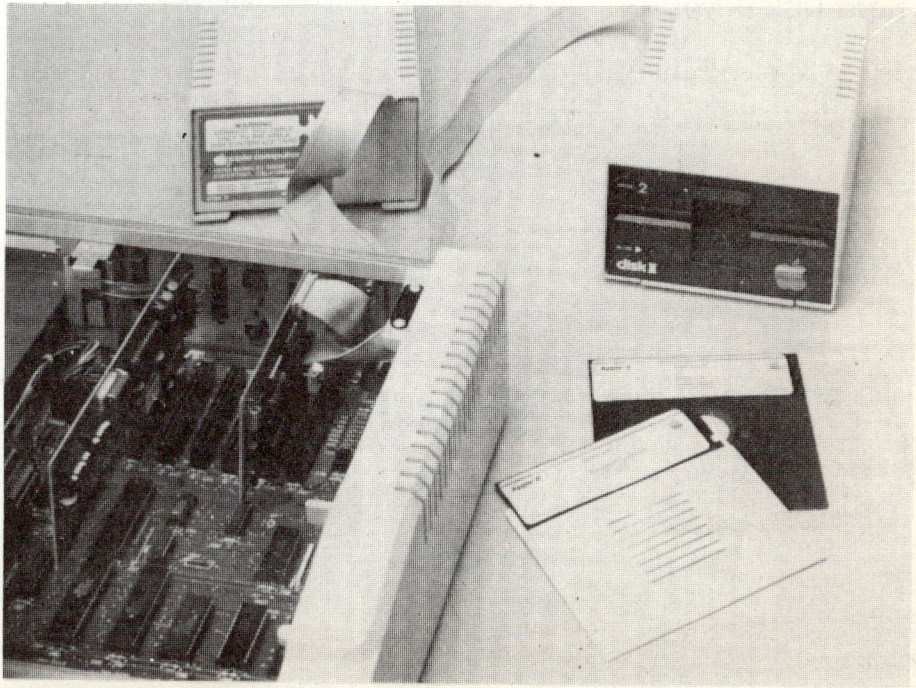

Figure 1-10. Disk II drives, controller cards, and disks

The drive grips the flexible plastic disk through the center hole and spins it inside the jacket. Through the windows cut out of the protective jacket, the drive records and retrieves information as magnetic variations in the coating of the disk.

The Disk II and Duodisk drives can store 140K bytes (143,360 characters) of information on each disk. Because the disk is removable, you can have many disks, each with different information recorded on it. However, a single Disk II drive holds only one disk at a time; a Duodisk drive holds two disks at once. You can attach up to six Disk II drives, three Duodisk drives, or an equivalent combination to one Apple II computer. (The recommended maximum is four Disk II drives, two Duodisk drives, or an equivalent combination.) The additional drives allow the computer to access more disks at once.

You can prevent the drive from writing on a disk. All you do is cover the notch on the side of the disk with a piece of opaque tape or with a small label made especially for this purpose, as shown in Figure 1-11.

Hard Disk Drives

The Apple Profile disk drive is called a *hard disk drive* because its built-in disks are rigid, not flexible. The disks inside a Profile

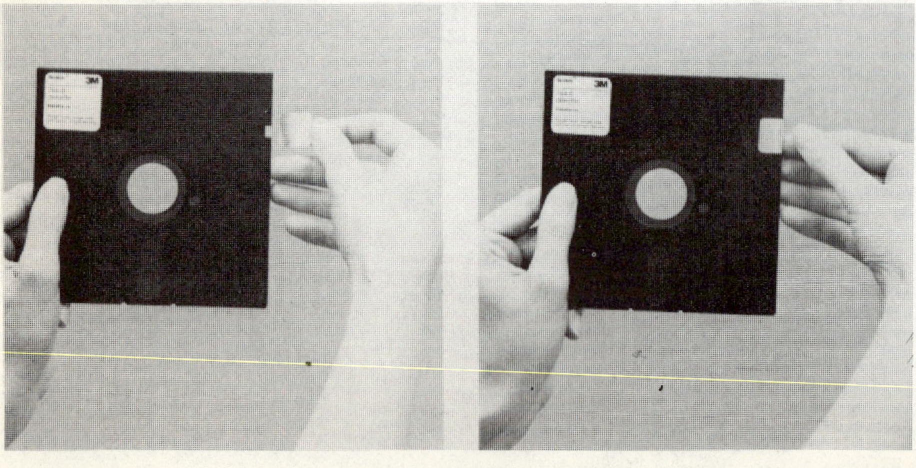

Figure 1-11. Write-protecting a 5¼-inch diskette

drive are not removable because the drive operates at very close tolerances and must be sealed against dust and smoke. The current model Profile uses two built-in disk platters to store 10 megabytes of information (one megabyte is 1024 kilobytes, or 1,048,576 bytes). Thus a single Profile drive can store more on its built-in disks than a Disk II or Duodisk could store on 70 removable diskettes. Figure 1-12 shows a Profile.

CASSETTE RECORDER

The Apple II can use an ordinary cassette tape recorder as a storage device. Tape recorders connect directly to the back of the Apple II (refer to Figure 1-13).

Write-Protecting Cassettes

Each cassette has two notches in the rear edge (see Figure 1-14). When the notches are uncovered, a cassette recorder can sense

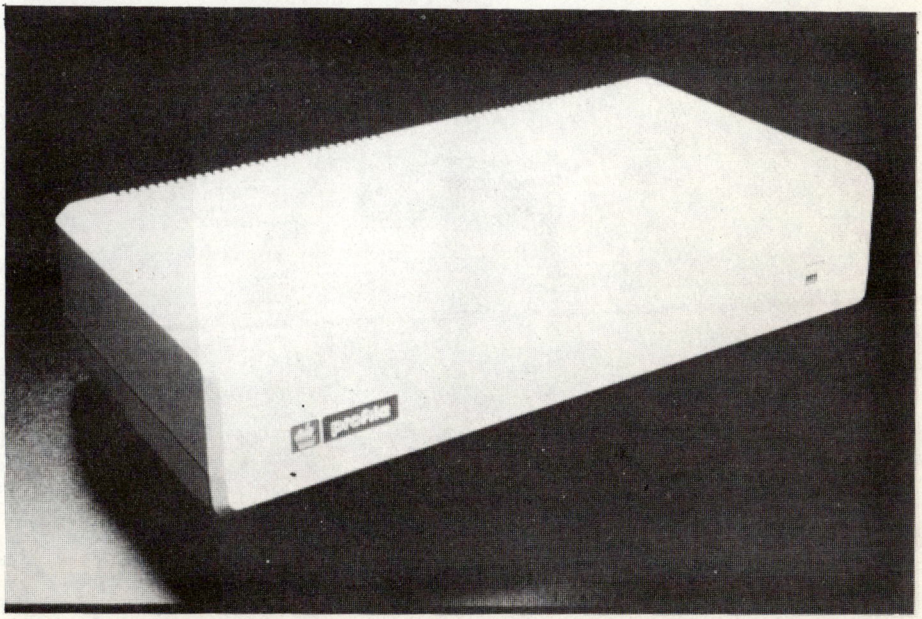

Figure 1-12. The Profile disk drive

Figure 1-13. Attaching a cassette recorder

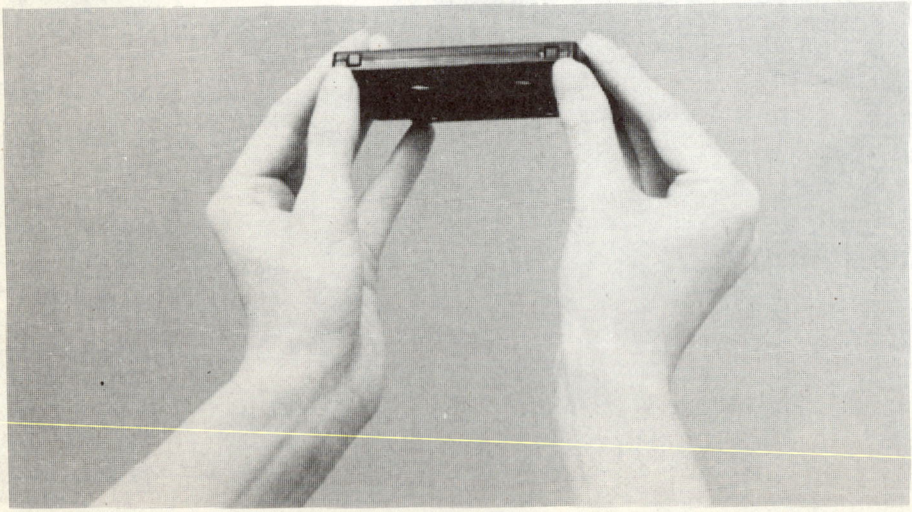

Figure 1-14. Cassette write-protect notches

the holes and will not record on the cassette. New blank cassettes have tabs covering the holes so information can be recorded on the tape. You can protect important programs by knocking out the correct tab and exposing the hole. Later, if you want to record over a protected tape, simply cover the holes with tape.

Each cassette has two sides. One notch protects one side, while the other notch protects the other side. To determine which tab to remove, hold the cassette so that the exposed tape is toward you and the side you wish to protect is facing up. Remove the tab on the left-hand side to prevent recording over the side facing up.

PRINTERS

With a printer, the Apple II can produce letters, reports, graphics, and more. There are printers of every size, price, and description as Figure 1-15 illustrates. Some will print correspondence that looks just as good as anything a typewriter can produce. Others can print graphics characters; a few can even print in color. Each printer provides a different combination of speed, print quality, number of character sets, types of paper that can be used, and other features.

Parallel and Serial Communications

The two most popular methods for communications between computers and printers are called *parallel* and *serial*. The differences between them are technical and unimportant here. The Apple II can use either method, but serial communications are slightly more common.

A printer connects to the Apple II via an accessory card (see Figure 1-16). Printers that use parallel communications require the Apple II Parallel Interface Card or its equivalent. Printers that use serial communications require the Apple II Super Serial Card or its equivalent.

When printing, the Apple II stands idle much of the time because its potential output rate far exceeds the print speed of even the fastest printer. You can plug in a device between the Apple II and the printer to act as a reservoir for characters waiting to be printed. Called a *printer buffer* or *print spooler*, this device contains read/write memory like that found inside the

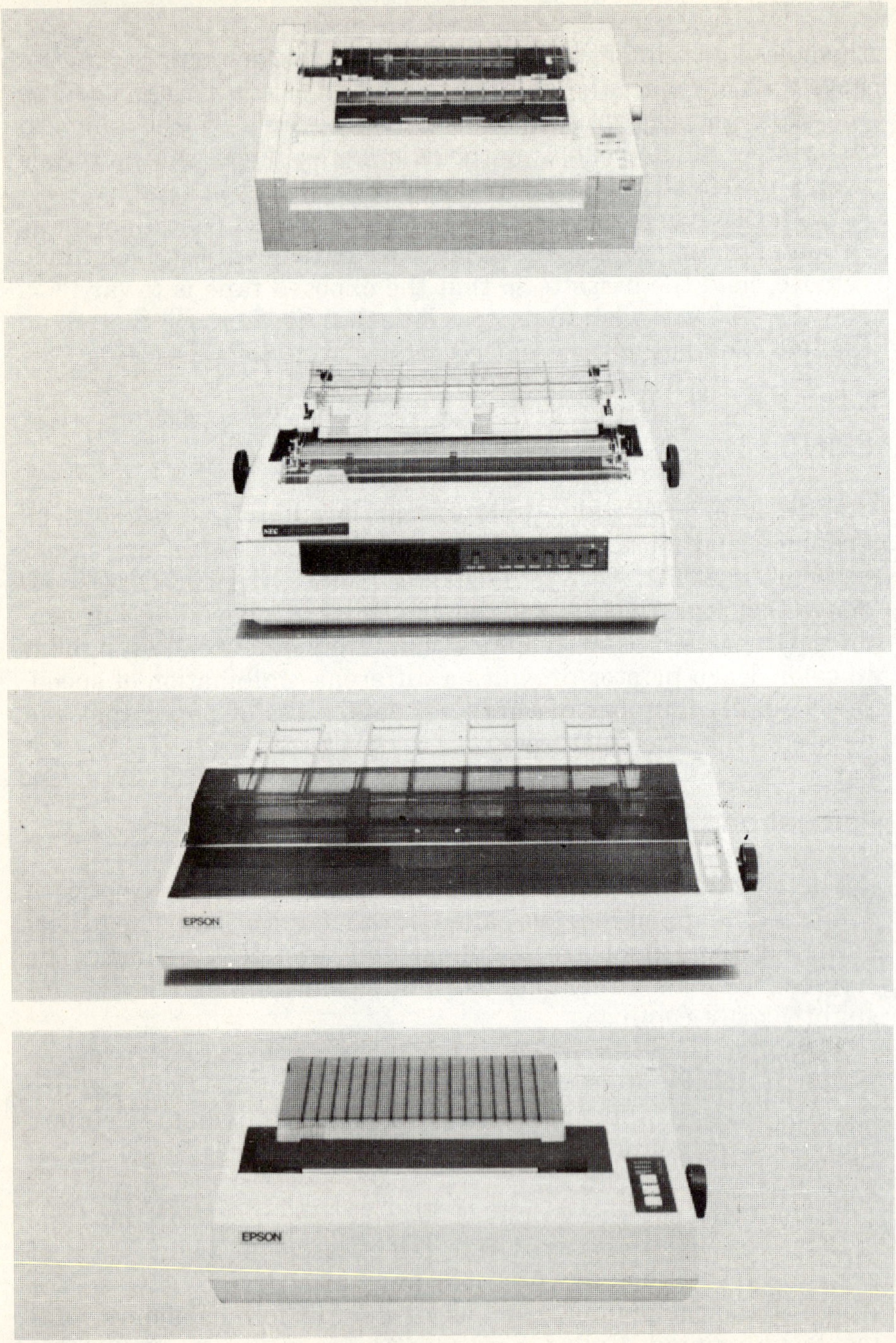

Figure 1-15. Some printers

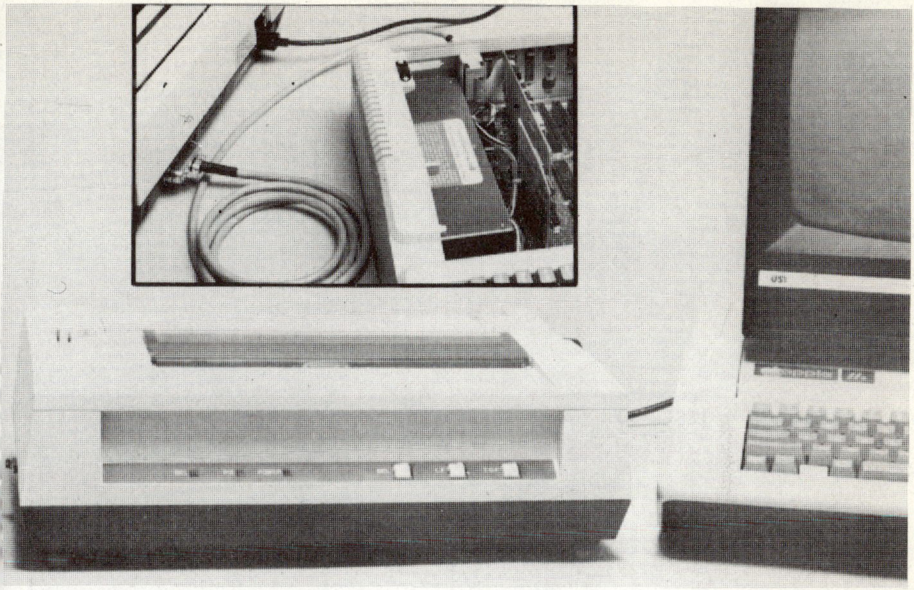

Figure 1-16. Attaching a printer

Apple II, but dedicated to storing information destined for the printer. The printer buffer accepts information at a fast rate, stores it, and gradually releases it as the printer is ready.

MODEMS

A *modem* is a device that allows a computer to communicate over telephone lines with other computers. The word modem is a shortened form of the term *mo*dulator/*dem*odulator: a modem modulates information and demodulates sound. In other words, it converts information from the Apple II into sound patterns and sends the sounds over the telephone line. It also converts sound patterns received over the phone line from another modem-equipped computer into information for the Apple II.

You plug one cable from the modem into a serial communications card at the back of the Apple II, another cable into a telephone wall jack, a third cable into an electrical outlet, and

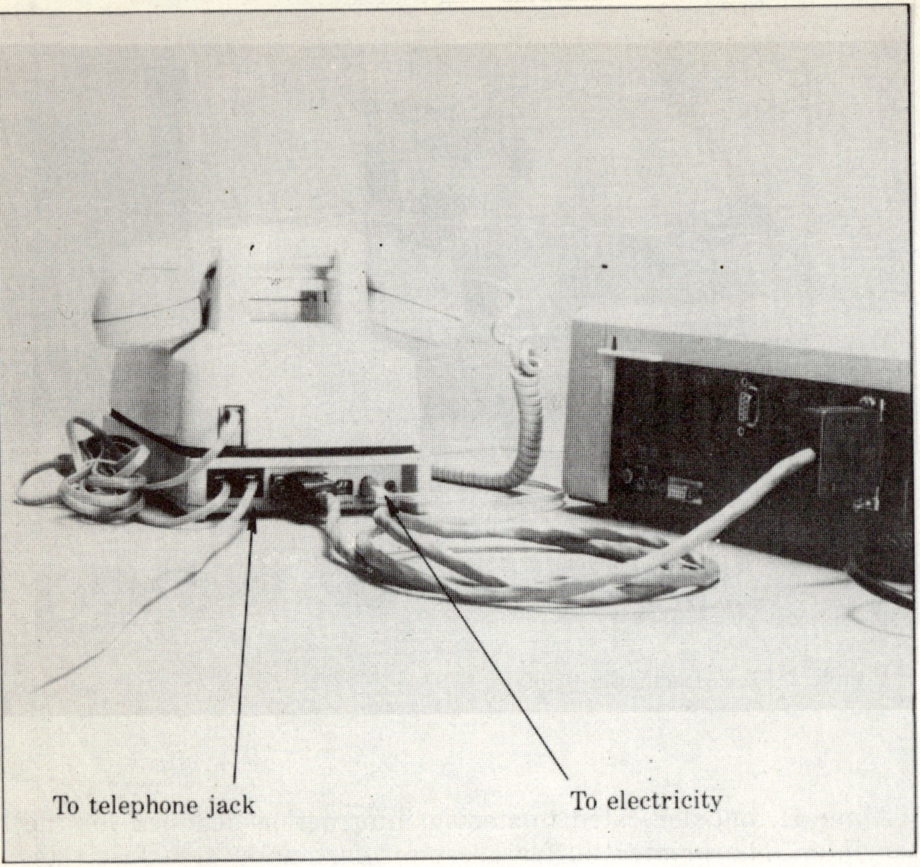

Figure 1-17. Attaching a modem

sometimes a fourth cable into a telephone (see Figure 1-17). Then, under your direction, the Apple II can dial a phone number and "talk to" another computer across town or around the world.

The computer on the other end of the line might be an Apple II, some other personal computer, or a huge computer belonging to an information service such as The Source or CompuServe. These information services offer electronic mail delivery, newspaper stories, airline flight schedules, games, stock market prices, sports scores, and more. Once you subscribe, you pay from $5 to $300 an hour (plus the cost of the telephone call) while you're connected to the service.

HAND-HELD CONTROLS

Mouse, *joystick*, and *paddle* hardly sound like the names of computer equipment, but they are. All are hand-held controls. A joystick or pair of paddles either plug into the back panel of an Apple IIe or attach inside an Apple II, Apple II Plus, or Apple IIe (Figure 1-18). The AppleMouse II plugs into its own accessory card that attaches inside the Apple II (Figure 1-19).

Joysticks and paddles are popular as game controls but are also useful for other applications. The mouse is most commonly used for selecting displayed information and choosing a command from a list of options on the screen. The mouse can reduce the amount of typing you have to do.

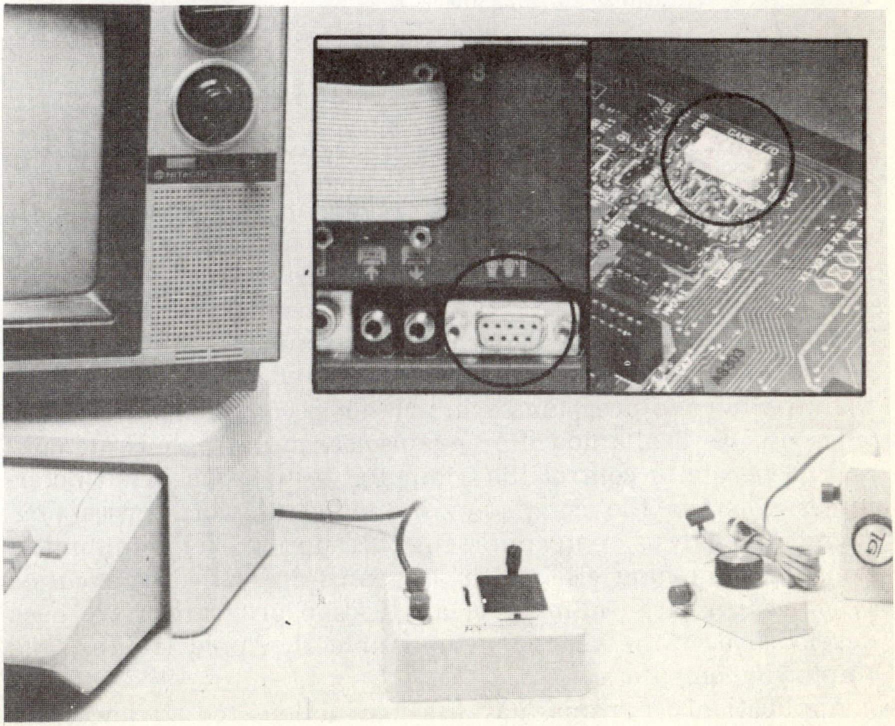

Figure 1-18. Attaching game controls

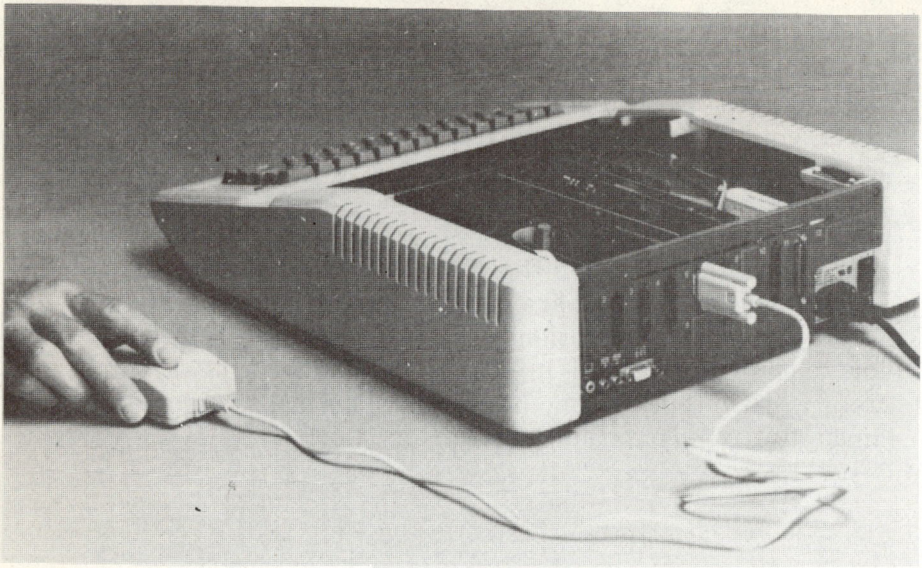

Figure 1-19. Attaching an AppleMouse II

SOFTWARE

An Apple II without a program is like an orchestra without a musical score: dormant. Any computer needs instructions to bring it to life, just as an orchestra needs sheet music. A program provides an orderly set of instructions that tell the computer how to do something. Programs are as important a part of the Apple II as its physical components. The term *software* refers to the repertoire of programs available for a computer.

Usually, several kinds of programs coexist in Apple II memory and cooperate to control the computer system. One kind determines whether the computer is applied to word processing, financial analysis, entertainment, accounting, telecommunications, or something else. Such programs are called *application programs.* A large number of application programs have been developed over the years for the Apple II, Apple II Plus, and Apple IIe computers.

Application programs may use instructions too advanced for the Apple II to understand without some help. In that case, a second kind of program translates the application program into instructions the Apple II understands. A *compiler* program prepares a translated version of an application program for subsequent use. Alternatively, an *interpreter* may translate an application program each time it is used. One interpreter for the BASIC programming language resides in part of the Apple II's read-only memory; others share read/write memory with the application program.

Application programs, compilers, and interpreters usually rely on the existence of another kind of program, called the *operating system*, to take care of fundamental communication with devices like the keyboard, display screen, disk drive, and printer. An application program can then delegate simple tasks—such as displaying each character of a message on the screen—without worrying about how they're done.

The principal operating system for the Apple II is called ProDOS. The Pascal operating system, which must be used with application programs written in the Pascal language, is also popular. Many of the application programs written for the Apple II, Apple II Plus, and Apple IIe computers use the original Apple operating system, called DOS 3.3 (Disk Operating System version 3.3) or its predecessor, DOS 3.2. Gradually, most of those application programs are being converted to use ProDOS.

Part of the programming needed by the BASIC interpreter and the operating system resides permanently in read-only memory. It is called the *Machine Language Monitor*. Chapter 14 describes the Machine Language Monitor in more detail.

Getting Started 2

You may never write a program yourself, but instead only use programs from the pool of software available for the Apple II. This chapter provides general instructions for starting up an existing program, but it does not replace the specific instructions that come with the program. There is no way this book could adequately explain the operating procedures for even the most popular programs, let alone all of the programs now available for the Apple II. Once started, however, a well-designed program displays enough specific instructions to get you going, and for details you can consult the program's manual or check with someone who already knows the program thoroughly.

STARTING THE APPLE II

Starting most Apple II systems requires turning on two power switches. If your Apple II has disk drives, you also need to put a disk into one of them. The program on the disk you insert is started automatically. If your Apple II has no disk drives, you must start a program from cassette tape instead. The following sections explain how to start up in more detail.

Switching On the Display Screen

If your Apple II uses a television set as a display screen, you must set it for computer reception and switch it on as shown in Figure 2-1. Locate the slide switch hanging from the TV antenna

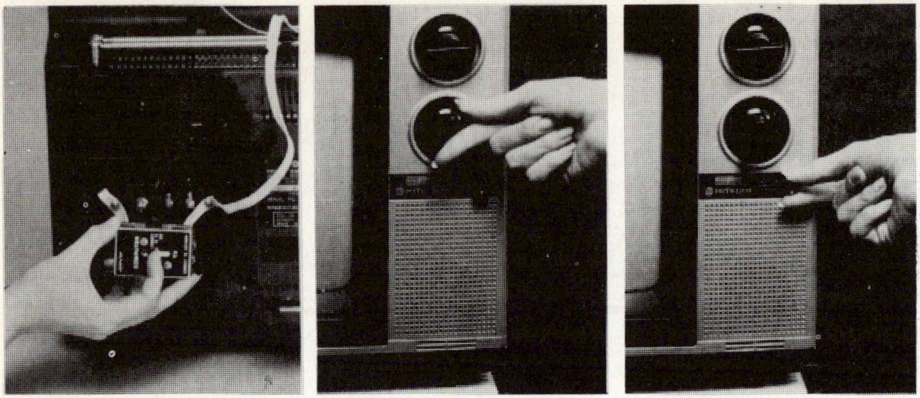

Figure 2-1. Setting a TV for computer reception

terminals and set it on the GAME or COMPUTER setting. Select the channel specified by the RF modulator instructions (usually channel 33). If you don't know which channel to use, ask someone else who uses the system or a dealer who sells the RF modulator. Switch on the TV and turn the volume all the way down. The Apple II uses only the television's picture, not its speaker.

A video monitor is even easier to use. There is no antenna switch to set or channel selector to tune. Just switch the monitor on, and if it has a volume control, turn it all the way down as Figure 2-2 illustrates.

Inserting a Start-Up Disk

Before starting an Apple II that has disk drives, you need to insert a program disk (see Figure 2-3). Program disks are also called *start-up disks* because you use them to start up the Apple II. Start-up disks always contain an operating system such as ProDOS and at least one application program. One start-up disk, the ProDOS User's Disk, comes with the Apple Disk II and Duodisk drives. It contains programs that help you organize disks that use the ProDOS operating system. Another start-up disk, the DOS 3.3 System Master disk, formerly came with Disk II drives and can now be purchased separately. You can purchase a wide variety of programs on other start-up disks.

The start-up disk goes into the drive whose cable is attached to slot 6 inside the Apple II console. If there are two drives attached

Figure 2-2. Switching on a video monitor

to that accessory card, use the one attached to the accessory card socket labeled *Drive 1.*

In order to insert a disk in the drive, you must open the disk drive door by lifting the flap in the center of the drive. If there is

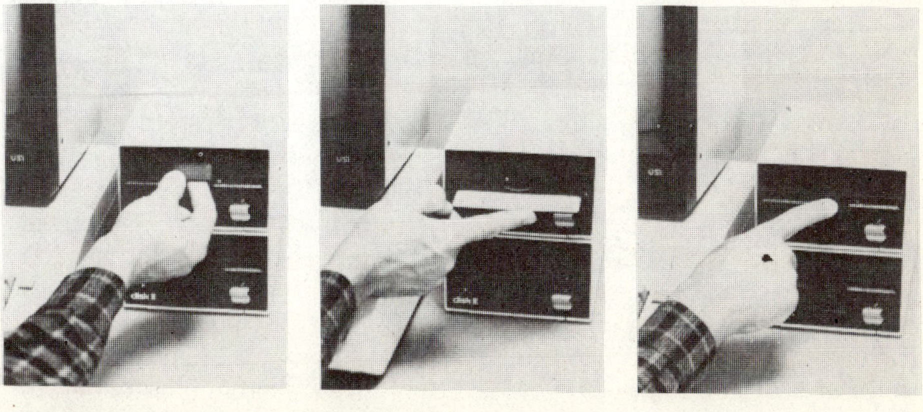

Figure 2-3. Inserting a disk in drive 1

already a disk in the drive, grasp it with your thumb and forefinger and pull it straight out. Be careful not to bend it as you pull it out. Do not touch the shiny inner surface through any of the cutouts in the protective outer jacket. Place the disk in a disk envelope and set it aside.

Hold the disk you want to insert so the label is face up. Gently slide the disk straight into the drive, taking care not to bend it. Push the disk all the way in. If it meets any resistance, stop. Remove it, check for obstructions, and try again. If it still sticks, try another disk. If that sticks too, there may be something wrong inside the drive, and you should have it checked.

When you have inserted the disk, slowly push down the drive door. If the door will only go down a fraction of an inch, the disk is not in far enough.

Switching On the Apple II Console

Locate the power switch on the rear of the Apple II, next to where the power cord plugs into the computer. Turn the switch on (Figure 2-4). You should hear a beep from inside the Apple II. The power lamp on the keyboard will now be on.

If you did not hear a beep, turn the switch off, then on again. If you still do not hear anything, turn the power off. Was the power lamp lit? If not, unplug the Apple II and plug in a lamp or a

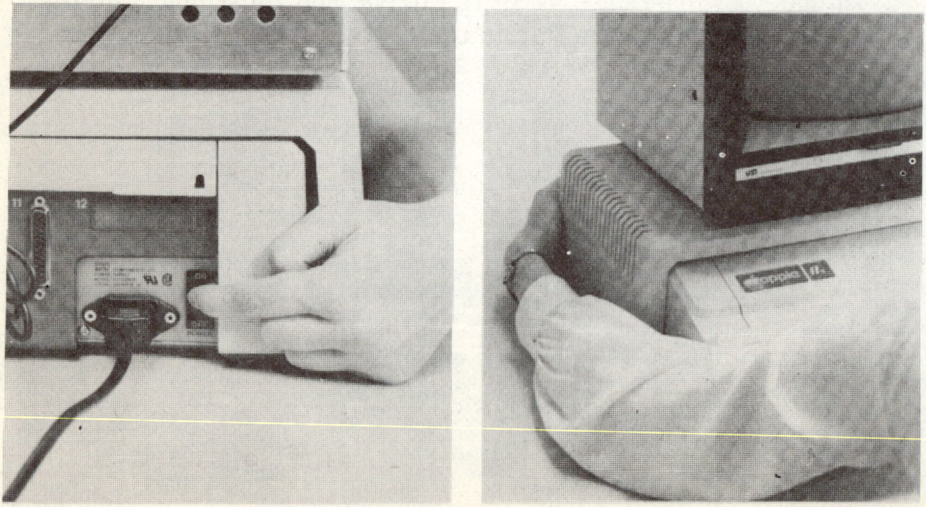

Figure 2-4. Switching on the Apple II console

radio to see if the wall outlet has power. If in doubt, get help from someone with more experience. You can ruin parts of the computer by ignorantly poking around inside it.

After Switching On the Console

Immediately after switching on the Apple II console, you see the message **Apple][** displayed in the middle of the screen. On an enhanced Apple IIe, the message *Apple IIe* appears instead. If your computer has no disk drives, a square right bracket (]) also appears at the left edge of the screen.

If your Apple II has disk drives, the message on the screen is accompanied by chattering sounds from inside drive 1. The "disk use" light on the Disk II or Duodisk begins to glow. Within a couple of seconds, the disk drive settles down to a smooth whirr as the computer reads the operating system from the disk. This is called *loading* or *booting* the operating system.

What happens next depends on which operating system the start-up disk uses. With the ProDOS operating system, the **Apple][** (or *Apple IIe*) message disappears about five seconds after start-up. Another message appears in the middle of the screen—something like **PRODOS 1.1.1 18-SEP-84**—and a copyright notice appears at the bottom of the screen. About five seconds later, those messages disappear and a square bracket (]) appears for a few seconds in the upper-left corner of the screen.

With the DOS 3.3 operating system, the **Apple][** (or *Apple IIe*) message disappears about five seconds after startup. A square bracket (]) appears for a few seconds in the lower-left corner.

With the Pascal operating system, the **Apple][** (or *Apple IIe*) message disappears about four seconds after startup. The screen fills with at-sign symbols (@) for an instant and then goes blank. A small square or rectangle may be displayed in the upper-left corner of the screen. If your Apple II has more than one drive, it may chatter and whirr briefly.

Usually within 45 seconds of startup the screen assumes the standard look for the application program you are starting. You can begin using the program according to its displayed or published instructions.

If the disk drive spins for several minutes with no change in the screen display, there is something wrong with the disk or the drive. Endless spinning usually means there is no disk in the drive or the drive door is not closed all the way. It's also possible the disk you inserted is upside down, blank, or not an Apple II disk. If the message *** **UNABLE TO LOAD PRODOS** *** appears on the screen, the disk you inserted is not a start-up disk. Try starting up again (or restart as described in the next section). Should a second start-up attempt fail, try another disk. If different disks fail repeatedly, there may be a problem with the disk drive, and you will need to have it serviced. Failure of just one disk indicates a damaged disk; in this case, use another copy.

Restarting With the Power On

On an Apple IIe, you can restart the program you are using or start a different program from the keyboard. Simply insert the disk that contains the program you want to start and then hold down the OPEN APPLE, CONTROL, and RESET keys all at the same time. Neither the Apple II Plus nor the original Apple II has an OPEN APPLE key, so you must switch the console power off and back on instead.

Warning: Do not restart the Apple II indiscriminately. Most programs have standard procedures for quitting. If you bypass them by restarting or by switching the computer off, you risk losing everything you did during the current session with the program. Restart a program or start another program only after quitting the current program normally.

USING PROGRAMS

Using almost any Apple II program involves some typing. You may not have to type whole paragraphs, but you will have to type some isolated letters or numbers and a few words. There are programs that let you use a mouse to reduce the amount of typing you must do. But even in those programs you must still do some typing, so you need to be familiar with the Apple II keyboard.

The Cursor

A special symbol, called the *cursor*, marks the location where your next typing will appear on the screen. In many programs the cursor is a blinking underline, but it can also be a blinking

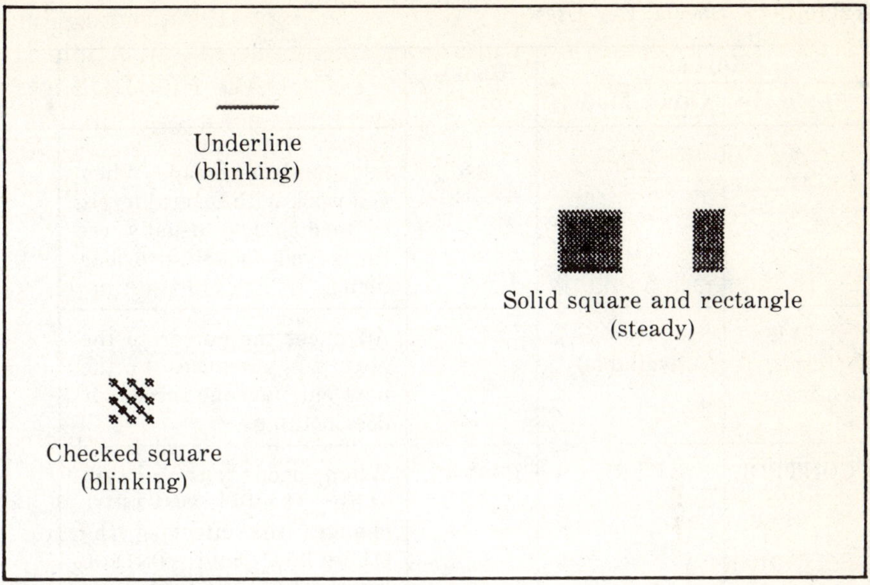

Figure 2-5. Standard cursor designs

vertical line, a blinking checked square, or a steady solid square or rectangle (see Figure 2-5).

The Keyboard

Most of the Apple II's keys are the same as the ones on a typewriter, but there are some special keys. Their functions vary from one program to the next. See Table 2-1 for a list of special keys and their most common functions.

Typing Pitfalls

As you type entries on your Apple II, you will discover that it takes everything you say literally. There are a number of typing pitfalls to trip up the unwary program user.

Many typists do not distinguish between the number 0 and the letter O or the number 1 and the lowercase letter l. A computer program cannot resolve this ambiguity. You must be very careful to type a numeral when you mean a numeral. To help you

Table 2-1. Special Key Uses

Keycap		Book's Notation	Use
Apple IIe	Other Models		
ESC	ESC	ESC	ESC stands for escape. When you work with several levels of menus, ESC usually returns you to the previous menu.
TAB	(Not available)	TAB	Advances the cursor to the next tab, advances to the next entry on the screen, or does nothing.
CONTROL	CTRL	CONTROL	When used with certain other keys, CONTROL changes the effect of the other key. Hold CONTROL down while you press and release another key.
SHIFT	SHIFT	SHIFT	Use like the shift keys on a typewriter to produce capital letters or the symbols at the tops of the numeral and punctuation keys. On most Apple II Plus and standard Apple II models, SHIFT has no effect on letters, since they are always capitals.
CAPS LOCK	(Not available)	CAPS LOCK	Locks the keyboard so it generates capital letters without using a SHIFT key. Affects only the 26 letters of the alphabet.
(Not needed)	REPT	REPT	Hold REPT down while you press another key to make the other key repeat.
DELETE	(Not available)	DELETE	With some programs, DELETE removes the character to the left of the cursor. Otherwise, it displays a white square.

Table 2-1. Special Key Uses (*continued*)

Keycap		Book's Notation	Use
Apple IIe	**Other Models**		
RETURN	RETURN	RETURN	Signifies the end of an entry. Most programs do not accept an entry until you press RETURN.
←	←	←	Usually moves the cursor left, like the backspace key on a typewriter. With some programs, it may also delete as it moves.
→	→	→	Usually moves the cursor right, as a reverse-backspace key would on a typewriter.
↓	(Not available)	↓	With some programs, allows you to move down the list of options in a menu. Has various other uses.
↑	(Not available)	↑	With some programs, allows you to move up the list of options in a menu. Has various other uses.
RESET	RESET	RESET	On an Apple IIe or Apple II Plus, RESET has no effect when pressed alone, but CONTROL-RESET halts the program with a loss of data likely. On an Apple IIe, CONTROL-OPEN APPLE-RESET restarts the computer as if you switched the power off and on. On a standard Apple II, RESET alone halts the program with a loss of data likely.
(open apple symbol)	(Not available)	OPEN APPLE	Has various uses. CONTROL-OPEN APPLE-RESET restarts the computer as if you

Table 2-1. Special Key Uses (*continued*)

Keycap		Book's Notation	Use
Apple IIe	**Other Models**		
			switched the power off and on.
	(Not available)	SOLID APPLE	Has various uses. CONTROL-SOLID APPLE-RESET initiates a series of diagnostic tests lasting about one minute.

remember, the Apple II displays the zero with a slash through it.

On the Apple IIe you can type small letters as well as capitals. However, some programs do not allow small letters in commands. If you're not sure whether a program allows lowercase letters, go ahead and try using some. If they don't work, press the CAPS LOCK key and stick to uppercase.

The Apple IIe has two keys that generate a single quote (apostrophe). In most cases, program commands that use a single quote require the conventional character, ', which slants to the right. The alternate single quote character, ‘, which slants to the left, will not work.

There is a DELETE key on the Apple IIe, but with many programs it will not back over your entry. Instead, use the ← key, as described later in this chapter.

Terminating Entries

Because the lengths of entries vary, the controlling program usually will not accept an entry until you signify that you are finished typing it. The RETURN key is the most common entry terminator. If you type an entry and nothing happens, you probably need to press the RETURN key. There are entries that don't need a terminator, and even a few that use a terminator other than RETURN, but such exceptions are well documented.

Combination Keystrokes

The SHIFT and CONTROL keys do nothing in and of themselves. Instead, they change the effect of other keys. To use one of these keys, you press it, hold it down, and press another key. As an obvious example, when you hold down the SHIFT key and press a letter, the letter will be capitalized. This book denotes such combination keystrokes by separating member keys with a hyphen. For example, CONTROL-X means "press the CONTROL and X keys simultaneously."

Automatic Key Repeat

You may have discovered that when you hold down a key on the Apple IIe, it repeats automatically. This feature works with all keys except OPEN APPLE, SOLID APPLE, and RESET.

Earlier models of the Apple II do not have the automatic key repeat feature. Instead, they have a REPT key. To make a key repeat, hold down the key and then press the REPT key. Release the REPT key and the repeating stops.

STARTING PROGRAMS FROM DISK

Some disk software starts itself. As described earlier in this chapter, you need only insert the disk in drive 1, close the drive door, and turn on the computer. For example, the ProDOS User's Disk contains a self-starting program (described in Chapter 3) that helps you organize ProDOS disks.

Not all programs are self-starting, however. The DOS 3.3 System Master disk, for example, contains several programs (described in Chapter 4) that help you organize DOS 3.3 disks. You must start such programs by typing commands at the keyboard.

The Command Prompt

Soon after starting an Apple II with a disk in drive 1 that lacks a self-starting program, you see the cursor near the left edge of the display screen. Next to the cursor is a special character, called the *command prompt* or *prompt.* It may be a square bracket (]), an angle bracket (>), or an asterisk. The Apple II is a multilingual computer, and the shape of the command prompt indicates in which language it expects instructions.

The] and > command prompts signify that the Apple II is ready to receive BASIC commands. There are two different prompt characters because some Apple II models have two different versions of BASIC, called *Integer BASIC* and *Applesoft*. Integer BASIC uses the > command prompt and Applesoft uses the] prompt. It turns out that both versions use the same commands for starting programs manually.

On early models of the Apple II the first command prompt you see is an asterisk (*). The asterisk is the command prompt for the Apple II Machine Language Monitor. In this case, you must switch control of the Apple II to BASIC by entering CONTROL-B (press the CONTROL and B keys in unison, then press the RETURN key).

Loading the Operating System

All Apple IIe and Apple II Plus computers—and many original Apple II computers—load the operating system automatically from the disk in drive 1 when you switch on the computer. If your Apple II does not automatically load DOS, or if you are unsure whether it has been loaded, you can load it manually.

To manually load an operating system, first determine which operating system your program uses. Next, select a disk that contains the right operating system, such as the ProDOS User's Disk or the DOS 3.3 System Master disk. Then put the selected disk in drive 1 and close the drive door. Now see which command prompt (], >, or *) is displayed. If the command prompt is] or >, type PR#6 and then press the RETURN key. If the command prompt is an *, type a 6, then press CONTROL-P, and finally press the RETURN key.

The "in use" lamp on the disk drive will light and you will hear noises from inside the drive. The operating system is being copied into the Apple II's memory. If you put the disk into the wrong drive, take it out and insert it in the one with its lamp lit. Soon a message appears on the display screen, telling you which operating system has been loaded.

Program Names

Every program on a disk has a name. You need to know the name in order to start the program manually. The name of a program that uses the DOS 3.3 operating system must be between 1 and 30 characters long, including blank spaces. It must begin with a letter, but the rest of the name can be any character except a comma. Chapter 4 explains how to display a list of all the program names on a DOS 3.3 disk.

A ProDOS program name starts with a letter. After that, it may contain any combination of letters, numerals, and periods. However, a simple name cannot be more than 15 characters long. With ProDOS, a program can be referred to by a compound name that is made up of several simple names separated by slashes (/). Chapter 3 explains how to display a list of all the program names on a ProDOS disk.

Starting a BASIC Program

To start a BASIC program, type the command RUN, a blank space, and the name of the program you want to start, like this:

```
RUN FILEM
```

After you press the RETURN key, the command above will start the program named FILEM. Chapter 4 explains how to use the FILEM program and several other programs on the DOS 3.3 System Master disk. For instructions on using another program, consult its manual.

If the program doesn't start and you get the message **FILE NOT FOUND**, it means you misspelled the program name, miscounted the number of spaces in it, used the wrong program name altogether, used the wrong disk, or put the disk in the wrong drive.

If the message **LANGUAGE NOT AVAILABLE** appears, then you must manually switch the Apple II to the other version of BASIC. Remember, the command prompt at the left edge of the screen tells you which version of BASIC the Apple II is currently using. A square bracket (]) means Applesoft, and an angle bracket (>) means Integer BASIC. To switch from Applesoft to Integer BASIC, type the command INT and press the RETURN key. Typing the command FP will switch from Integer BASIC to Applesoft. On some models of the Apple II, a disk drive will come to life when you use the FP or INT commands. If the message **LANGUAGE NOT AVAILABLE** appears again, insert a DOS 3.3 System Master disk and type the command again. (There are some Apple II models that have only Applesoft, and some that have only Integer BASIC.)

Starting a Machine Language Program

Some programs are written in the Apple II's machine language, or in assembly language, which is essentially the same thing. To start one of these programs, use the BASIC command BRUN, like this:

```
BRUN FID
```

After you press the RETURN key, the command above will start the program named FID. The FID program is described in Chapter 4. For instructions on using another program, consult its manual.

If the program doesn't start and you get the message **FILE NOT FOUND**, it means you misspelled the program name, miscounted the number of spaces in it, used the wrong program name altogether, used the wrong disk, or put the disk in the wrong drive.

Specifying the Drive

If your Apple II has more than one disk drive, you can start a program from any drive you want. Be aware, however, that some programs are designed to work only in a certain drive. Starting a program in any drive does not guarantee it will work there; check the program's manual for details.

On an Apple II with a pair of disk drives, each drive is identified by number, 1 or 2. To designate a specific drive with the RUN or BRUN command, append a comma, the letter D, and the drive number. The following example specifies a file called COPYA on drive 2:

```
RUN COPYA,D2
```

To designate a specific drive on an Apple II with more than two drives, you must state the slot number of the accessory card to which the drive is attached. Append a comma, the letter S, and the slot number, like this:

```
RUN MASTER,S3
```

Once you issue a command with an explicit drive or slot number, that drive or slot will be used until another command specifies another drive or slot number. Turning off the Apple II or reloading the operating system resets the slot to 6 and the drive to 1.

You can combine slot and drive specifications. Here is an example:

```
BRUN FID,S6,D2
```

Caution: Use only drive and slot numbers that actually have drives attached. If you specify a nonexistent or vacant slot or drive, the computer may lock up, forcing you to reset or restart it.

Earlier Versions of DOS 3.3

DOS 3.3 was first released in August 1980. Programs written before that were distributed on disks for use with an earlier version, such as DOS 3.2.1, DOS 3.2, or some lower number. The chief difference between DOS 3.3 and earlier versions is in the number of sectors into which the disks are divided. DOS 3.3 uses 16-sector disks, but earlier versions used 13-sector disks. If you try to use a 13-sector disk with DOS 3.3, the message **UNABLE TO READ/WRITE** appears on the display screen.

In order to use a 13-sector disk with DOS 3.3, you must follow a slightly more complicated procedure than the one outlined above. After loading DOS 3.3, either automatically or manually, you must run the Applesoft program named START13 or the machine language program named BOOT13. Both programs are on the DOS 3.3 System Master disk. The disk drive goes to work. After a few seconds a message appears, asking which slot you wish to use for your 13-sector disk. Before responding, put the disk that was prepared by the earlier version of DOS (DOS 3.2.1, DOS 3.2, and so on) into drive 1. Then type the drive's slot number and press the RETURN key. After the disk drive stops, you can start your program with the RUN or BRUN command, as appropriate.

STARTING PROGRAMS FROM CASSETTE

If your Apple II has no disk drives, you can start programs manually from cassette tapes instead. This section only presents general instructions for getting a program started from cassette. For information on how to use the program once it is started, you must consult the program's manual or someone who already knows how to use it.

When you turn on an Apple II that has no disk drives, you hear it beep and immediately see the cursor near the left edge of the display screen. Next to the cursor is the command prompt, either], >, or *. Remember,] and > are command prompts for Applesoft and Integer BASIC, and * is the command prompt for the Machine Language Monitor.

Adjusting the Playback Volume

Before a cassette recorder will work properly with an Apple II, you must set its volume control. If the volume is too low or too high, the information on the tape will be distorted and the Apple II will not be able to understand it.

Trial and error is the only method for determining what volume level is correct for your tape recorder. Here is the general procedure. First, you set the volume control very low and try to transfer a program from cassette to the Apple II's memory. If the low setting does not work, you set the volume a little higher and try again. You keep adjusting the volume upward until the program is successfully transferred.

You can use any of the tapes that came with the Apple II to set the recorder volume. If the command prompt is a square bracket (]), try the cassette labeled COLOR TESTSOFT. If the command prompt is an angle bracket (>), try the tape labeled COLOR TEST. Put the cassette into the recorder. Be sure that the program label faces up. Then for each position of the volume control, perform the following steps:

1. Rewind the tape completely.
2. Type the word LOAD at the keyboard.
3. Press the PLAY button on the cassette recorder to start the tape.
4. Press the RETURN key.

When you press the RETURN key, the cursor disappears. After 15 or 20 seconds you can analyze your success.

If you get the message **?SYNTAX ERROR** or **?***SYNTAX**

ERR, do not adjust the volume, just go back to step 1 and try again. If this keeps happening, try cleaning the cassette recorder heads, or use a different tape.

If nothing happens, or if the message **?ERR** or **?***MEM FULL ERR** appears, reset the computer by pressing CONTROL-RESET. If doing this makes the * command prompt appear, restart BASIC by pressing first CONTROL-B and then the RETURN key. Next, set the tape recorder volume a little higher and try again.

If you hear a beep and no message appears, things are going well. The Apple II has found the beginning of the program on the tape and is transferring it. After about 15 more seconds (depending on the length of the program on the tape) you will hear another beep, and the command prompt and cursor will reappear on the screen. The program has been successfully transferred. You can now stop the tape by depressing the STOP button on the tape recorder. Make a note of the volume setting so you don't have to repeat this procedure after using the recorder away from the Apple II.

Starting a BASIC Program

Before you start a BASIC program from cassette, the Apple II must be ready for the correct version of BASIC. To switch from Applesoft to Integer BASIC, type the command INT and press the RETURN key. Typing the command FP will switch from Integer BASIC to Applesoft.

On some models of the Apple II, Integer BASIC is not available. If you have no disk drives and the Applesoft command prompt character appears when you first switch on the console, your machine does not have Integer BASIC. There are also some Apple II Plus machines with disk drives that have only Applesoft.

With some standard Apple II machines, Integer BASIC is always available, but you must get Applesoft from cassette. If your machine is one of those, find the tape labeled APPLESOFT II. Put it in the recorder and rewind it all the way. Type the word LOAD, but before you press the RETURN key, press the PLAY button on the cassette recorder to start the tape moving. Then press the RETURN key, and soon you will hear the Apple II beep. In about two minutes, the computer will beep again, and the Applesoft command prompt (]) will appear. Stop the tape.

With the proper version of BASIC selected, these are the steps for starting a program from cassette:

1. Position the tape to the beginning of the program. This will usually be the beginning of the tape, in which case you must rewind the tape completely. If the program you want is not the first program on a cassette, you must go through these steps for each program that precedes it on the tape. Repeat the following steps for each extra program you must pass over.
2. Type the word LOAD at the keyboard.
3. Press the PLAY button on the cassette recorder to start the tape.
4. Press the RETURN key. The cursor disappears.
5. After a few seconds, the Apple II beeps to signal that it has started to transfer the program into the Apple II's memory.
6. Some time later, the Apple II beeps again, signaling that it has finished the transfer. Use the STOP button on the tape recorder to stop the tape.
7. Type the word RUN, press the RETURN key, and the program begins.

If you hear no beeps or if you get any error messages during steps 5 and 6, recheck the volume control adjustments according to the directions given earlier in this chapter. If you still have problems, the cassette you are using is probably defective and you will have to replace it.

USING A PRINTER

In spite of the diversity of printer features, operating one printer is much the same as operating another. There are variations in the way you feed paper into the printer or install a new ribbon, but most of the differences show up only if you program the printer. As long as you stick to existing programs, you need only make sure your printer is listed among those supported by a program you want to use. This chapter only addresses the operating procedures that apply to all printers. For specific details on your printer, refer to its manual.

The Printer Controls

Your printer probably has an on/off switch, some buttons for manual control, and several status lamps grouped together in a control panel (see Figure 2-6). The on/off switch may be on the side or at the back of the printer. There may be secondary control switches and levers located inside the printer. Table 2-2 lists the most common printer controls and status lamps.

Many printers know how far the current line is from the bottom of the page and will eject the paper at the press of a button. At the end of a page printed on continuous paper, the printer automatically advances to the top of the next page. For this feature to work properly, you must align the paper before you turn the printer on, thereby giving the printer a place from which to start reckoning the page length. Some printers have a button you can push while the printer is on to reestablish the top of a page at the current line.

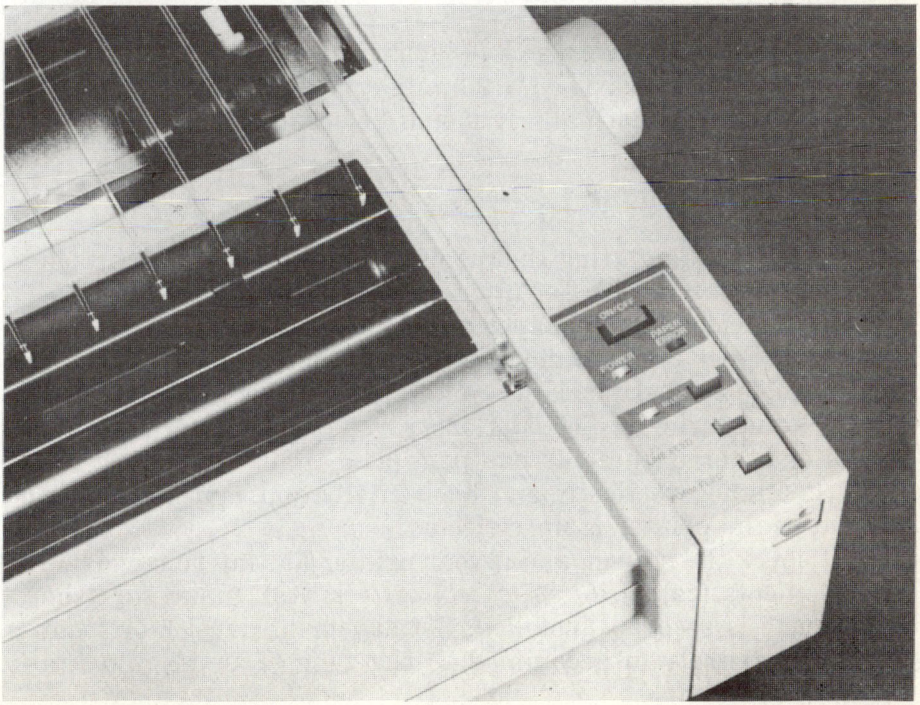

Figure 2-6. A typical printer control panel

Table 2-2. Common Printer Controls and Status Lamps

Switches and Buttons	Function
ON/OFF	Turns the printer on and off
SELECT	Suspends/resumes printing
FORM FEED	Advances paper to next page
LINE FEED	Advances paper one line
CLEAR	Resets printer after error
OVERRIDE	Finishes printing last page

Status Lamp	Meaning (when lit)
Power	Power on
Ready	Printer ready to print
Select	Permits printing to proceed
Paper Out	Almost out of paper
Alarm	Ribbon out or broken, or printer error

Your printer may have a switch labeled AUTO LINE FEED or LOCAL LINE FEED. The switch might be on the front panel or it might be inside; normally it should be set in the off position.

Preparing for Printing

The first step in getting the printer ready to print is to attach it to the computer via a serial or parallel accessory card. Then you must select the right paper and load it into the printer. Use continuous forms for uninterrupted printing, multiple-part for carbon copies, label stock for mailings, and so forth. If your printer accepts single-sheet stationery, you can use it for printing letters or other documents one page at a time. Make sure the paper is aligned vertically and horizontally and that its path in and out of the printer is unrestricted.

Next check the ribbon, and if your printer has interchangeable type elements (called *daisy wheels* or *thimbles*), make sure the correct one is securely installed. Set any print density or form thickness controls to accommodate the type of paper you are using.

Lastly, close all the printer covers and guards. An open cover will activate an interlock switch, which will temporarily disable the printer. Switch the printer on and set the SELECT or ONLINE switch if there is one. The READY and SELECT status lights must be lit for the printer to work.

RESETTING THE APPLE II

You can interrupt an Apple II program by pressing CONTROL-RESET. On standard Apple II machines, pressing RESET alone (without CTRL) will work. However, this feature is of little practical use, because you usually cannot resume a program from where you left off. If you use the RESET key, you may have to redo any work you did since you started the program. You can even ruin a disk by using the RESET key while the drive it's in is in use.

Accidental Reset

On Apple II Plus and standard Apple II keyboards, the RESET key is located very near the RETURN key. It's all too easy to hit

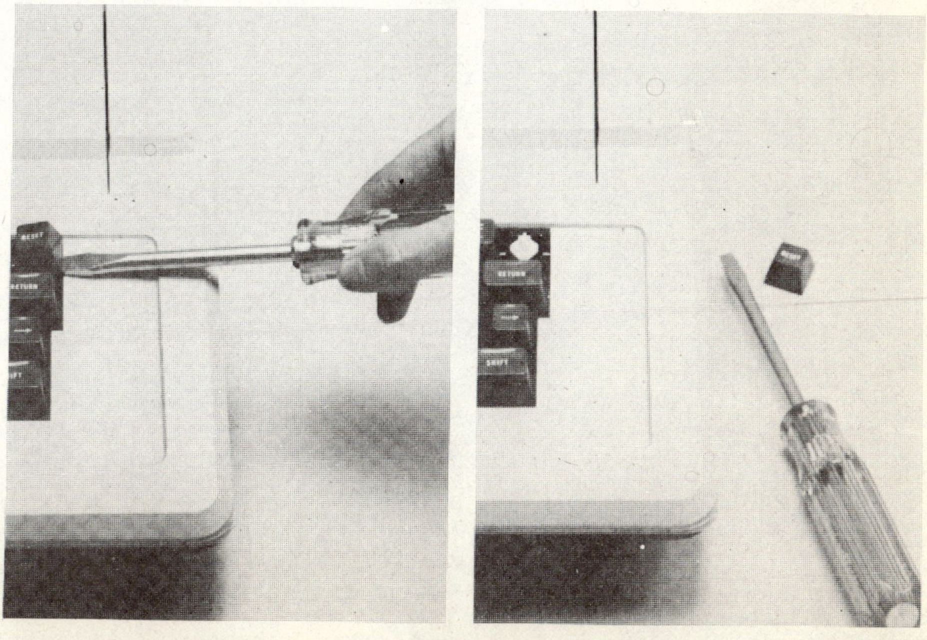

Figure 2-7. Guarding against accidental reset on a standard Apple II

RESET when you meant to hit RETURN . This is not a big problem on an Apple II Plus or Apple IIe, since you must press the CONTROL key along with the RESET key for anything to happen. The danger is further minimized on an Apple IIe, since its RESET key is also recessed and moved away from the other keys. But there is a constant danger of accidental reset on an original Apple II. You can reduce the chance of an accidental reset on an original Apple II keyboard by carefully prying off the plastic key top, leaving just the shaft of the key switch available (see Figure 2-7).

Organizing ProDOS Disks 3

The STARTUP program on the ProDOS User's Disk lets you work on disks and the program and data files they contain without memorizing and typing commands. Instead, you choose options from displayed menus. From the STARTUP program, you can do the following:

- Identify disk contents.
- Prepare a new disk for use.
- Erase a disk.
- Duplicate a disk.
- Copy program and data files between disks.
- Remove selected program and data files from a disk.
- Rename selected program and data files.
- Rename a disk.
- Lock selected program and data files against change or removal.
- Unlock selected program and data files for change or removal.
- Convert disks from ProDOS to DOS 3.3 and vice versa.
- Compare two files or two disks.
- Determine what accessory cards are installed in which slots.

PRODOS DISK ORGANIZATION

Before diving into the STARTUP program, you should understand how information is organized on a ProDOS disk. A single disk can store a large amount of information. Rarely is all this storage space used for one purpose, however. Several small, independent parcels of information usually coexist on a single disk. Every operating system has a scheme for keeping track of all the separate parcels of information.

Files

The ProDOS operating system treats each disk as a filing cabinet and each parcel of information as a file in the filing cabinet. In fact, parcels of information on a disk are called *files.* A ProDOS file may contain a program, a collection of data, or even other files.

Most data files are automatically created by programs as needed. Program files are created by the people who write the programs. Until you start writing your own programs, you will have little occasion to create a program file or data file yourself.

Directories

A file that contains other files is called a *directory file,* or simply a *directory.* If you think of a disk as a filing cabinet, you might think of a directory as a drawer in the filing cabinet—that is, as the drawer itself, not what may be in the drawer. Every disk has at least one directory, called the *volume directory.* It is the main directory for the whole disk and contains as many as 51 other program files, data files, or directories. ProDOS creates a volume directory automatically when you first prepare a disk for use, as described later in this chapter.

Any directory in the volume directory can contain other directories, and these directories can contain other directories, and so on. It's as if a filing cabinet could have drawers inside of drawers inside of drawers. You can theoretically have up to 64 directory levels on a single disk, although it's hard to use more than half a dozen. You can create subdirectories with the ProDOS User's Disk STARTUP program as described later in this chapter. Figure 3-1 diagrams a typical directory setup on a disk.

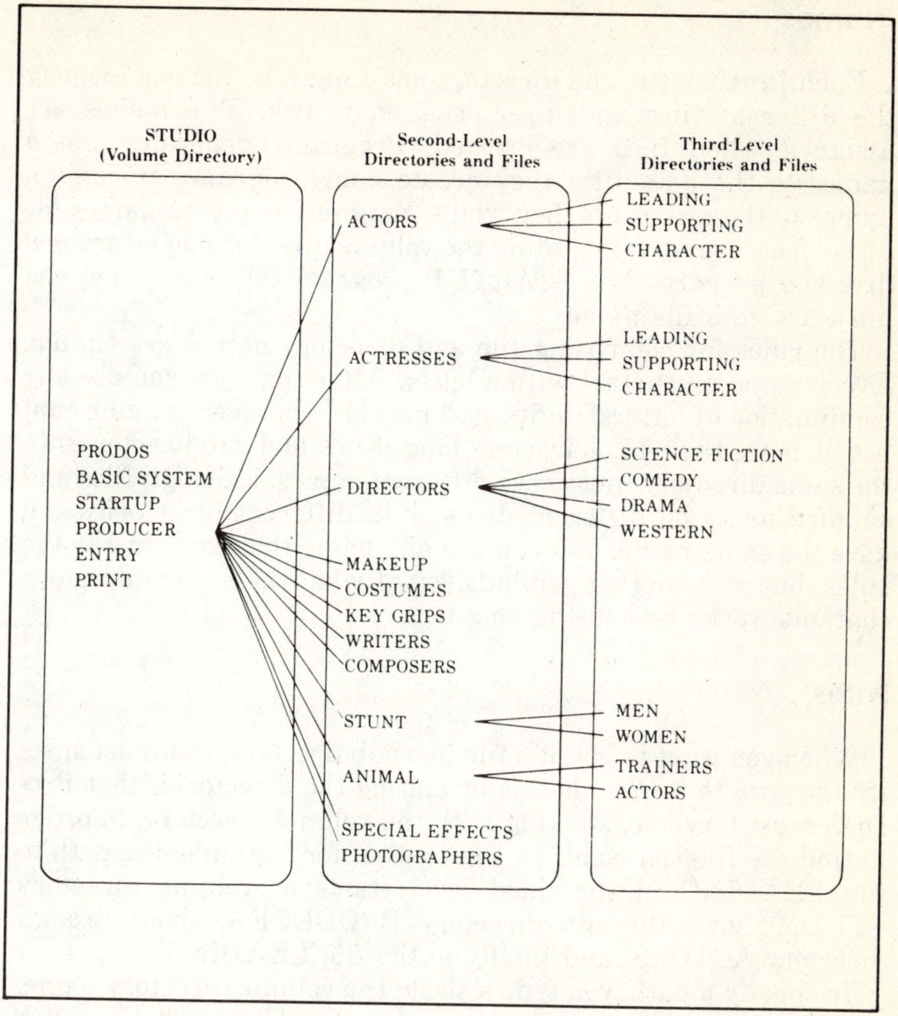

Figure 3-1. Directories on a hypothetical disk (64 directory levels allowed)

Unlike the volume directory, subdirectories have no specific limit on the number of files they contain. The only limit is the amount of space still available on the disk. Imagine a file drawer that can grow to the size of the filing cabinet but no larger.

Names

Each ProDOS file and directory has a name so you can identify the different files and directories on a disk. File names are assigned when files are created. Programs generally assign names to the data files they create, and programmers assign names to the programs they write. You must make up names for directories yourself, including the volume directory on every new disk you prepare. The STARTUP program tells you when you must assign a file name.

The rules for composing file and directory names are simple. Every name must start with a letter. After that, you can use any combination of letters, digits, and periods. However, a name cannot be more than 15 characters long. Files and subdirectories in the same directory must have different names, although files and subdirectories on different disks or in different directories can have the same name. You can use any name that conforms to the rules, but a name that reminds you of what the file or directory contains works best in the long run.

Paths

When you want to get at a file in a subdirectory, you must specify the *path* to it. You do this by stating the directories that ProDOS must traverse, starting with the volume directory, in order to find the file you want. In Figure 3-1, for example, the path to file LEADING in the third level starts at volume directory STUDIO, goes through directory PRODUCER, then through directory ACTORS, and finally to the file LEADING.

To specify a path, you type a slash, the volume directory name, another slash, the next directory name, and so on, listing each directory name with a slash in front of it and ending with the name of the file you want. The result is called a *pathname*. The pathname for the example cited in the previous paragraph is /STUDIO/PRODUCER/ACTORS/LEADING.

The Prefix and Partial Pathnames

Typing pathnames can be a tedious proposition, especially if you're using files buried several directory levels below the volume directory. ProDOS provides a shortcut to repeatedly typing in all or part of a pathname. It allows you to define a prefix and after that to type only partial pathnames. To every partial pathname you type, ProDOS automatically adds the prefix you defined. The result, prefix plus partial pathname, is the complete pathname.

In Figure 3-1, for example, if the prefix were /STUDIO/PRODUCER/, you could type the partial pathname COSTUMES for the file /STUDIO/PRODUCER/COSTUMES, and DIRECTORS/DRAMA instead of the full pathname /STUDIO/PRODUCER/DIRECTORS/DRAMA.

STARTING THE STARTUP PROGRAM

Now that you understand how ProDOS organizes information on disks, you can use the STARTUP program on the ProDOS User's Disk to do all the tasks listed at the beginning of this chapter and more.

To start the STARTUP program when the Apple II is on, insert the ProDOS User's Disk and restart the computer by pressing CONTROL-OPEN APPLE-RESET. If the Apple II is off, insert the disk, switch on the display (TV or monitor), and switch on the computer. As usual, the message **Apple][** or **Apple IIe** appears on the screen immediately, followed in about five seconds by ProDOS version and copyright information.

Four or five seconds after the ProDOS version-number message appears, the screen goes blank again. Seven or eight seconds after that (about thirteen seconds after switching on or restarting the Apple II), the screen displays the Startup Menu, shown in Figure 3-2.

General Instructions

The Startup Menu lists six options. Two of the options, F and C, lead to other menus of more options, all of which do something different with a disk or disk files. The Startup Menu options ?, S, T, and B do not directly affect disks or disk files.

In spite of its diversity, the STARTUP program uses fairly consistent procedures. You only have to learn once how to choose from a menu, get on-screen help, change menu levels, and type entries. Let's take a look at how you do those things before investigating the menu options.

```
*************************************
*                                   *
*         PRODOS USER'S DISK        *
*                                   *
* COPYRIGHT APPLE COMPUTER, INC. 1983 *
*                                   *
*************************************

YOUR OPTIONS ARE:

     ? - TUTOR: PRODOS EXPLANATION

     F - PRODOS FILER (UTILITIES)

     C - DOS <-> PRODOS CONVERSION

     S - DISPLAY SLOT ASSIGNMENTS

     T - DISPLAY/SET TIME

     B - APPLESOFT BASIC

PLEASE SELECT ONE OF THE ABOVE
```

Figure 3-2. The Startup Menu

CHOOSING A MENU OPTION Every menu option is keyed by a letter or by a question mark. To choose an option, you type its key letter but do not press RETURN.

ESC TO PREVIOUS MENU Many menu requests invoke other menus; however, during most phases of the STARTUP program you can return to the previous menu by pressing the ESC key. This allows you to cancel a menu choice before any irreversible action occurs, in case you make a wrong choice or change your mind. In the upper-right portion of the screen, the program sometimes displays the effect of pressing the ESC key.

TYPING ENTRIES For some menu options, you have to type the name of a file, path, directory, and so on. The ProDOS User's Disk STARTUP program has a standard procedure for requesting such information from you. First it prompts you with a brief message, such as **PATHNAME:**. Then it displays some blank spaces enclosed in parentheses, showing you how many characters you can type and where they will appear on the screen. A cursor in the form of a blinking checkerboard marks the spot where the next character you type will appear. As you type, the characters appear between the parentheses and the cursor moves to the right. Figure 3-3 shows a typical entry in progress.

```
****************************************
*                                      *
*           RENAME A VOLUME            *
*                                      *
****************************************

--RENAME--
  THE VOLUME IN SLOT:  6
               DRIVE:  1



  NEW VOLUME NAME: (/LETTERS.85▒    )








--PRESS <RET> TO ACCEPT:<ESC> TO EXIT--
```

Figure 3-3. A typical keyboard-entry scenario

While typing, you can use the ← and → keys to move the cursor back and forth. In some cases, pressing ESC restores the original entry line.

Sometimes the program displays the existing value of an entry, or a standard value for an entry, between the parentheses. You can accept the proposed entry by just pressing the RETURN key, or you can change or replace the proposal by typing another response before pressing RETURN.

ON-SCREEN HELP FROM THE TUTOR The main menu and several other menus in the ProDOS User's Disk STARTUP program contain a "tutor" option, which you choose by typing a question mark. The tutor option displays several paragraphs that explain the program features and options available from the menu currently displayed.

THE PRODOS FILER

Typing the letter F from the Startup Menu chooses the ProDOS Filer Menu (Figure 3-4). This menu's five options allow you to read some explanatory text, work on individual files, work on whole disks, change some of the the program's standard responses, or return to the Startup Menu.

Working on Individual Files

Typing the letter F from the ProDOS Filer Menu chooses the File Commands Menu, which contains a tutor option and eight commands for working on individual files (Figure 3-5). You can copy, delete, lock, unlock, or rename one or more files at a time. You can also list the files in a directory, compare two files, make a new directory, or change the ProDOS prefix.

FILE NAMES AND PATHS IN THE PRODOS FILER As part of every Filer Menu option, you must specify a pathname for one or two files. Each pathname you type must conform to the normal ProDOS rules described earlier in this chapter. The ProDOS prefix, which is initially set to the name of the volume directory (that is, the disk name), is added to the beginning of a pathname you type, unless the pathname you type begins with a / character.

```
****************************************
*                                      *
*   APPLE'S PRODOS SYSTEM UTILITIES    *
*                                      *
*         FILER VERSION 1.1            *
*                                      *
*  COPYRIGHT APPLE COMPUTER,  1983-84  *
*                                      *
****************************************

         ? - TUTOR

         F - FILE COMMANDS

         V - VOLUME COMMANDS

         D - CONFIGURATION DEFAULTS

         Q - QUIT

  PLEASE SELECT AN OPTION:
```

Figure 3-4. The Filer Menu

You can always type an explicit pathname, but sometimes it is more convenient to specify a group of files to be acted on at once. The ProDOS Filer lets you do that by specifying an ambiguous pathname, that is, a single name that can identify several files. To specify an ambiguous pathname, you include the character = or ? as a "wild card" that stands for any character or string of characters. For example, the simple pathname "PRODUCERS/=" specifies every file in directory PRODUCERS. As another example, the name "PRODUCERS/A=" specifies all files in directory PRODUCERS that have names starting with the letter A. Similarly, the name "DIRECTORS/=N" specifies all files in directory

```
****************************************
*                                      *
*            FILE COMMANDS             *
*                                      *
****************************************

            ? - TUTOR

            L - LIST PRODOS DIRECTORY

            C - COPY FILES

            D - DELETE FILES

            K - COMPARE FILES

            A - ALTER WRITE-PROTECTION

            R - RENAME FILES

            M - MAKE DIRECTORY

            P - SET PREFIX
SELECT AN OPTION OR <ESC>: ▒
```

Figure 3-5. The File Commands Menu

DIRECTORS that have names ending with the letter N. Only one wild card character is allowed in a pathname.

The ? wild card specifies an ambiguous pathname in the same manner as the = wild card. If you use a = wild card, the program acts without further approval on every file identified by the ambiguous file name. If you use a ? wild card, the program gets your approval before it acts on any file specified by the ambiguous file name. It does this by displaying a file name and waiting for your reponse. Type Y if you want the file acted on, N if you want it skipped, or press ESC if you want to cancel the command at that point and return to the File Command Menu.

IDENTIFYING DISK CONTENTS Menu option L (List ProDOS Directory) lists all the files and subdirectories in one disk directory. You must specify the pathname of the directory to be listed. For example, typing the wild card = and pressing RETURN specifies the directory named by the ProDOS prefix.

If there are more than 18 names to list, they are listed in pages, with 18 names to a page. After displaying each page, the program waits until you press the RETURN key before it begins the next page.

Figure 3-6 shows a sample ProDOS directory listing. At the top is the directory name. Following that is a list of file and

```
DIRECTORY:/USERS.DISK

 NAME               TYP  BLOCKS  MODIFIED

*PRODOS             SYS      30  18-SEP-84
*BASIC.SYSTEM       SYS      21  18-JUN-84
*FILER              SYS      51  18-JUN-84
*CONVERT            SYS      42   1-NOV-83
*STARTUP            BAS      24  26-JUL-84
*MOIRE              BAS       3  15-OCT-83
*HYPNOSIS           BAS       3  15-OCT-83
*ANIMALS            BAS      10  15-OCT-83

 BLOCKS FREEE:     89       USED:     191




--PRESS <RET> TO BEGIN: <ESC> TO EXIT--
```

Figure 3-6. A sample ProDOS directory listing

directory names, including the name, type, and size of each. Table 3-1 identifies the file types used by the ProDOS operating system. At the end of the listing is the amount of disk space used and the amount available. All sizes are reported as a number of blocks, each of which is 512 bytes.

COPYING FILES With menu option C (Copy Files), you can copy one or more files from one disk to another. You can also copy a file from one directory to another directory on the same disk. You must specify the source and destination pathnames in the usual manner. Remember, the program prefixes the pathname you type with the ProDOS prefix unless you type a / as the first pathname character.

If the ProDOS Filer finds that you have specified the name of an existing file for the destination, it asks whether you want to delete the existing file and replace it with the source file.

If you are copying from one disk to another and using a single drive, you will have to swap disks at least once for each file copied. For a long file, you may have to swap more than once. No swapping is required if you copy from a disk in one drive to a disk in the other drive, or from one ProDOS directory to another on the same disk.

DELETING FILES To delete one or more files and make the space they occupy on the disk available for other files, choose option D (Delete Files) from the File Commands Menu. You must specify a pathname for the files you want to delete. Menu option D can also delete a ProDOS subdirectory, but only if it is empty.

Table 3-1. ProDOS File Types

Abbreviation	Type
DIR	Directory
TXT	Text or other data
BAS	Applesoft program
VAR	Applesoft variables
BIN	Binary
REL	Relocatable
$F *n*	User defined (*n* = a number from 1 to 8)
SYS	ProDOS system program or system file

COMPARING FILES Menu option K (Compare Files) allows you to compare two ProDOS files to see if their contents are identical. You specify the pathnames. If the files match, the message **COMPARE COMPLETE** appears. If the files do not match, the message **FILES DO NOT MATCH** appears.

LOCKING AND UNLOCKING FILES Some programs, data files, or ProDOS directories must be kept permanently. To protect such files against accidental erasure, renaming, or change, ProDOS supports file *locking.* To lock or unlock a file or ProDOS directory, choose option A (Alter Write-Protection) from the File Commands Menu. Specify an explicit pathname for a single file or directory, or an ambiguous pathname for a group of files and directories. The ProDOS Filer displays the message **LOCK FILES?**; type Y if you want the file or files to be locked, or N if you want them to be unlocked.

RENAMING FILES You can change the name of any file or ProDOS directory with menu option R (Rename Files). You specify the current pathname and the new pathname. Both pathnames must specify a file in the same directory, and the new pathname cannot already be used by another file in the directory.

CREATING A PRODOS SUBDIRECTORY Menu option M (Make Directory) allows you to make a new subdirectory in any other directory. You must enter a pathname for the new directory. Remember, the new subdirectory name is automatically prefixed with the current ProDOS prefix.

SETTING THE PRODOS PREFIX The normal ProDOS prefix is the name of the volume directory of the last disk you used. By choosing option P (Set Prefix) from the File Commands Menu, you can specify a new prefix. The current prefix is proposed as a basis for the new prefix. You can edit the proposal with the ← and → keys before pressing RETURN to confirm the name.

Working on Entire Disks

Typing the letter V from the ProDOS Filer Menu chooses the Volume Commands Menu, which contains a tutor option and seven commands for working on whole disks (Figure 3-7). You can format, copy, or rename a disk. You can also list the names of the disks known to ProDOS, compare two disks, check for disk defects, and review disk space allocation.

SPECIFYING THE DISK TO USE As part of most volume commands, you must specify slot and drive numbers for one or two disks. You are asked first for a slot number and then for a drive number. The slot you specify must have disk drives attached, and the drive number must be 1 or 2. In addition, an Apple IIe with 128K of RAM can use part of the memory for an electronic "disk drive;" it has slot number 3 and drive number 2.

```
****************************************
*                                      *
*            VOLUME COMMANDS           *
*                                      *
****************************************

         ? - TUTOR

         F - FORMAT A VOLUME

         C - COPY A VOLUME

         L - LIST VOLUMES

         R - RENAME A VOLUME

         D - DETECT BAD BLOCKS

         B - BLOCK ALLOCATION

         K - COMPARE VOLUMES

SELECT AN OPTION OR <ESC>: ▒
```

Figure 3-7. The Volume Commands Menu

FORMATTING A DISK Before you can use a brand-new disk, you must use option F (Format a Volume) from the Volume Commands Menu to map the disk surface, check for defects, and set up a blank volume directory. This initialization process is called *formatting.* You can also format a used disk in order to erase it completely.

Be careful when you specify the slot and drive numbers. If you specify the wrong ones, you may accidentally format (and erase) the wrong disk. As a safeguard, you must approve formatting if the disk already has a recognizable ProDOS name.

You must specify a name for the volume directory on a newly formatted disk. The name BLANK, followed by a couple of digits, will be proposed. You can accept the proposal by pressing RETURN or replace it by typing a name of your own choosing.

Formatting a 5 1/4-inch diskette takes about 20 seconds. Other types of disk drives may take more or less time. While formatting is in progress, the message **FORMATTING** appears alongside the slot number on the screen. When formatting is finished, the message **FORMAT COMPLETE** appears near the bottom of the screen.

DUPLICATING A DISK Option C (Copy a Volume) of the Volume Command Menu is important because it can make backup copies of your disks. Before choosing option C, get the original and duplicate disks ready. First, cover the write-enable notch on the original disk with a write-protect sticker. This simple precaution may save you considerable grief if you make a mistake later in the procedure. Choose any spare disk for the duplicate, even a new, unformatted one. Duplicating a disk automatically formats the duplicate disk just as menu option F does, completely erasing the former contents of the duplicate disk before making the copy.

You must specify slot and drive numbers for the original and duplicate disks. The duplicate disk can use the same drive as the original disk, though the copy is made much faster if the disks are placed in separate drives.

At this point the program tells you to place the original and duplicate disks in their respective drives. If both disks share the same drive, the copy utility asks you to insert the original disk and then remove the original disk and insert the duplicate disk.

Before the duplication begins, you must specify a name for the volume directory on the duplicate disk; the name of the original disk is proposed. You can accept the suggestion by pressing RETURN, or you can type a different name before pressing RETURN.

If the original and duplicate disks use the same drive, the screen displays messages asking you to insert one disk and then the other, over and over again. You have to swap disks many times before the copy process is finished. Each time you insert the original disk, a small part of it is read into the Apple II's memory. Then when you insert the duplicate disk, the part that was read into memory is written onto the disk. If the original and duplicate disks use different drives, you do not need to swap disks.

An error message appears during the copying procedure if you leave a drive door open, forget to insert a disk, or try to copy information onto a write-protected disk. If this happens, try the duplicating procedure again.

Warning: Some programs are produced on copy-protected disks to prevent copyright infringement. Menu option C cannot successfully duplicate a copy-protected disk. The disk may appear to be duplicated successfully but will not work properly when you try to use it later. Always try a duplicate program disk before assuming that it works.

LISTING AVAILABLE DISKS When you choose option L (List Volumes) from the Volume Commands Menu, a list of currently inserted disks is displayed. On an Apple IIe with 128K of memory, the list may include an electronic disk. The slot number, drive number, and volume directory name are given for each disk on the list.

RENAMING A DISK Menu option R (Rename a Volume) allows you to change a disk name (the name of its volume directory). You specify slot and drive numbers. The program proposes the existing name, which you can accept by pressing RETURN or change by typing a new name before pressing RETURN.

CHECKING DISK CONDITION Menu option D (Detect Bad Blocks) checks the disk whose slot and drive numbers you specify for unusable areas. It reads the disk and reports **0 BAD BLOCKS** if it finds no problems, or it lists the block numbers where the problems exist. If you have a disk with bad blocks, try copying all its files to a newly formatted disk and reformatting the bad disk.

CHECKING DISK USAGE To get a report of disk space allocation, choose option B (Block Allocation) from the Volume Commands Menu. For the disk you specify by slot and drive numbers, the program displays the number of 512-byte blocks in use, the number not in use, and the total number on the disk.

COMPARING DISKS Menu option K (Compare Volumes) allows you to compare two disks to see if their contents are identical. You specify slot and drive numbers for each disk. If the files match, the message **COMPARE COMPLETE** appears. If the disks do not match, the disparate block numbers are listed.

Changing ProDOS Filer Standard Responses

Recall that when you choose any of the options in the Volume Commands Menu, the ProDOS Filer normally proposes that it act on the disk in slot 6, drive 1. If the option you choose requires two disks, the ProDOS Filer proposes that it use the disk in slot 6, drive 2 for the second disk. Of course you can override the proposals each time you choose an option from the Volume Commands Menu. However, option D (Configuration Defaults) of the main ProDOS Filer Menu allows you to change the slot and drive numbers proposed by default. The Filer calls these numbers *defaults*.

Option D of the main Filer Menu allows you to choose another default: whether output will appear on the screen or on the screen and the printer. The output is affected from options L, D, and K of the Volume Commands Menu and from options L and K of the File Commands Menu.

To change the slot, drive, or output defaults, choose option S (Select Defaults) from the Configuration Defaults Menu. As shown in Figure 3-8, you must specify the slot and drive numbers you want proposed for both source and destination drives, and you must specify where you want output sent. The Filer proposes entries that you can accept by pressing RETURN or reject by typing your own entries.

To restore the Filer defaults to their initial values, choose option R (Restore Defaults) from the Configuration Defaults Menu.

```
****************************************
*                                      *
*           SELECT DEFAULTS            *
*                                      *
****************************************

--SELECT DEFAULTS--
     FOR SOURCE SLOT:  6
              DRIVE:   1

    DESTINATION SLOT:  6
              DRIVE:   2

 SELECT AN OUTPUT DEVICE:          P

   PRINTER SLOT: (▒)




--PRESS <RET> TO ACCEPT:<ESC> TO EXIT--
```

Figure 3-8. Selecting Filer defaults

Quitting the Filer

To quit the Filer, press the ESC key repeatedly until the main Filer Menu appears. Then choose option Q (Quit). You must specify the pathname of a file of type SYS to which the Filer can transfer control of the Apple II. For example, specifying the name BASIC.SYSTEM transfers control to the BASIC interpreter and then automatically starts the BASIC program named STARTUP.

DOS 3.3-PRODOS CONVERSION

Typing the letter C from the Startup Menu chooses the Convert Menu (Figure 3-9), which you can use to convert ProDOS files to DOS 3.3 files or vice versa. Its options allow you to designate the direction of conversion, specify the location of the source and destination disks, set a date to be attached to new ProDOS files, and mark files to be converted.

```
                CONVERT Menu
Direction: DOS 3.3 S6,D2 ---> ProDOS
Date: <NO DATE>
Prefix: /USERS.DISK/
---------------------------------------


   R - Reverse Direction of Transfer

   C - Change DOS 3.3 Slot and Drive

   D - Set ProDOS Date

   P - Set ProDOS Prefix

   T - Transfer (or List) Files


---------------------------------------

Enter Command: ▒   ? - Tutor,  Q - Quit
```

Figure 3-9. The Convert Menu

Reversing Conversion Direction

The second line of the Convert Menu screen shows which way files will be converted, DOS 3.3 to ProDOS or ProDOS to DOS 3.3. You can change the direction by choosing option R (Reverse Direction of Transfer) from the Convert Menu.

The DOS 3.3 Disk Drive

Normally, the DOS 3.3 disk is assumed to be in a drive other than the one occupied by the ProDOS disk (as determined by the ProDOS prefix). You can specify any drive for the DOS 3.3 disk by choosing option C (Change DOS 3.3 Slot and Drive) from the Convert Menu.

The ProDOS Date

ProDOS can "stamp" a date on a file when the file is written on a disk. Some Apple II machines have an accessory card with a clock/calendar that provides the current date automatically. You can enter a date by choosing option D (Set ProDOS Date) from the Convert Menu. If you choose option D, you must enter a legitimate date in the format 28-FEB-85. The year must be any number between 0 and 99, the month must be a three-letter abbreviation such as JAN or SEP, and the day number must make sense with the month (for example, 31-FEB is not allowed).

Entering a date via the Convert Menu does not set an accessory clock card if one is installed. Also, the accessory clock card may reset the date at midnight after you set the date via the Convert Menu.

The ProDOS Prefix

The ProDOS prefix designates which disk to use for the ProDOS files and may specify a partial pathname for them as well. The prefix is initially set to the name of the volume directory that contains file CONVERT. Option P (Set ProDOS Prefix) allows you to change the prefix. You may specify a prefix by typing a partial pathname directly or by entering the slot and drive numbers of a disk from which the volume directory name can be read.

Selecting and Converting Files

Files are converted individually, not en masse, so you must specify which files to convert. After you choose option T (Transfer or List Files) from the Convert Menu, you are asked to enter a file name. You may type a single explicit file name or an ambiguous file name. The explicit file name specifies one file to be converted, but an ambiguous file name specifies a group of files.

You specify an ambiguous name by including the character = or ? as a "wild card" that stands for any character or string of characters. For example, the simple name "=" specifies every file, the name "VISI=" specifies all files that have names starting with the letters VISI, and the name "=.TEXT" specifies all files that have names ending with .TEXT. The ? wild card specifies an ambiguous name in the same manner as the = wild card. Only one wild card character is allowed in a name.

Use a = wild card to convert all files identified by the ambiguous file name. You make no further entries or choices.

Use a ? wild card if you wish to convert only some of the files identified by the ambiguous file name. A list of the matching file names is displayed (Figure 3-10), and one of the file names is highlighted in inverse characters. You can pick the highlighted file by pressing the SPACEBAR; an arrow will appear next to the file name. You can move down the list of file names by pressing ↓ or → and up the list by pressing ↑ or ←. To unmark a file if you change your mind, move to it and press the SPACEBAR again. When you have marked all the files you want to convert, press RETURN and the conversion begins. You can cancel the conversion by pressing ESC.

ProDOS has more stringent rules for naming files than does DOS 3.3. When going from DOS 3.3 to ProDOS, all blanks, punctuation, and symbols are changed to periods. In addition, long DOS 3.3 names are shortened to 15 characters.

A DOS 3.3 directory can hold up to 105 files, but a ProDOS volume directory is limited to 51 files. Therefore, when converting from DOS 3.3 to ProDOS, it's possible to fill the ProDOS volume directory before all files are converted. If this happens, the conversion stops and an advisory message appears. To convert a DOS 3.3 disk with more than 51 files to ProDOS, specify a ProDOS subdirectory, not the volume directory, as the destination. ProDOS subdirectories can hold any number of files as long

```
           Transfer (or List) Files
Direction: ProDOS ---> DOS 3.3 S6,D1
Date: 13-JUN-85
Prefix: /EXAMPLES/PROGRAMS/
                          ESC: CONVERT Menu
-------------------------------------------
    ->WHIZBOOM            BAS 01-OCT-83
      TWO.LINER           BAS 01-OCT-83
      VERY.SHORT          BAS 01-OCT-83
    ->ONERR.DEMO          BAS 01-OCT-83
      PART1               BAS 01-OCT-83
      PART2               BAS 01-OCT-83
      E.S.P.              BAS 01-OCT-83
      LISTSELF            BAS 01-OCT-83
      MAKE.FRUIT          BAS 01-OCT-83
      GET.FRUIT           BAS 01-OCT-83
      CONJUGATE           BAS 01-OCT-83
      CONJUGEATEN         BAS 01-OCT-83
      CONJUGEAT           BAS 01-OCT-83
      USE.SUB             BAS 01-OCT-83
      MAKE.TEXT           BAS 01-OCT-83
----------------- More --------------------

Enter Command:                     ? - Help
```

Figure 3-10. Selecting files to be converted

as there is space available on the disk.

ProDOS files of type DIR, VAR, BIN, REL, and $F*n* cannot be converted to DOS 3.3. DOS 3.3 files of type I (Integer BASIC programs) can be converted to ProDOS but cannot be executed.

You can use some files immediately after converting them to a different operating system. This is generally true of data files consisting of text or binary numbers. Program files, however, often require additional changes that must be made manually. For this reason, do not expect a program from a DOS 3.3 disk to work with ProDOS just because you transferred it to a ProDOS disk.

Quitting File Conversion

To quit converting files from one operating system to another, press the ESC key repeatedly until the main Convert Menu appears. Then type the letter Q. You must specify the pathname of a file of type SYS to which the Filer can transfer control of the Apple II. For example, specifying USERS.DISK BASIC.SYSTEM transfers control to the BASIC interpreter and automatically starts the BASIC program named STARTUP, thereby returning you to the Startup Menu.

REVIEWING SLOT ASSIGNMENTS

To review the configuration of your Apple II, choose option S (Display Slot Assignments) from the Startup Menu. As shown in Figure 3-11, the displayed summary includes the name of the volume directory on the last disk accessed, model of Apple II, amount of memory (RAM), version of BASIC in ROM, and names of accessory cards installed in slots 1 through 7 (0 to 7 for the Apple II Plus and the standard Apple II).

SETTING THE TIME AND DATE

The ProDOS operating system keeps track of a date and time, which you can set by choosing option T (Display/Set Time) from the Startup Menu. When you choose option T, the current date and time are displayed and you are asked whether you wish to change them (Figure 3-12). The date and time are not displayed unless you have already set them or unless your Apple II has a clock/calendar accessory card that sets them automatically.

Should you choose to enter the date and time, you will be required to enter them completely—you cannot cancel this procedure by pressing ESC. The date format is 01-APR-86. The year must be any number between 0 and 99, the month must be a three-letter abbreviation such as JAN or SEP, and the day number must make sense with the month (for example, 31-JUN is not allowed). A 12-hour clock format is used, not a 24-hour format. You enter the hours, minutes, and A for A.M. or P for P.M.

```
***************************************
*                                     *
*     DISPLAY SLOT ASSIGNMENTS        *
*                                     *
***************************************

STARTUP DISK: /USERS.DISK/

YOUR Apple //e HAS:

    128K OF RANDOM ACCESS MEMORY

    APPLESOFT IN ROM

    SLOT 1: I/O CARD
    SLOT 2: PARALLEL CARD
    SLOT 3: 80-COLUMN CARD
    SLOT 4: MOUSE/JOYSTICK
    SLOT 5: EMPTY
    SLOT 6: DISK DRIVE
    SLOT 7: EMPTY

PRESS RETURN TO DIPLAY MAIN MENU
```

Figure 3-11. Reviewing Apple II configuration

QUITTING THE STARTUP PROGRAM FOR BASIC

To exit the ProDOS User's Disk STARTUP program altogether, choose option B (Applesoft BASIC). When you do, the STARTUP program ends, leaving you on a BASIC command line. Chapter 5 begins to explain what you can do from there.

```
***************************************
*                                     *
*     SYSTEM DATE AND TIME UTILITY    *
*                                     *
***************************************



       THE CURRENT SETTINGS ARE:

             DATE: <NO DATE>

             TIME: <NO TIME>

    UPDATE SYSTEM DATE AND TIME? Y/N
```

Figure 3-12. Setting the date and time

Organizing DOS 3.3 Disks 4

The DOS 3.3 System Master disk contains several programs that help you organize the programs and data files on DOS 3.3 disks without memorizing and typing DOS 3.3 commands. Instead, you choose options from displayed menus and select programs and data files from lists of displayed names. With programs on the DOS 3.3 System Master disk, you can do the following:

- Duplicate a disk.
- Identify disk contents.
- Copy program and data files between disks.
- Remove selected program and data files from a disk.
- Lock selected program and data files against change or removal.
- Unlock selected program and data files for change or removal.
- Check disks for readability.

DOS 3.3 DISK ORGANIZATION

Before using the programs on the DOS 3.3 System Master disk, you must understand how information is organized on a DOS 3.3 disk. Although a single disk can store a large amount of information, all the storage space is rarely used for one purpose. Instead, several small, independent parcels of information usually coexist on a single disk. Every operating system has a scheme for keeping track of all the separate parcels of information.

DOS 3.3 Files

The DOS 3.3 operating system treats each disk as a filing cabinet and each parcel of information as a file in the filing cabinet. In fact, parcels of information on a disk are called *files.* A DOS 3.3 file may contain a program or a collection of data.

Most data files are automatically created by programs as needed. Program files are created by the people who write the programs. Until you start writing your own programs, you will have little occasion to create a program file or data file yourself.

DOS 3.3 File Names

Each DOS 3.3 file has a name so you can identify the different files on a disk. File names are assigned when files are created. The programs on the DOS 3.3 System Master disk tell you when you must assign a file name.

The rules for composing file names are simple. Every name must start with a letter. After that, you can use any combination of letters, digits, symbols, blank spaces, and other characters that can be typed on the keyboard—but no commas. A DOS 3.3 file name cannot be more than 30 characters long. You can use any name that conforms to the rules, but a name that reminds you of what the file contains works best in the long run.

DUPLICATING DISKS

The DOS 3.3 System Master disk contains a program for duplicating disks. There are two versions of the program. One, named COPY, is used with Integer BASIC, when the command prompt > is next to the cursor. The other version, COPYA, is used with Applesoft, when the command prompt] is next to the cursor.

Before starting the duplication program, get the original (source) and duplicate (destination) disks ready. First, write-protect the original disk. This simple precaution may save you considerable grief if you make a mistake later in the procedure.

Choose any spare disk for the duplicate, even a brand-new one. Make sure the duplicate disk is not write-protected.

To start the duplication program, insert the DOS 3.3 System Master disk and type a RUN COPYA or RUN COPY command. When you press the RETURN key, the disk drive becomes active, and soon the message **APPLE DISK DUPLICATION PROGRAM** appears at the top of the screen.

The duplication program begins by requesting the slot number of the drive that will hold the original (source) disk. On the right side of the display screen, the message **DEFAULT=6** tells you that if you enter no slot number, but just press the RETURN key instead, the program will use slot 6 by default. If you want to use a different slot, type its number now and press RETURN.

Next the program asks you to enter the number of the drive, 1 or 2, that the original disk will occupy. It also tells you that if you specify no drive number, but just press the RETURN key, it will use drive 1.

After you designate the slot and drive numbers for the original disk, the program requests the slot and drive numbers for the duplicate (destination) disk. You can specify any drive for the duplicate disk, including the same drive as the original disk. This time if you enter no numbers, but just press the RETURN key, the program will use slot 6 and drive 2 by default.

At this point you will see the message **—PRESS 'RETURN' KEY TO BEGIN COPY—** on the display screen. If you wish to abort the copy operation you can do so now, but only by pressing CONTROL-RESET. The procedure from this point on differs depending on whether you are using one or two drives for the duplication.

If the original and duplicate disks use the same drive, press the RETURN key now to proceed. Messages appear on the display screen asking you to insert first one disk, then the other. The program tells you to swap disks several times. You insert the original disk and the program reads part of it into memory, then you insert the duplicate disk and the program writes part of it out, and so on until the whole disk is duplicated. The first time you insert the duplicate disk, the program displays the message **INITIALIZING**.

If the original and duplicate disks are in separate drives, the program does not tell you to insert them. You must do that before pressing the RETURN key in response to the message **—PRESS**

'RETURN' KEY TO BEGIN COPY—. There is no need to swap disks; the copy proceeds without intervention.

When the copy is finished, the message —**DO YOU WISH TO MAKE ANOTHER COPY?**— appears on the display screen. You can choose to make another copy using the same slot and drive numbers, or you can end the program.

An error message appears during the copying procedure if you leave a drive door open, forget to insert the disk, or try to duplicate onto a write-protected disk. If this happens, restart the program with another RUN command.

THE FILEM AND FID PROGRAMS

The DOS 3.3 System Master disk includes a file developer program, named FID, that lets you catalog, lock, unlock, delete, and verify files. It can also report the amount of space available on a disk. With the FID program you can copy a file or a set of files from one disk to another, even if your system has only one drive.

To start the FID program, insert the DOS 3.3 System Master disk and type a RUN FILEM command as described in Chapter 2. When you press the RETURN key, the disk drive becomes active and the message **EXECUTING FID** appears in the center of the screen. The FILEM program is starting the machine language program named FID. Soon the menu of FID program commands appears on the display screen (Figure 4-1). To execute one of the listed commands, type the number displayed next to it and press RETURN.

File Names in the FID Program

Some of the commands in the FID program require you to enter file names. You can always type an explicit file name, but sometimes it is easier to refer to a whole set of files at once. In the FID program, you can do that by using an ambiguous file name, that is, a single name that can identify any of several files.

The FID program treats an equal sign (=) as a "wild card" that stands for any character or string of characters. For example, the simple file name "=" specifies every file on the disk. As another example, the name "H=" specifies all files that have names starting with the letter H. Similarly, the name "=O" spec-

```
***************************************
*        APPLE ][ FILE DEVELOPER       *
*                                      *
*             FID VERSION M            *
*                                      *
* COPYRIGHT APPLE COMPUTER,INC. 1979  *
***************************************

CHOOSE ONE OF THE FOLLOWING OPTIONS

        <1>    COPY FILES
        <2>    CATALOG
        <3>    SPACE ON DISK
        <4>    UNLOCK FILES
        <5>    LOCK FILES
        <6>    DELETE FILES
        <7>    RESET SLOT & DRIVE
        <8>    VERIFY FILES
        <9>    QUIT

WHICH WOULD YOU LIKE?
```

Figure 4-1. FID program command menu

ifies all files that have names ending with the letter O. You can use more than one = character in an ambiguous file name. The name "=L=" specifies any file that has a name with the letter L in it. In fact, all of the examples in this paragraph would specify the standard greeting program name, HELLO.

The presence of an = character in a file name signals the FID program to ask this question: **DO YOU WANT PROMPTS?** If you answer N (for no), the FID program acts without further approval on every file identified by the ambiguous file name. If you answer Y, the FID program gets your approval before it acts on any file specified by the ambiguous file name. It does this by displaying a file name and waiting for your response. Type Y if you want the file acted on, N if you want it skipped, or Q if you want to quit the command at that point and return to the command menu.

Specifying a Drive

The FID program identifies drives by slot and drive number, a concept explained in Chapter 2. When you first start the FID program, it does not know which drive to use. Therefore, on the first command you request, it asks for a slot and drive number. If the first command you choose is <1> COPY FILES, you must specify two drives, one to copy from and one to copy to (this process is described in detail later in this chapter).

Once you specify a drive, the FID program continues to use that drive with subsequent commands until you specify a different drive using command <7> RESET SLOT AND DRIVE, as described later in this chapter. Also, if you switch back and forth between command <6> COPY FILES and any other command, you must specify the slot and drive again at each command.

If you specify a slot or drive number that has no drive attached, you will eventually see the message **INVALID SLOT** or **INVALID DRIVE**. If that happens, press any key to return to the command menu.

Copying Files

The FID command <1> COPY FILES copies one or more files from one disk to another. You must enter the name of the file you wish copied; use an ambiguous file name to specify a set of files. The program tells you to insert the appropriate disks; you may want to first affix a write-protect label to the source disk as a safety measure.

After typing a file name to copy, you may abort the copy operation by pressing the ESC key. Press any other key to proceed. If the file or files you specify exist on the source disk and there is room for them, they will be copied. As each file is copied, it is announced on the display screen. If problems arise, you will see an error message and the copy operation will be canceled. Copies made before the error occurred will be intact.

If the FID program discovers a file on the destination disk that has the same name as the source file, it asks you what to do about it. Press CONTROL-C, followed by RETURN, to skip copying that file. Or type a new destination file name, and the source file will be copied under that name. Press only the RETURN key and the source file will replace the destination file. However, if the destination file is locked, the FID program requests your permission to ignore the lock before it goes ahead with the replacement.

You can copy from one disk to another using a single drive by specifying the same slot and drive numbers for both the source and destination drives. If you do, the FID program has you insert the source disk first so it can transfer the file into the Apple II's memory. Then it asks you to replace the source disk with the destination disk so it can copy the file from memory to the destination disk. If the file is too large to fit in memory all at once, or if there are several files involved, the copy operation occurs piecemeal: the FID program asks you to switch disks several times.

Identifying Disk Contents

Menu choice <2> CATALOG lists all the file names on a disk. If the disk contains more than 18 files, the FID program displays the first 18 names and waits until you press a key; it then displays the next 20 names. The pause gives you time to read a screenful of file names before they disappear off the top of the screen.

The catalog listing includes three items for each file on the disk, as shown in Figure 4-2. From left to right, it reports

1. The file type (A=Applesoft, I=Integer BASIC, B=Binary, T=Text). If the file is locked, the file type is prefixed with an asterisk.
2. The amount of disk space the file currently uses, as a number of 256-byte blocks. When the file size reaches 256 blocks, the number that appears in the catalog starts over at 0 and thus does not reflect the true size of the file.
3. The file name.

In addition, the disk volume number appears on the first line of the catalog listing.

```
CATALOG

DISK VOLUME 254

*A 003 HELLO
*I 003 APPLESOFT
*B 006 LOADER.OBJ0
*B 042 FPBASIC
*B 042 INTBASIC
*A 003 MASTER
*B 009 MASTER CREATE
*I 009 COPY
*B 003 COPY.OBJ0
*A 009 COPYA
*B 003 CHAIN
*A 014 RENUMBER
*A 003 FILEM
*B 020 FID
*A 003 CONVERT13
*B 027 MUFFIN
*A 003 START13
*B 007 BOOT13
```

Figure 4-2. Partial catalog of a DOS 3.3 System Master disk

Space on Disk

To learn the amount of disk space used and available, choose command <3> SPACE ON DISK. Disk space is measured in 256-byte blocks that the FID program calls *sectors*.

Locking and Unlocking Files

Some program or data files on a disk must be kept permanently. To protect such files against accidental erasure, renaming, or change, DOS 3.3 supports file *locking*. To lock a file, choose the command <5> LOCK FILES and specify the file's name. To unlock a file, choose the command <4> UNLOCK FILES and specify the file's name. You can lock or unlock more than one file at a time by specifying an ambiguous file name.

Deleting Files

With command <6> DELETE FILES, you can delete a single file or, by using an ambiguous file name, you can delete several files at once. Be careful about deleting with ambiguous file names; it is all too easy to delete files you want to keep.

The disk space formerly occupied by deleted files becomes available immediately for other files.

Resetting the Slot and Drive

Choosing command <7> RESET SLOT & DRIVE forces the FID program to ask you for slot and drive numbers immediately after you choose the next command from the menu.

Verifying Files

Command <8> VERIFY FILES checks a file or files you specify for readability. If it detects any problems, the message **I/O ERROR** appears. You may check out a whole set of files by specifying an ambiguous file name.

Quitting FID

To end the FID program and return to the BASIC command prompt, choose command <9> QUIT.

FID Program Errors

One of the following error messages may appear during a FID program command: **DISK FULL**, **DISK WRITE PROTECTED**, **FILE LOCKED**, or **I/O ERROR**. Press any key and the command menu will reappear.

Should an error code number appear instead of one of the messages cited in the last paragraph, you must restart the Apple II by pressing CONTROL-OPEN APPLE-RESET or switching the console off and back on. Then you must restart the FID program.

If an error occurs during a file copy operation, immediately check the catalog of the destination disk for an incomplete file. The incomplete file will have the same name as the last source file displayed (or a different name if you gave it one) but will use fewer sectors than the source file. Delete the incomplete file at once, before attempting to copy any more files to the same disk.

Fundamentals of BASIC Programming 5

This chapter teaches you how to start writing your own programs on the Apple II using the BASIC programming language. It explains the two different modes of operation available in BASIC, tells you how to type BASIC commands, and details advanced techniques for correcting and changing those commands.

PROGRAMMING LANGUAGES

A programming language is the medium of communication between you and the computer. You use it to tell the computer exactly how to perform a given task. A program is simply a list of instructions that the computer follows to get a job done.

There are many programming languages. Some, like BASIC, are general-purpose languages, while others are designed for specific areas like business, science, graphics, and text manipulation. Programming languages are as varied as spoken languages. In addition to BASIC, other common programming languages are Pascal, C, FORTRAN, COBOL, PILOT, Logo, and FORTH.

Apple II computers can use several programming languages, BASIC and Pascal among them. This book concentrates on describing how to program the Apple II in BASIC.

Syntax

No matter what the programming language, every program statement must be written following a well-defined set of rules.

These rules taken together are referred to as *syntax*. Each programming language has its own syntax.

Some programming language syntax rules are obvious. For example, a plus sign (+) represents addition. You do not have to be a programmer to understand that. Normally, you would use an × or · for multiplication, but computer keyboards have no such symbols. Therefore, most programming languages use an asterisk (*) to represent multiplication. You will simply have to memorize that fact, along with some other rules that may seem arbitrary and meaningless at first.

About BASIC

BASIC is a popular programming language because it is easy to learn but still powerful enough to handle most applications in business, industry, and at home. Its roots date to 1964, when it emerged from Dartmouth College as an introductory language for programmers who shared a single large computer system. Those programmers never saw the computer itself, only a teletype. Since then, dozens of computer manufacturers have expanded and improved BASIC to enable it to handle keyboards, display screens, printers, disk drives, and so on. Each manufacturer changed the language in its own way. The result is that BASIC, like English, has many dialects.

Dialects of BASIC

Apple II computers give you a choice of two dialects of BASIC: Integer BASIC and Applesoft. Most programmers choose Applesoft over Integer BASIC. Applesoft has more commands and features, including more graphics commands and the ability to use numbers with decimal fractions. Integer BASIC programs, however, execute faster than Applesoft programs.

Because of the differences between the two dialects, programs written in one dialect usually do not work correctly when the Apple II is expecting instructions in the other dialect. Furthermore, a BASIC program written for the Apple II may not work on another computer, even if the other computer also claims to be programmable in BASIC. You must manually translate an existing BASIC program to the dialect of BASIC that is used by the computer on which you wish to run the program.

Generally speaking, the descriptions and examples in this chapter and throughout the rest of the book pertain equally to Applesoft and Integer BASIC. Any features peculiar to one version will be clearly identified. Unless the text states otherwise, all program examples will work in Integer BASIC or Applesoft.

STARTING BASIC

There are many ways to start BASIC on an Apple II. The method you use depends on which model you have, what accessories it has, and which operating system—ProDOS or DOS 3.3—you use. Also, the method for starting Applesoft differs from the method for starting Integer BASIC.

All the instructions in this section assume you have already turned on your computer as described in Chapter 2.

Starting Applesoft on an Apple IIe

If you wish to use the ProDOS operating system, you can start Applesoft as follows:

1. Insert the ProDOS User's Disk in drive 1.
2. Press CONTROL-OPEN APPLE-RESET to restart the computer.
3. When the STARTUP program's main menu appears, choose Applesoft by pressing the B key.

If you wish to use the DOS 3.3 operating system, you can start Applesoft as follows:

1. Insert the DOS 3.3 System Master disk in drive 1.
2. Press CONTROL-OPEN APPLE-RESET to restart the computer.

If your Apple IIe has no disk drives, or if its drives are not working, you can also start Applesoft without an operating system. Follow these steps:

1. Open the door on drive 1, and leave it open. (Skip this step if your computer does not have drives.)
2. Press CONTROL-OPEN APPLE-RESET to restart the computer.
3. If drive 1 starts chattering and whirring, press CONTROL-RESET.

Starting Applesoft on an Apple II Plus

If your Apple II Plus has 64K or more of read/write memory (RAM), follow the instructions in the previous section for starting Applesoft on an Apple IIe.

If your Apple II Plus has less than 64K of RAM, you cannot use ProDOS. Follow the instructions in the previous section for starting with the DOS 3.3 System Master disk or for starting with no disk on an Apple IIe.

Starting Applesoft On a Standard Apple II

If your standard Apple II has a Language card installed, follow the instructions in the section above for starting Applesoft on an Apple IIe using a DOS 3.3 System Master disk.

If your standard Apple II has an Applesoft ROM accessory card inside the computer in slot 0, you have *firmware* Applesoft. You can follow the instructions in the section above for starting Applesoft on an Apple IIe using a DOS 3.3 System Master disk. You can also start Applesoft without an operating system as follows:

1. Locate the switch that protrudes through the back panel from the Applesoft ROM accessory card. Flip the switch up.
2. Press the RESET key.
3. Press CONTROL-B and then RETURN.

If your standard Apple II has neither a Language card nor an Applesoft ROM card in slot 0, you must load Applesoft from cassette tape. The procedure is explained in Chapter 2.

After Starting Applesoft

You can tell Applesoft is started and ready when you see its prompt character, a square bracket (]), at the left edge of the screen with the cursor next to it. At this point, the Apple II is waiting for you to type an Applesoft command.

Switching to Integer BASIC

You can switch to Integer BASIC from Applesoft by typing the command INT and pressing the RETURN key. After you switch to Integer BASIC, the command prompt is an angle bracket (>). You can switch back to Applesoft by typing the command FP and pressing the RETURN key.

Integer BASIC is not available on any Apple II when you use the ProDOS operating system. It is available on an Apple IIe or Apple II Plus when you use the DOS 3.3 operating system, but unavailable when you use no operating system. Integer BASIC is available on any standard Apple II when you use the DOS 3.3 operating system or no operating system.

Creating a ProDOS BASIC Disk

Using the STARTUP program on the ProDOS User's Disk as described in Chapter 3, you can easily create a disk that starts Applesoft automatically. First you format a disk (remember that formatting erases all the information on the disk). Then you copy the files named PRODOS and BASIC.SYSTEM from the ProDOS User's Disk to the newly formatted disk.

Now to start BASIC, merely insert the newly created BASIC disk in drive 1 and switch on the computer. You no longer have to go through the main menu in the STARTUP program on the ProDOS User's Disk. If the computer is already on, you can start BASIC by inserting your BASIC disk and pressing CONTROL-OPEN APPLE-RESET to restart the Apple II.

TYPING COMMANDS

When the Apple II seems to be doing nothing except flashing the cursor, it is probably waiting for a command. You issue BASIC commands by typing them on the keyboard. The BASIC interpreter (Applesoft or Integer BASIC) examines each command you enter and tries to determine what to do. If you type everything correctly, the BASIC interpreter can direct the computer to carry out your command. Thus, the BASIC interpreter, not the Apple II, determines the validity of the commands you type.

On any machine except an enhanced Apple IIe, you must type commands in capital letters. To avoid confusion, you should depress the CAPS LOCK key if you have an original Apple IIe. On an enhanced Apple IIe, you can type commands in any combination of uppercase and lowercase letters.

If you make a mistake while typing in a command, you cannot use the DELETE key to correct it. The DELETE key does not back up along a command line. Instead, use the ← key as described later in this chapter.

Terminating Commands

In most cases, the BASIC interpreter does not act on a command until you press the RETURN key to indicate you are finished typing it. If you type a command and nothing happens, you probably forgot to terminate it by pressing RETURN.

You can cancel a command by pressing CONTROL-X instead of RETURN.

Display Screen Line Length

All Apple II models can display 40 characters on each screen line. Many have a special accessory card installed that makes it possible to display up to 80 characters per screen line. This feature is especially common on Apple IIe machines.

When you first turn on an Apple II, the 80-column adapter is inactive, so each display line is 40 characters wide. To activate the adapter and enable 80-character lines, use the following command:

```
]PR#3
```

The command above works only if the 80-column adapter is installed either in slot 3 of a standard Apple II or Apple II Plus, or in the special auxiliary slot provided for it on an Apple IIe. If the adapter card is in a different slot, use that slot number instead of the 3 in the PR# command. If you use the PR# command with the wrong slot number, the computer will behave unpredictably, and may even lock up, forcing you to reset it with CONTROL-RESET.

Many companies make 80-column adapter cards for the Apple II, and while all enable 80-character display lines, there are some differences among them. The following description of 80-character mode applies specifically to an Apple IIe fitted with an Apple brand 80-column adapter card.

When you press the RETURN key after typing a PR#3 command, the Apple IIe clears the display screen. The cursor and command prompt reappear in the upper left-hand corner of the screen, which is called the *home* position. The cursor changes from a flashing checked square to a solid-color rectangle. Like the cursor, characters you type now will be half their former width. This is called *active-80 mode,* because the 80-column adapter is active and enabling 80-character lines.

If the characters are too small to read easily, you can shift back to the wider size by pressing the ESC key, releasing it, and then pressing the 4 key. Every character on the left half of the display screen doubles in size, and the characters on the right half are lost. This is called *active-40 mode.* The 80-column adapter is still active, but has switched over to 40-character lines. To switch back to active-80 mode and its 80-character lines, press ESC, then 8.

You may notice that when you switch between active-80 and active-40 modes, the cursor design changes momentarily. Pressing the ESC key when the 80-column adapter is active etches a cross onto the cursor. The cross disappears as soon as you press the 4 or 8 key. You can ignore the cross for now; you will use it when editing commands and program lines, topics discussed later in this chapter.

Typing ESC-CONTROL-Q changes the cursor back to a blinking checked square and the line width to 40. Notice that none of these ESC key commands require you to press the RETURN key. Typing CONTROL-RESET also deactivates the 80-column adapter, but may leave meaningless random characters on the display screen.

IMMEDIATE MODE COMMANDS

When you first start BASIC, it is in *immediate mode,* also called direct or calculator mode. In this mode, the computer responds immediately to any instructions you issue.

Displaying Characters

The PRINT command lets you write your own messages on the display screen. Try typing in this example:

```
]PRINT "LET SLEEPING DOGS LIE"
```

Don't forget to press the RETURN key after the last quotation mark. The Apple II prints the following message:

```
LET SLEEPING DOGS LIE

]▒
```

A PRINT command like the one above instructs the computer to display everything between the quotation marks. The cursor disappears momentarily while the computer executes the command, then reappears, telling you the computer is ready for another command.

There is a limit to the length of the message you can put between quotation marks. The limit is different for Integer BASIC and Applesoft, but in both cases it exceeds the width of the display screen. This means a command can occupy more than one display line. Long commands like this automatically wrap around to the next line on the display screen. Try this command:

```
]PRINT "UNDER NORMAL CIRCUMSTANCES, THE
MAN WOULD BE CONSIDERED CRAZY"
```

When you press RETURN, you'll see this (on a 40-column screen):

```
UNDER NORMAL CIRCUMSTANCES, THE MAN WOUL
D BE CONSIDERED CRAZY

]▒
```

Integer BASIC allows about 120 characters per command. If you exceed the limit, you will get the message ***** TOO LONG ERR** after you press the RETURN key.

Applesoft allows 255 characters per command. As you approach the limit, the Apple II starts beeping. When you exceed the limit, it displays a backslash (\ ) and automatically cancels your entry, as if you had pressed CONTROL-X.

Displaying Calculations

You can use the PRINT command in immediate mode as you would use a calculator; it responds directly with the answers to arithmetic calculations. Try these examples:

```
]PRINT 4+6
10

]PRINT 500-437
63

]PRINT 100*23
2300

]PRINT 3^2
9

]PRINT 3*4*10-800
-680

]▒
```

In each calculation above, the answer will appear on the line immediately following the command when you press RETURN. Notice that you do not use quotation marks in these examples. Type one of the examples above with quotation marks and watch what happens. (The computer prints the problem, not the answer.)

Integer BASIC has a maximum and minimum limit on the value of a calculation. If the value of a calculation is more than 32767 at any point during the calculation, the error message ***** >32767 ERR** appears. If the value is less than −32767, the message **−*** >32767 ERR** appears. Some examples of these errors are shown below. The last example shows division by zero.

```
>PRINT -32766-2
-*** >32767 ERR
>PRINT 2^15-1
*** >32767 ERR
>PRINT 10/0
*** >32767 ERR
>▒
```

Decimal fractions are not allowed in Integer BASIC. If you

perform a division calculation that does not come out even, the remainder will be discarded. For example, try this calculation:

```
>PRINT 9/2
4
>▒
```

Applesoft does allow fractions. Numeric values can have a total of nine *significant digits*, including both fractional and nonfractional parts. This means that values with more than nine digits are rounded off to nine or fewer nonzero digits. The following examples illustrate how this works:

```
]PRINT  12.34567896
12.345679

]PRINT  12.34567894
12.3456789

]▒
```

If you try some of your own arithmetic calculations in immediate mode in Applesoft, you will notice that the result is sometimes displayed using scientific notation.

```
]PRINT 10^9
1E+09

]▒
```

If you do not understand scientific notation, stick to simple calculations for now. We will investigate scientific notation and numeric values in the next chapter.

Mixing Characters and Calculations

The PRINT command can also mix messages and calculations. To do that, type the command word PRINT, then type the first message or calculation. Next, type a semicolon, and after that type the second message or calculation. Here is an example:

```
]PRINT  2*8*11+2*8*14;" SQ.  FT."
400 SQ. FT.

]▒
```

You can include as many messages and calculations as you like, in any combination. Just separate one from another with a semicolon.

Abbreviated PRINT Command

Applesoft allows you to abbreviate the PRINT statement as a question mark. Here are some examples you can try:

```
]?"TIME MARCHES ON"
TIME MARCHES ON

]?13-46*6
-263

]▒
```

Error Messages

Both Applesoft and Integer BASIC are very fussy about the way you type commands. If you make a spelling or punctuation error in a command, the Apple II beeps to draw your attention to the error, and a message appears to suggest the likely cause of trouble. Applesoft and Integer BASIC have limited diagnostic abilities, so do not expect a definitive analysis of your error. They must choose from fewer than 40 messages to describe one of the thousands of errors and combinations of errors that can occur.

There are some errors the computer cannot detect. Suppose you want to multiply 28 times 187, and you type this by mistake:

```
]PRINT 28+187
215

]▒
```

In this example, the Apple II has responded with the correct answer to the calculation. It cannot tell that you accidentally typed the wrong arithmetic operation. Likewise, neither Applesoft nor Integer BASIC check the accuracy of text you type between quotation marks, so they do not detect mistakes there.

Error messages have a slightly different format in Integer BASIC than in Applesoft, as the following shows.

Applesoft

```
]PRNIT "THE LAVA FLOWS"

?SYNTAX ERROR
]▒
```

Integer BASIC

```
>PRNIT "THE LAVA FLOWS"
*** SYNTAX ERR
>▒
```

EDITING COMMAND LINES

The simplest way to change a command line is to retype it. This is unsatisfactory for several reasons. Retyping is a time-consuming chore and the chances of typographical errors are high. Fortunately, there is a way to modify command lines you have already typed, as long as they are still visible. This is possible both in Integer BASIC and in Applesoft because anything displayed on the screen is *live*. In other words, you can edit anything on the screen. By using the ESC key in conjunction with several other keys, you can move the cursor around on the screen at will. This allows you to position the cursor to the beginning of any line that is displayed on the screen. Then you can use the → key to pass over parts of the command line you wish to leave unchanged. You can replace, insert, or delete characters anywhere on the line.

Moving the Cursor

There are three ways to move the cursor using keystrokes. The easiest method works only on the Apple IIe; a slightly less convenient method works on most Apple II models; and the most awkward method works on any Apple II.

On the Apple IIe, you can use the ←, →, ↓, and ↑ keys to move the cursor around on the display screen. But first you must press the ESC key to put the computer in *escape mode* (sometimes called *edit mode*). If the Apple IIe is in active-40 or active-80 mode (80-column adapter active), pressing ESC etches a cross on the solid white cursor. The cross reminds you that the computer is in

ILLUSTRATION COURTESY OF APPLE COMPUTER, INC.

Figure 5-1. Cursor movement keys in escape mode (most Apple II models)

escape mode. If the 80-column adapter is inactive (or not installed), pressing the ESC key still puts the computer in escape mode, even though the cursor remains a flashing checked square.

On an Apple II Plus (or Apple IIe), you can use the I, J, K, and M keys for cursor movement in escape mode. Because of the way these four keys are situated on the keyboard, they form a directional control pad (Figure 5-1). As with the arrow keys on the Apple IIe, you must press the ESC key to put the computer in escape mode before the I, J, K, or M key will move the cursor.

On any Apple II, you can move the cursor around on the screen by pressing two keys in sequence. First press and release the ESC key, then press either the A, B, C, or D key. The A key moves the cursor right, the B key moves it left, C moves it down, and D moves it up (Figure 5-2). Each time you want to move the cursor one position, you must press the ESC key and the appropriate letter key, A, B, C, or D.

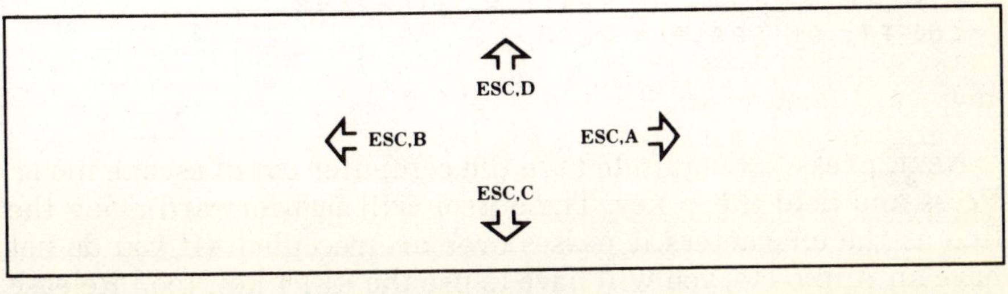

Figure 5-2. Cursor movement (any Apple II)

On an Apple IIe, the ←, →, ↓, and ↑ keys will repeat if you hold them down, moving the cursor longer distances with fewer keystrokes. On an Apple II Plus, you can use the REPT key with the I, J, K, and M keys to do the same thing.

Changing Characters

Replacing one character with another is easy. Using one of the methods described above, move the cursor to the first character of the line in which you want to make a change. Then, making sure the computer is *not* in escape mode, use the → key to copy over the characters you want to leave alone. Stop when you get to the first character you want to change. Type the new characters right over the old ones. Use the → key again to recopy to the end of the line. Finally, press the RETURN key to effect the change.

For example, suppose you have just typed the following command to calculate the cubic feet of storage space in a 10 × 25 × 8-foot storage locker:

```
]PRINT "CU. FT. OF SPACE = ";10*25*8
CU. FT. OF SPACE = 2000

]■
```

You can easily change this immediate mode line to calculate the storage space in storage lockers of different sizes. To change the dimensions to 10 × 25 × 14, for example, first position the cursor at the beginning of the immediate mode line. Use any of the cursor movement techniques described above. On an Apple IIe, for example, press the ESC key to put the computer in escape mode and then press the ↑ key three times to move the cursor up to the line where you want to make the change.

```
]::RINT "CU. FT. OF SPACE = ";10*25*8
CU. FT. OF SPACE = 2000

]
```

Next, press ESC again to take the computer out of escape mode. Press and hold the → key. The cursor will fast-forward along the line as the characters it passes over are recopied. (If you do not have an Apple IIe, you will have to use the REPT key, too.) Release the key (or keys) in time to stop the cursor when it gets to the 8.

If you overshoot or undershoot by not releasing the key at the proper time, backspace or recopy one character at a time by tapping the ← and → keys.

```
]PRINT "CU. FT. OF SPACE = ";10*25*█4
CU. FT. OF SPACE = 2000

]
```

With the cursor positioned over the 8, type in the new room dimension of 14 and press the RETURN key.

```
]PRINT "CU. FT. OF SPACE = ";10*25*14
CU. FT. OF SPACE = 3500

]█
```

Deleting Characters

With a slight change, the general procedure outlined above for changing characters will also work for deleting them. The only difference comes when, instead of typing new characters over old, you use cursor movement techniques to skip over the old, unwanted characters. On an Apple IIe, you can use the → key to skip over characters. Be sure the computer is in escape mode, or you will recopy the characters instead of deleting them. For example, with the cursor like this,

```
]█RINT "OUT, DAMNED SPOT! OUT, I STRAY!"
```

use the → key (*not* in escape mode) to recopy the characters up to the mistake:

```
]PRINT "OUT, DAMNED SPOT! OUT, I S█RAY!"
```

Using cursor movement keys only, skip over the two extra characters T and R. On an Apple IIe, for example, you would press the ESC key to put the computer in escape mode and then press the → key twice.

```
]PRINT "OUT, DAMNED SPOT! OUT, I STR::Y!"
```

Now press ESC again to take the computer out of escape mode, and recopy the remaining characters with the → key. Press the RETURN key, and the message is printed correctly.

```
]PRINT "OUT, DAMNED SPOT! OUT, I STRAY!"
OUT, DAMNED SPOT! OUT, I SAY!

]■
```

You can also use the SPACEBAR to delete characters by replacing them with blank spaces. To blank out all characters from the cursor position to the end of the display line, press ESC and then E. This has the same effect as pressing the SPACEBAR repeatedly until you reach the end of the display line, but in this case the cursor doesn't move. Characters on the next display line are not erased from the screen even if they were part of the same command.

Inserting Characters

Inserting characters into a line may seem confusing at first because the final results are not immediately apparent. The Apple II cannot push apart characters on a line to make room for insertions. Instead, you insert text above the line with the aid of the cursor movement keys. You must remember that the command line displayed on the screen is not necessarily an exact replica of the command line stored in the computer's memory.

For example, suppose you want to insert the word BAND in front of the word WAGON in the example below:

```
]PRINT "ON THE WAGON"
ON THE WAGON

]■
```

Press ESC to put the computer in escape mode. Then use the cursor movement keys (↑, ←, I, J, and so on) to position the cursor so it is on the first character of the command line, as follows:

```
]::RINT "ON THE WAGON"
ON THE WAGON

]
```

Press ESC again to take the computer out of escape mode, and use the → key to copy over the first part of the line, stopping at the W. Make sure the computer is not in escape mode while you do this.

```
]PRINT "ON THE █AGON"
ON THE WAGON

]
```

Press the ESC key followed by the ↑ key (or I key) to move the cursor up one line. If there are characters to the right of the cursor on this line, you can erase them by first pressing the E key and then ESC to get back into escape mode).

```
                ▒
]PRINT "ON THE WAGON"
ON THE WAGON

]
```

Press ESC again to take the computer out of escape mode, and type the word BAND.

```
               BAND█
]PRINT "ON THE WAGON"
ON THE WAGON

]
```

In escape mode again, position the cursor on the letter W on the original line. Remember, if you're not in escape mode the ← key will erase the characters it passes over; do not un-insert your insertions!

```
               BAND
]PRINT "ON THE ▒AGON"
ON THE WAGON

]
```

Finally, use the → key to copy over the rest of the line. (Make sure the computer is not in escape mode.) Press the RETURN key to reexecute the command.

```
               BAND
]PRINT "ON THE WAGON"
ON THE BANDWAGON

]█
```

PROGRAMMED MODE STATEMENTS

There is only so much you can do in immediate mode. Instead of typing commands for immediate execution, you can type them into a program and defer their execution until later. This is called *programmed mode* (also called deferred mode or indirect mode). In programmed mode, the computer accepts and stores commands in its memory, but does not act on them until you tell it to do so. In this mode, commands are usually called *statements*, but people do use the terms interchangeably. Most immediate mode commands can be used as programmed mode statements, and vice versa, although there are a few that work in only one mode. Appendix A lists all commands and statements and specifies those that are limited to immediate or programmed mode.

Line Numbers

Most immediate mode commands can be converted to program statements by adding a *line number*. A line number is simply a one- to five-digit number entered at the beginning of a program line. Here is an example:

```
]10 PRINT "RUBBER BABY BUGGY BUMPERS"
```

In Applesoft, line numbers can range between 0 and 63999. Integer BASIC allows line numbers between 0 and 32767.

Line numbers determine the sequence of program lines in a BASIC program. The first line must have the smallest line number, and the last line must have the largest. Even if you type the lines out of order, the Apple II will internally rearrange them in the proper sequence by line number.

Listing Program Lines

You can see what program lines the computer has stored in its memory at any time by typing the command LIST. Suppose you type in the following program:

```
]30 PRINT "CUT"
]10 PRINT "FISH"
]20 PRINT "OR"
]40 PRINT "BAIT"
]▒
```

Looking back at your work, you notice that the lines are out of order. This makes no difference, because the Apple II has internally rearranged them by line number. To reassure yourself, you can list the lines the computer has in its memory with a LIST command:

```
]LIST

10  PRINT "FISH"
20  PRINT "OR"
30  PRINT "CUT"
40  PRINT "BAIT"

]▒
```

This is called a *program listing.* There are variations of the LIST command that allow you to list one line at a time or a group of lines. This latter option is especially handy when you have a long program that will not fit on the display screen all at once. With the last example program still in the computer's memory, the command LIST 10 will list just line 10, like this:

```
]LIST 10

10  PRINT "FISH"

]▒
```

To list several sequential program lines, you must specify both the starting and ending line numbers, as in this example:

```
]LIST 20,40

20  PRINT "OR"
30  PRINT "CUT"
40  PRINT "BAIT"

]▒
```

In Applesoft, you can list all program lines up to and including a specific program line. You can also list all program lines from a specific line to the end of the program. Here are examples of those two versions of the LIST command:

```
]LIST ,20

10  PRINT "FISH"
20  PRINT "OR"
```

```
]LIST 20,

20 PRINT "OR"
30 PRINT "CUT"
40 PRINT "BAIT"

]▒
```

You can halt a listing before it reaches the end by typing CONTROL-C. This is especially useful for halting the interminable listing of a long program.

On Apple IIe and Apple II Plus machines you can temporarily suspend the listing of a program by pressing CONTROL-S. The listing resumes when you press CONTROL-S again. This feature allows you to review the listing of a long program at your own pace.

Program Execution

The computer *executes* or *runs* a program when it performs the operations the program specifies. An immediate mode command is like a one-line program that is executed as soon as you press the RETURN key. In programmed mode you must issue the RUN command to execute a program. Each time you do so, the entire program runs again. The following example illustrates this:

```
]LIST

10 PRINT "FISH"
20 PRINT "OR"
30 PRINT "CUT"
40 PRINT "BAIT"
50 END

]RUN

EITHER
FISH
OR
CUT
BAIT

]▒
```

An END statement like the one on line 50 in the example above tells BASIC to stop executing the program and to then return to immediate mode. Therefore an END statement should be the last statement your program executes. Applesoft does not require an END statement. It ends a program automatically when it runs out of statements. Still, it's a good idea to end your programs properly, with END statements.

A plain RUN command like the one in the previous example starts the program at its lowest line number. With a variation of the RUN command, you can specify which line to start on. The following RUN command executes the last two lines of the previous program:

```
]RUN 30
 CUT
 BAIT

 ]▒
```

Multiple-Statement Lines

You can put more than one statement on a single program line. The first statement follows the line number. The second statement follows the first, with a colon (:) in between. In other words, use colons to separate the statements on a multiple-statement line. Here is an example:

```
]10 PRINT "FISH":PRINT "BAIT":END
```

Applesoft allows multiple-statement program lines in both programmed and immediate modes. In both cases, the line length limit is 255 characters, as described earlier in this chapter.

Integer BASIC allows multiple-statement lines only in programmed mode. Immediate mode lines can have just one command each. Line length is limited to approximately 150 characters. The exact line length limit depends on the content of the line.

Program Comments

If you write a short program with five or ten statements, you will probably have little trouble remembering what the program does—unless you leave it around for six months and then try to use it again. If you write a longer program with 100 or 200 statements, then you are quite likely to forget something important about the program the very next time you use it. After you have written dozens of programs, you will stand no chance of remembering each program in detail. The solution to this problem is to document your program by including comments or remarks that describe what is going on.

Use REM statements to put remarks in your program. Here is an example:

```
]10 REM DISPLAY BOILING POINT OF WATER
]20 REM IN SEVERAL TEMPERATURE SCALES
]30 PRINT 212: REM FAHRENHEIT
]40 PRINT 100: REM CELSIUS
]50 PRINT 80: REM REAUMUR
```

The computer skips over REM statements; it does not execute them. Everything on a program line that follows the command word REM is treated as an explanatory comment, so a REM statement must come last on a multiple-statement line.

Automatic Line Numbering

Integer BASIC will automatically number your program lines for you. Use the AUTO command to institute this feature. The computer will then supply the next line number each time you press the RETURN key. Here is an example:

```
>AUTO 1000

>1010 PRINT "HOW MANY YARDS IN A MILE?"
>1020 PRINT 5280/3
>1030
>▒
```

As you can see from the example, the AUTO command requires you to specify the line number where automatic line numbering should start. You can also specify the increment between line numbers. The following example illustrates this:

```
>AUTO 1000, 100

>1100 PRINT "HOW MANY YARDS IN A MILE?"
>1200 PRINT 5280/3
>1300
>▒
```

In the example above, line numbers are incremented by 100. If you do not specify the increment, the Apple II uses an increment of 10 by default.

The computer will not advance to the next line number if it finds an error on the line you just finished, or if you entered nothing on the line except RETURN.

To get out of the automatic line numbering mode, type CONTROL-X. This cancels the line number provided by the computer. Following that, type the command MAN to return to manual line numbering.

EDITING BASIC PROGRAMS

Few programmers can write perfect programs and type them in without a mistake. Even fewer can avoid making changes and improvements as they go along. Fortunately, the techniques presented earlier in this chapter for editing command lines also work with programmed mode lines. There are also ways to add, delete, and replace entire program lines.

Changing Lines

In order to edit anything, whether it is an immediate mode command or a program line, it must be visible on the display screen. In the case of an immediate mode line, if it's not visible you'll have to retype it. But you can redisplay programmed mode lines with the LIST command. Simply specify starting and ending line numbers for a screen-sized section of the program. If you list too much, stop the listing by pressing CONTROL-C while the line you want to change is still on the screen. It doesn't matter how a line gets on the screen; once it's there, you can change it.

When a program line is too long to fit on one display line, the LIST command automatically continues it on the next display line. The continuation lines are indented five spaces. You can keep the LIST command from indenting continuation lines. First, clear the entire display screen by pressing ESC followed by @. Then type the following command:

```
POKE 33,30
```

In addition to suppressing the indentation, the preceding command reduces the width of the display screen to 30 characters. This technique works only when the screen width is 40 and does not change the character size. Don't worry for now about how the POKE command works; we will explore it in more detail in Chapter 8.

To return the display to a width of 40, type this:

```
POKE 33,40
```

Replacing Lines

To replace a program line with a new one, just type in the new line using the old line number. The Apple II automatically deletes an existing program line that has the same line number as one you type in later.

Deleting Lines

To delete an entire line, type its line number and then press the RETURN key. When you list the program, you will see that the line and line number are no longer part of the program. Here is an example:

```
]100 PRINT "VIRTUE IS ITS OWN REWARD"
]110 PRINT "IF THE SHOE FITS, WEAR IT"
]120 PRINT "WHERE THERE'S SMOKE, THERE'S
 FIRE"
]130 PRINT "LOOK BEFORE YOU LEAP"
]140 PRINT "BREVITY IS THE SOUL OF WIT"
]150 END
]110
]130
]LIST

100 PRINT "VIRTUE IS ITS OWN REW
   ARD"
120 PRINT "WHERE THERE'S SMOKE,
   THERE'S FIRE"
140 PRINT "BREVITY IS THE SOUL O
   F WIT"
```

```
150 END

]▒
```

You can use the DEL command to delete a block of program lines. Continuing the example above,

```
]DEL 110,140

]LIST

100 PRINT "VIRTUE IS ITS OWN REW
   ARD"

150 END
]▒
```

In the example above, the command DEL 110,140 deletes all program lines starting at line number 110 and ending with line number 140. Even though line 110 does not exist, all lines between 110 and 140 are deleted.

Adding Lines

You can type in new program lines in any order, at any time. Their line numbers determine their position in the program. The Apple II automatically merges them with any other program lines currently in memory. Try adding lines 120 and 110 back into the example above.

```
]120 PRINT "WHERE THERE'S SMOKE, THERE'S
 FIRE"
]110 PRINT "IF THE SHOE FITS, WEAR IT"
]LIST

100 PRINT "VIRTUE IS ITS OWN REW
   ARD"
110 PRINT "IF THE SHOE FITS, WEA
   R IT"
120 PRINT "WHERE THERE'S SMOKE,
   THERE'S FIRE"
150 END

]▒
```

Renumbering Program Lines

The DOS 3.3 System Master disk contains a program, named RENUMBER, that can renumber the lines in an Applesoft program. You must run RENUMBER before you start typing any program lines; you may want to do this right after starting the computer. The RENUMBER program adds a new command to Applesoft and displays a summary of its options (Figure 5-3).

Running the RENUMBER program adds the ampersand

```
&&&&&&&&&&&&&&&&&&&&&&&&&&&&&&&&&&&&&&&
&                                     &
&          APPLESO¯T RENUMBER         &
&                                     &
&  COPYRIGHT APPLE COMPUTER,INC. 1978 &
&                                     &
&&&&&&&&&&&&&&&&&&&&&&&&&&&&&&&&&&&&&&&


RENUMBER    (DEFAULT VALUES)

& {FIRST 10] [,INC 10] [,S 0] [,E 63999]


MERGE

&H   PUT PROGRAM ON HOLD
&M   MERGE TO PROGRAM ON HOLD



PRESS 'RETURN' TO CONTINUE...█
```

Figure 5-3. Renumber (& command) options

command, &, to Applesoft. It can go through your program and assign new, equally spaced line numbers. The following example illustrates this:

```
]LIST

6 PRINT "FISH"
73 PRINT "OR"
85 PRINT "CUT"
99 PRINT "BAIT"
1400 END

]&

]LIST

10 PRINT "FISH"
20 PRINT "OR"
30 PRINT "CUT"
40 PRINT "BAIT"
50 END

]▒
```

The & command has two options that let you restrict the part of the program that is renumbered. The S option specifies the line number to start on and the E option specifies the number to end on. To use these options, add an S followed by the starting line number, then a comma, and after that an E followed by the ending line number, like this:

```
]LIST

6 PRINT "FISH"
73 PRINT "OR"
85 PRINT "CUT"
99 PRINT "BAIT"
1400 END

]&S73,E99
]LIST

6 PRINT "FISH"
10 PRINT "OR"
20 PRINT "CUT"
30 PRINT "BAIT"
1400 END

]▒
```

Two other options, F and I, let you designate the first new line number to use and the increment between newly assigned line numbers. Here is an example:

```
]LIST

6 PRINT "FISH"
73 PRINT "OR"
85 PRINT "CUT"
99 PRINT "BAIT"
1400 END

]&F100,I20

]LIST

100 PRINT "FISH"
120 PRINT "OR"
140 PRINT "CUT"
160 PRINT "BAIT"
180 END

]▒
```

You can use all four options in one & command, and can list them in any order. You can also use one option alone, any two options, or any three options. If any option is missing, the & command uses a standard number by default, as listed in Table 5-1. If an error occurs during the renumbering process, a message explains the problem. The messages are listed in Appendix B.

A program may contain statements that refer to other program line numbers. The & command automatically corrects the

Table 5-1. Renumber Command Options

Option	Specifies
S	Line number to start renumbering
E	Line number to end renumbering
F	First new line number to use
I	Increment between newly assigned line numbers

line number references in those statements. That includes DEL, LIST, and RUN when they are used in programmed mode. It also includes some statements that are covered in later chapters: GOTO, ON-GOTO, GOSUB, ON-GOSUB, and IF-THEN. The & command does not correct line numbers that are in REM statements.

Caution: Do not reset the computer by pressing CONTROL-RESET while renumbering is in process, or you will destroy your program. The FP command may destroy the & command, forcing you to rerun the RENUMBER program to restore it. Doing that erases your Applesoft program.

Clearing Out Old Programs

Because the Apple II stores programs in its memory, you must specifically instruct it to erase an old program before you type in a new one. Do this by typing the command NEW. If you forget to type NEW, your new program will be mixed in with your old program.

ENDING BASIC

Switching off the Apple II ends a session with Applesoft or Integer BASIC, as does restarting with another disk (by inserting the new disk and pressing CONTROL-OPEN APPLE-RESET). Be careful not to switch off or restart the computer while it is executing a command or program.

BASIC Programs on Disk and Cassette 6

Since the Apple II can keep only one BASIC program in its memory at a time, you need some way to store a program outside memory and retrieve it on demand. Depending on how you start the Apple II and on which dialect of BASIC you use, you can store programs on cassettes only, DOS 3.3 disks and cassettes, or ProDOS disks. Table 6-1 lists the possibilities.

Applesoft and Integer BASIC have commands for working with programs and other files on disk. In many cases, the commands parallel features of the STARTUP program on the ProDOS User's Disk and the FILEM program on the DOS 3.3 System Master disk. The commands for ProDOS disks are similar to the commands for DOS 3.3, but they are not identical. (ProDOS commands are not available in Integer BASIC.)

This chapter presents the disk and cassette commands in three sections: one for ProDOS disks, one for DOS 3.3 disks, and one for cassettes. The sections are completely self-contained, so read only the ones that interest you. You will find additional information about using cassettes in Chapter 2. Chapter 4 contains an introduction to DOS 3.3 files, catalogs, and names. The introduction to ProDOS files, directories, names, paths, and prefixes is in Chapter 3.

PRODOS COMMANDS

When you start an Apple II with a ProDOS disk, Applesoft includes commands for storing and retrieving programs on disks.

Table 6-1. Disk and Cassette Command Availability

Startup Disk	BASIC Dialect	Commands Available
ProDOS	Applesoft	ProDOS
DOS 3.3	Applesoft	DOS 3.3 and cassette
DOS 3.3	Integer BASIC	DOS 3.3 and cassette
None	Applesoft	Cassette
None	Integer BASIC	Cassette

It also includes commands that mimic many of the menu choices in the STARTUP program on the ProDOS User's Disk, which is described in Chapter 3. There are commands to change the program name prefix, to display and create directories, and to delete, rename, lock, and unlock files and directories. For file copying, disk duplication, and disk formatting, you must use the STARTUP program on the ProDOS User's Disk.

Saving Programs

The SAVE command writes onto disk a copy of the BASIC program currently in the computer's memory. You specify the program's name. For example:

```
]SAVE MONEY
```

This statement saves the BASIC program currently in memory under the name MONEY. It uses the volume directory on the drive where the last disk activity occurred (unless you have specified a prefix, as described later in "Changing the Prefix").

You can also specify a full pathname when you save a file. The following example saves a file named LEADING, which is located in a directory named ACTOR that is on a disk volume named PRODUCER:

```
]SAVE /PRODUCER/ACTOR/LEADING
```

Warning: Be careful which name you use when saving a program. If another file with the same pathname already exists, ProDOS replaces it with the program you are saving.

Loading Programs

The LOAD command reads a program file from disk into the computer's memory. The incoming program replaces any existing program. You must specify the name of the file to be loaded. The following example loads a program named HELLO:

```
]LOAD HELLO
```

If the name you specify is not in the volume directory, you will get the message **PATH NOT FOUND**. If the name exists but does not identify a BASIC program file, the message **FILE TYPE MISMATCH** appears.

As with the SAVE command, you can specify a full pathname as part of a LOAD command. The following statement loads the file LEADING that was saved earlier:

```
]LOAD /PRODUCER/ACTOR/LEADING
```

Changing the Prefix

When most of your files are in the same directory, you can save yourself some typing by using a ProDOS prefix to specify the part of the pathname they all have in common. You do this with the PREFIX command. Here is an example:

```
]PREFIX /PRODUCER/ACTOR
```

This sets the prefix to the volume (that is, the disk) named PRODUCER and the directory named ACTOR. The prefix is added to the file names or partial pathnames in any subsequent ProDOS commands such as LOAD and SAVE.

To learn the current prefix, type the PREFIX command alone (without any pathname) in immediate mode. Unless you change the prefix, it is set to the volume directory name of the disk you used most recently.

Starting a BASIC Program

After loading a BASIC program with the LOAD command, you can execute it with the RUN command. As a shortcut, you can both load and run a BASIC program with just the RUN command. All you do is add the program name or pathname, like this:

```
]RUN /MAIL.LIST/ENTRY
```

If you entered this example and pressed the RETURN key, the command would start the program named ENTRY from the disk volume named MAIL.LIST.

The Disk Directory

Both the CAT and CATALOG commands display a listing of the programs and other files in a directory. You can specify a pathname for the directory or let ProDOS use the current prefix directory. Here is an example that specifies a pathname:

```
]CATALOG /PRODUCER/STUNT/WOMEN
```

For each file in the directory, the CATALOG command displays seven items across 80 columns, as shown in Figure 6-1. (If your screen is set for 40 columns, two lines are used to display the nine items for each file.) From left to right, it reports:

1. The file name. If the file is locked, the name is prefixed with an asterisk.

```
]CATALOG

/USERS.DISK

 NAME            TYPE  BLOCKS  MODIFIED          CREATED          ENDFILE SUBTYPE

*PRODOS          SYS       30  18-SEP-84  0:00   18-SEP-84 13:51    14848
*BASIC.SYSTEM    SYS       21  18-JUN-84  0:00   18-JUN-84  0:00    10240
*FILER           SYS       51  <NO DATE>         18-JUN-84  0:00    25600
*CONVERT         SYS       42   1-NOV-83  0:00    1-NOV-83  0:00    20481
*STARTUP         BAS       24  26-JUL-84  0:00   26-JUL-84  0:00    11470
*MOIRE           BAS        3  15-OCT-83  0:00   15-OCT-83  0:00      941
*HYPNOSIS        BAS        3  15-OCT-83  0:00   15-OCT-83  0:00      637
*ANIMALS         BAS       10  15-OCT-83  0:00   15-OCT-83  0:00     4578

BLOCKS FREE:   89     BLOCKS USED:  191      TOTAL BLOCKS:  280

]
```

Figure 6-1. A ProDos CATALOG command directory listing

2. The file type (see Table 6-2).
3. The amount of disk space the file currently uses, as a number of 512-byte blocks.
4. The last date the file was modified.
5. The date the file was created.
6. The amount of space allotted for the file, as a number of bytes.
7. A random-access file's record length, a binary file's load address, or a blank space for any other type of file.

In addition, the CATALOG command displays the directory name at the top of the listing. It also displays the number of 512-byte blocks free, the number of blocks used, and the total number of blocks on the disk at the bottom of the listing. The endfile and subtype columns are of interest primarily to advanced programmers.

The CAT command displays an abbreviated version for 40-column screens. It displays only the first four items from the CATALOG listing, plus the directory name, the number of blocks free, and the total blocks on the entire disk.

Creating a Directory

You can create new directories with the CREATE command. You specify the directory name (or the pathname ending with the

Table 6-2. ProDos File Type Abbreviations

Abbreviation	Type
DIR	Directory
TXT	Text or other data
BAS	Applesoft program
VAR	Applesoft variables
BIN	Binary
REL	Relocatable
$F *n*	User defined (*n* = a number from 1 to 8)
SYS	ProDOS system program or system file

new directory name) as follows:

```
]CREATE /PRODUCER/SPECIAL.EFFECTS
```

After creating a directory, you can save programs and other files or create more directories (subdirectories) in it. If you try to create a file or directory that already exists, the error message **DUPLICATE FILE NAME** will appear on the screen.

Deleting Files and Directories

With the DELETE command you can remove a file or directory from the disk. You specify a file name, pathname, or partial pathname for the file. Here is an example:

```
]DELETE /PRODUCER/ANIMAL/TRAINERS
```

The DELETE command cannot remove a locked file (indicated by an asterisk in a directory listing) or a directory that is not empty. It can never remove the volume directory.

Renaming Files and Directories

To change the name of a file or directory (including the volume directory), use the RENAME command. You first specify the old name and then the new name, as in the following example:

```
]RENAME MAKE.UP, MAKEUP
```

This renames the file MAKE.UP to MAKEUP in the directory specified by the ProDOS prefix.

The RENAME command cannot move a file from one directory to another, so both names must be in the same directory. You cannot rename a locked file or directory. Nor can you rename a file to a file name that already exists. If you do, you will be greeted by the error message **DUPLICATE FILE NAME**.

Locking and Unlocking Files and Directories

The LOCK command protects a file or a directory against removal, renaming, or having any modifications made to it. The UNLOCK command removes this protection. Here is an example of each command.

```
]LOCK COSTUMES
]UNLOCK COSTUMES
```

Specifying the Drive

On an Apple II that has more than one disk drive, you can use the ProDOS commands with any drive you want. If you specify a volume name that doesn't match the name of the disk in the start-up drive, ProDOS automatically checks all other disk drives. In fact, ProDOS can find a disk by its volume name even if you switch drives between commands.

Another way to specify a disk drive—and the disk in it—is by number. Drives are identified by the numbers 1 and 2. If your Apple II has more than two drives, the additional drives are also numbered 1 and 2, in pairs. Drive pairs are identified by the slot number of the accessory card to which they are attached. To add a drive number to a ProDOS command such as LOAD or SAVE, type a comma, the letter D, and the drive number at the end of the command. To specify a slot number, append a comma, the letter S, and the slot number. For example, the following command saves the current program under the name ENTRY on drive 2, slot 5:

```
]SAVE ENTRY,D2,S5
```

You can add just a drive number or a slot number and have ProDOS supply the missing information. If you omit the slot number, ProDOS uses the slot where the last disk activity occurred. Similarly, if you omit the disk drive number, ProDOS uses the same disk drive number as the most recent ProDOS command.

If you specify a drive or slot number in a ProDOS command and the ProDOS prefix is just a volume directory name (no subdirectory name included), the prefix changes to the name of the volume directory in the specified drive. Subsequent ProDOS commands will use that same drive until you specify another drive or slot number, or until you change the prefix with the PREFIX command.

However, specifying a drive or slot number has no effect on the ProDOS prefix if the prefix includes more than a volume directory. In this case, the prefix determines which drive and which slot subsequent ProDOS commands use (unless they include an explicit drive or slot number).

If you specify a drive or slot number where no drive is connected, the message **NO DEVICE CONNECTED** appears.

Confused? The relationship between the drive and slot numbers and the prefix is complicated. You may wish to take the safe but tedious approach: never use drive or slot numbers; only use pathnames and prefixes.

DOS 3.3 COMMANDS

When you start an Apple II with a DOS 3.3 disk, Applesoft includes commands for storing and retrieving programs on disks. It also includes commands that mimic many of the menu choices in the FILEM program on the DOS 3.3 System Master disk, which is described in Chapter 4. There are commands to display the disk catalog, initialize a disk, and to delete, rename, lock, unlock, and verify files. For file copying and disk duplication you must use the FILEM and COPYA programs on the DOS 3.3 System Disk.

Saving Programs

The SAVE command writes a copy of the BASIC program currently in the computer's memory onto disk. You specify the program's name. For example:

```
]SAVE MONEY
```

This statement saves the BASIC program currently in memory under the name MONEY.

Warning: Be careful which name you use when saving a program. If another file with the same name already exists, DOS 3.3 replaces it with the program you are saving.

Loading Programs

The LOAD command reads a program file from disk into the computer's memory. The incoming program replaces any existing program. You must specify the name of the file to be loaded. The following example loads a program named HELLO.

```
]LOAD HELLO
```

If the name you specify is not in the volume directory, you will get the message **FILE NOT FOUND**. If the name exists but does not identify a BASIC program file, the message **FILE TYPE MISMATCH** appears.

Starting a BASIC Program

After loading a BASIC program with the LOAD command, you can execute it with the RUN command. As a shortcut, you can load and run a BASIC program with just the RUN command. All you do is add the program name, like this:

```
]RUN ENTRY
```

If you entered this example and pressed the RETURN key, the command would start the program named ENTRY from the disk most recently used.

The Disk Catalog

The CATALOG command displays a listing of the programs and other files on a disk. Here is an example:

```
]CATALOG
```

For each file on the disk, the CATALOG command displays three items across 40 columns, as shown in Figure 6-2. From left to right, it reports:

1. The file type (A=Applesoft, I=Integer BASIC, B=Binary, T=Text). If the file is locked, the type is prefixed with an asterisk.
2. The amount of disk space the file currently uses, as a number of 256-byte blocks. When the file size reaches 256 blocks, the number that appears in the catalog starts over at zero, and thus does not reflect the true size of the file.
3. The file name.

In addition, the CATALOG command displays the volume number at the top of the listing (DISK VOLUME 254 in Figure 6-2).

If there are more than 18 files in the catalog, DOS 3.3 splits the

```
DISK VOLUME 254

*A 003 HELLO
*I 003 APPLESOFT
*B 006 LOADER.OBJ0
*B 042 FPBASIC
*B 042 INTBASIC
*A 003 MASTER
*B 009 MASTER CREATE
*I 009 COPY
*B 003 COPY.OBJ0
*A 009 COPYA
*B 003 CHAIN
*A 014 RENUMBER
*A 003 FILEM
*B 020 FID
*A 003 CONVERT13
*B 027 MUFFIN
*A 003 START13
*B 007 BOOT13
*A 004 SLOT#

]
```

Figure 6-2. A DOS 3.3 CATALOG command listing

listing into "pages." The first page lists the first 18 files and subsequent pages list 21 files each. DOS 3.3 waits at the end of each page for you to press a key. When you do, it goes on to the next page.

Initializing Disks

The INIT command prepares brand-new disks for the DOS 3.3 operating system by mapping the disk surface and setting up a blank catalog. You can also initialize a used disk in order to erase it completely. The INIT command specifies the name of the greeting program, which will be run automatically if you later start the Apple II with the initialized disk. Here is an example:

```
]INIT HELLO
```

This example initializes the disk and saves the BASIC program currently in memory as the greeting program. It uses the standard greeting program name, HELLO.

Deleting Files

With the DELETE command you can remove a file from the disk. You specify the name of the file to be deleted, as in this example:

```
]DELETE TRAINERS
```

The DELETE command cannot remove a locked file (indicated by an asterisk in a catalog listing).

Renaming Files

To change the name of a file, use the RENAME command. You first specify the old name and then the new name, as in the following example:

```
]RENAME MAKE.UP, MAKEUP
```

This renames the file MAKE.UP to MAKEUP.

Warning: The RENAME command does not check to see if the new file name is already in use. If it is, you will end up with two files that have the same name. This can be very confusing and difficult to fix.

Locking and Unlocking Files

The LOCK command protects a file against removal, renaming, or having any modifications made to it. The UNLOCK command removes this protection. Here is an example of each command:

```
]LOCK COSTUMES
]UNLOCK COSTUMES
```

Specifying the Drive

If your Apple II has more than one disk drive, you can use the DOS 3.3 commands with any drive you want. Drives are identified by the numbers 1 and 2. If your Apple II has more than two drives, the additional drives are also numbered 1 and 2, in pairs. Drive pairs are identified by the slot number of the accessory card to which they are attached.

To add a drive number to a DOS 3.3 command such as LOAD or SAVE, type a comma, the letter D, and the drive number at the end of the command. To specify a slot number, append a comma, the letter S, and the slot number. For example, the following command saves the current program under the name ENTRY on drive 2, slot 5:

```
]SAVE  ENTRY,D2,S5
```

You can add just a drive number or a slot number and have DOS 3.3 supply the missing information. If you omit the slot number, DOS 3.3 uses the slot where the last disk activity occurred. Similarly, if you omit the disk drive number, DOS 3.3 uses the disk drive number most recently specified. And if you omit both the drive and slot numbers, DOS 3.3 uses the drive and slot where the last disk activity occurred.

If you specify a drive or slot number where no drive is connected, the message **I/O ERROR** appears.

BASIC PROGRAMS ON CASSETTE

The Apple II can save and retrieve programs on cassette even if no disk drives are present. The cassette commands work with DOS 3.3, but not with ProDOS. They also work on an Apple II started without a disk, in which case neither ProDOS nor DOS 3.3 is present.

Saving a Program on Cassette

To save the program currently in memory on cassette, put a tape in the cassette recorder and follow these steps:

1. Rewind the cassette to the beginning.

2. Type the command word SAVE, but do not press the RETURN key yet.
3. Depress the cassette recorder's RECORD and PLAY buttons simultaneously.
4. Now press the RETURN key.
5. The Apple II beeps as it starts recording the program on the tape.
6. The Apple II beeps again when it finishes the recording.
7. Depress the STOP button on the recorder after the second beep.

Loading a Program From Cassette

To replace the program currently in memory (if any) with one from tape, put the tape in the cassette recorder and follow these steps:

1. Rewind the tape to the beginning.
2. Type the command word LOAD, but do not press the RETURN key yet.
3. Depress the PLAY button on the cassette recorder.
4. Now press the RETURN key.
5. The Apple II beeps as it starts to load the program from the tape.
6. The Apple II beeps again when it finishes.
7. Depress the STOP button on the recorder after the second beep. Use the LIST command to verify that the program is in memory.

Saving Multiple Programs

It doesn't take very much tape to record a single BASIC program. There is usually enough tape on one cassette to hold several programs. You can record programs one after another if you omit step 1 above. Instead of rewinding to the beginning of a new tape, start recording after the end of a program on a used tape.

Loading the second, third, and subsequent programs on a cassette is not as straightforward as loading the first. After you rewind the tape to the beginning, you must get past the first program in order to load the second, past the second to get at the third, and so on. You can do this by issuing the LOAD command repeatedly until the program you want is in memory. This is a slow process, but it works.

You can speed things up considerably if your cassette recorder has a tape counter. When you rewind the tape to the beginning before saving a program, reset the tape counter to zero. After saving the first program, jot down the tape counter reading. This is the starting tape counter reading for the second program. Save the second program and note the tape counter reading at the end of it (for the start of the third program).

To load the second program, rewind the tape to the beginning and once again reset the tape counter to zero. Then use the FAST FORWARD button on the cassette recorder to position the tape counter to the reading for the start of the second program. You can use the REWIND button on the cassette recorder to back up the tape if you overshoot with the FAST FORWARD button. Now use the LOAD command to load the second program.

Using Strings And Numbers 7

The business of computer programs is to input, manipulate, and output data. So the way a programming language handles data, whether numbers or text, is very important. This chapter describes the types of data you may encounter in an Applesoft or Integer BASIC program.

STRINGS

A *string* is any character or sequence of characters enclosed in quotation marks. You have already seen strings with the PRINT statement as messages to be displayed on the screen. Here are some more examples of strings:

"IGNORANCE IS BLISS"
"ACCOUNT 4019-181-324-837"
"NICK CHARLES"
"SAM & ELLA CAFE"
"MARCH 18, 1956"

With a few exceptions, a string can contain any character you can produce at the keyboard using the letter and number keys, with or without the CONTROL or SHIFT key. The keys you cannot use to generate characters are ←, →, ↑, ↓, RETURN, ESC, CONTROL-H, CONTROL-M, CONTROL-U, and CONTROL-X, because they either move the cursor or end the line you're working on, or both.

Strings can be any length from 0 to 255 characters. A string with no characters in it is called a *null string*. There are some invisible characters you can produce by pressing certain combinations of keys. For example, if you press the CONTROL and G keys simultaneously, the computer beeps. You can put this character in a string. Try pressing CONTROL-G between quotation marks in a PRINT statement.

```
]PRINT ""

] ▒
```

In this example you can hear the characters between the quotation marks even though you can't see them. There are other characters that are invisible and inaudible. Such characters are used for controlling printer functions, communications devices, and other components you can attach to the Apple II.

In order to make full use of strings, you must understand how characters are stored in the computer's memory. It's really very simple. Computer memory can store numbers, but it cannot store characters. When you type a character, the computer automatically converts it to a number, using a standard code called *ASCII* (American Standard Code for Information Interchange). Later, as the computer gets ready to display character strings, it automatically converts the code numbers back to characters. All this happens behind the scenes, so most computer users aren't even aware of how it works. If you write programs in BASIC, however, you may have to work directly with the code numbers. The ASCII code for the letter A is 65, for B it is 66, C is 67, and so on. You will find a complete table of characters and their ASCII code numbers in Appendix E.

In Applesoft, there is a way to generate a character by specifying its ASCII code number. This technique, described at the end of this chapter, lets strings include characters that move the cursor or cannot be generated from the keyboard for other reasons.

NUMBERS

There are two kinds of numbers that can be stored in the Apple II: *integers*, which are numbers without any fractional part, and *real numbers* (also called floating point numbers), which can have fractional parts. As you might suspect, Integer BASIC only recognizes integers. Applesoft uses both integers and real numbers.

You must express all numbers without commas. For example, you must use 32000, not 32,000.

Integers

An integer is a number that has no fractional portion or decimal point. The number can be negative (−) or positive (+). An unsigned number is assumed to be positive. Integer numbers must have values in the range −32767 to 32767. The following are examples of integers:

0
1
44
32699
−15

Real Numbers

A real number can be a whole number, a whole number with a decimal fraction, or just a decimal fraction. The number can be negative (−) or positive (+). If the number has no sign, it is assumed to be positive. The smallest (most negative) real number is

−100000000000000000000000000000000000000

and the largest is

100000000000000000000000000000000000000

Here are some examples of real numbers:

5
−15
65000
161
0
0.5
0.0165432
−0.0000009
1.6
24.0055
−64.2

When the value of any fractional number gets closer to zero than about 0.000000000000000000000000000000000000003, it will be converted to zero.

Scientific Notation

Very large and very small real numbers are presented in Apple using *scientific notation.* Any number that has more than nine digits in front of the decimal point will be expressed in scientific notation. Any fractional number closer to zero than ±0.01 will be expressed in scientific notation.

Scientific notation simply expresses a number as a multiple of 10, 100, 1000, or some other power of 10 (see Figure 7-1). Therefore it is a convenient way of expressing very large and very small numbers. The maximum and minimum values for real numbers, which we just expressed with dozens of zeros, can also be expressed using scientific notation as 1E+38 and −1E+38, respectively. Expressed in scientific notation, the closest a number can get to zero is 3E−38.

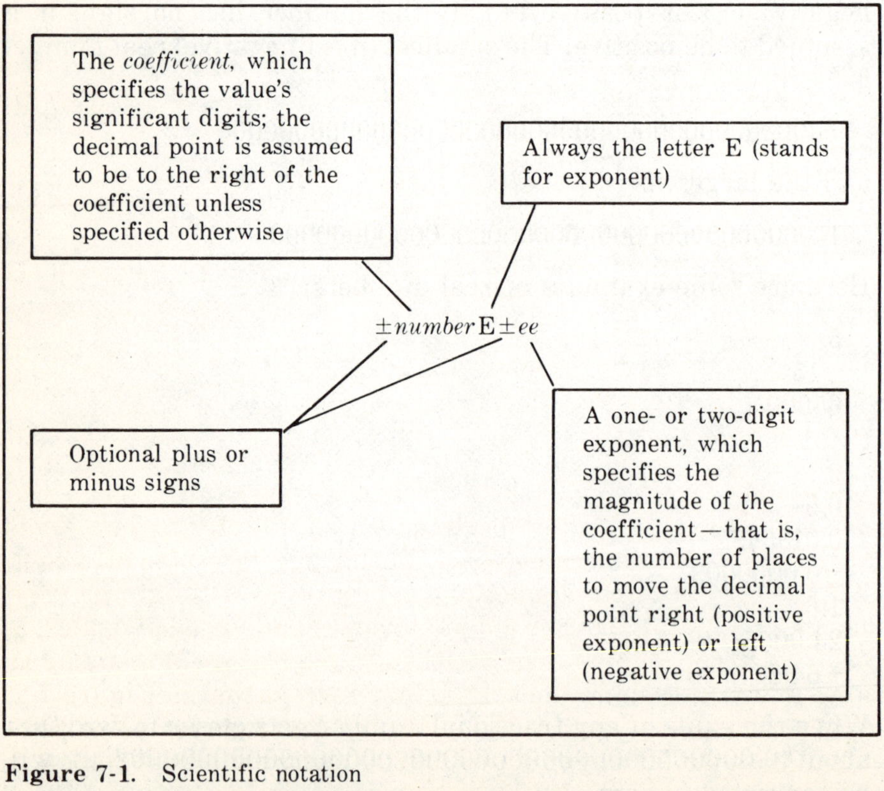

Figure 7-1. Scientific notation

Roundoff

We saw earlier that real numbers can have as many as nine digits of precision. For a number greater than 1 or less than −1, this means only the leftmost nine digits can be nonzero. Applesoft rounds off any digits in excess of nine. Here are some examples (note that large numbers are printed in scientific notation):

```
]PRINT 1234567891
1.23456789E+09

]?-123456789123456789
-1.23456789E+17

]?-150000475.75
-150000476

]?90000000.7558
90000000.8

]▒
```

Fractional numbers (those between 1 and −1) are subject to the same limitation. In this case, though, the nine digits of precision start with the first nonzero digit to the right of the decimal point. Here are some examples:

```
]PRINT .1234567891

]?.000000000900000007558
9.00000008E-10

]▒
```

VARIABLES

Thus far in our discussions of data we have only considered constant values. It is often more convenient to refer to data items by name rather than value. That is what *variables* are all about.

If you have studied elementary algebra, you will have no trouble understanding the concept of variables and variable names. If you have never studied algebra, then think of a variable name as a name that is assigned to a letter box such as that in Figure 7-2. Anything that is placed in the letter box becomes the value associated with the letter box name, until something new is placed in

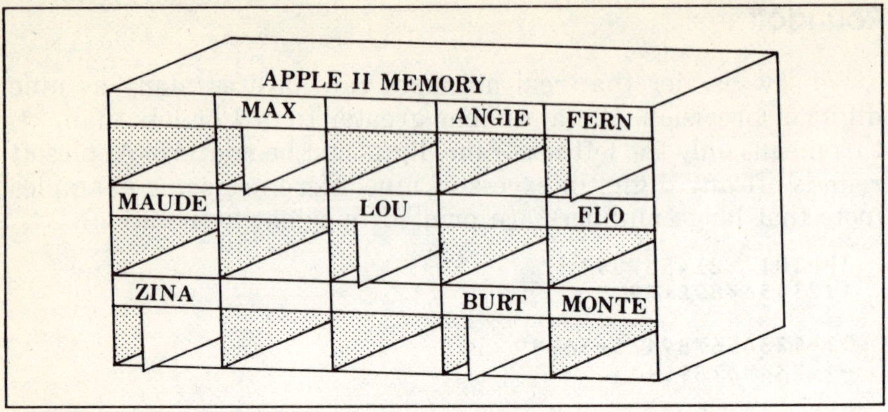

Figure 7-2. Variables are like letter boxes

the letter box. In computer jargon we say a value is stored in a variable.

A variable does not always have to refer to the same value. That is its real power—it can represent any legal value. You can change a variable's value during the course of a program. Applesoft and Integer BASIC have a number of statements that do this; we will investigate them later in this chapter.

Variable Names in Applesoft

As Figure 7-3 illustrates, Applesoft uses one, two, or three characters in variable names. The first character must be a letter. The second character, which is optional, can be any letter or digit. The third character is a suffix that designates the type of value the variable has. A dollar sign suffix designates a variable with a string value. A percent sign designates a variable with an integer value. A variable whose name has no suffix can have any numeric value, including a fractional one.

A string variable in Applesoft can store a string value of any length from 0 to 255 characters. Here are some examples of string variable names, both legal and illegal:

Legal	Illegal
A$	0$
MN$	M!$
F6$	77$

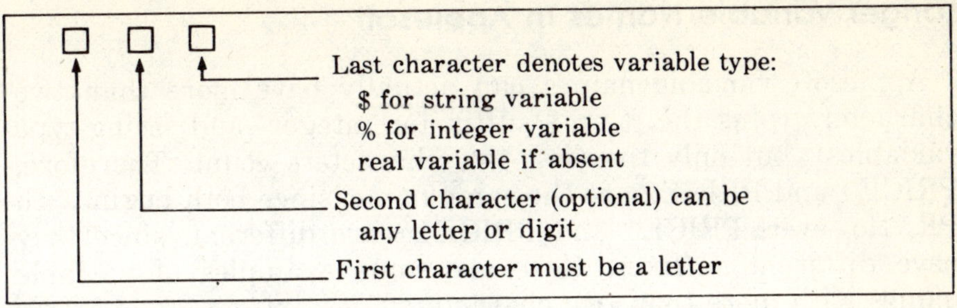

Figure 7-3. Applesoft variable name rules

Integer variables can refer to whole numbers between −32767 and +32767. If you attempt to exceed this limit, you will get the **?ILLEGAL QUANTITY ERROR** message. If you try to store a real value in an integer variable, Applesoft will convert the real value to an integer value first. We'll cover the rules for the conversion shortly. Here are some examples of legal and illegal integer variables in Applesoft:

Legal	**Illegal**
A%	A$%
B%	31%
A1%	3D%
X4%	

Real variables can refer to numeric values generally restricted to the range from -10^{38} to $+10^{38}$, although you may be able to compute values as large as 1.7×10^{38} or as small as -1.7×10^{38} under some circumstances. If you attempt to store a value that is too large in magnitude in a real variable, you will get the **?OVERFLOW ERROR** message. When the value of a real variable gets closer to zero than $\pm 2.9388 \times 10^{-39}$, Applesoft converts it to zero. Also, real variables can have integer values, since an integer is a real number with a fractional part of zero. Here are some examples of legal and illegal real variables:

Legal	**Illegal**
A	0
B	7B
A1	A#
AA	

Longer Variable Names in Applesoft

Applesoft variable names can actually have more than two characters (plus the % or $ suffix for integer- and string-type variables), but only the first two characters count. Therefore, PRICE1 and PRICE2 are the same name, since both begin with PR. However, PRICE1 and PRICE1% are different, since they have different suffixes. Here are some examples of variable names with more than two characters:

Legal	Illegal
COUNTER%	ITEM#%
ACCOUNTBALANCE	2NDRATE
NAME$	CUSTOMER.ADDRESS$

Keep the following points in mind if you use variable names with more than two characters:

- Only the first two characters and the variable type suffix ($ or %) are significant. Do not use extended names like LOOP1% and LOOP2%; these refer to the same variable: LO%
- Additional characters need extra memory space, which you might need for longer programs. But the advantage of using longer variable names is that they make programs easier to read. PARTNO, for example, is more meaningful than PA as a variable name describing part numbers in an inventory program.

Variable Names in Integer BASIC

Variable names in Integer BASIC can have from 1 to 100 characters (refer to Figure 7-4). The first character must be a letter, but the rest can be either letters or digits. A dollar sign as the last character of the variable name designates a string variable. A letter or digit as the last character designates a numeric variable.

String variables can refer to strings of any length between 0 and 255 characters. Blank spaces in a string count toward its total length. Before you use a string variable in Integer BASIC, you must specify the maximum length it will have. You do this with the DIM statement, which will be described later in this chapter. If you fail to declare the maximum length, you will get a

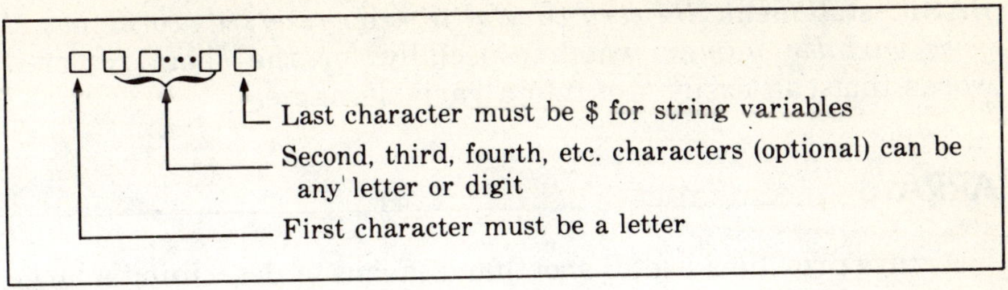

Figure 7-4. Integer BASIC variable name rules

*** **STR OVFL ERR** message. Here are some examples of string variable names, legal and illegal:

Legal	Illegal
A$	$
CUSTNAME$	8$
PART1$	BRAND.NAME$
X8$	

Numeric variables in Integer BASIC must have values between −32767 and +32767. If you exceed these bounds, you will get the *** **> 32767 ERR** message. Here are some examples of numeric variable names in Integer BASIC, both legal and illegal:

Legal	Illegal
A	APPLICANT'S AGE
CUSTZIPCODE	3X4Z
X0	$TOTAL

Reserved Words

All of the command words in BASIC commands and statements are reserved and cannot appear in variable names. Appendix A lists all Applesoft and Integer BASIC reserved words.

When executing BASIC programs, the Apple II scans every BASIC statement, seeking out any character string that constitutes a reserved word. (The only exception is text strings enclosed in quotation marks.) This can cause trouble if a reserved word is embedded anywhere within a variable name. The Apple II is not smart enough to identify a variable name by its location in a

BASIC statement. *Be very careful to keep reserved words out of your variable names;* watch especially for the short reserved words that can easily slip into a variable name.

ARRAYS

Arrays provide a useful shorthand means of describing a large number of related variables. Consider, for example, a table of 200 numbers. How would you like it if you had to assign a unique variable name to each of the 200 numbers? It would be far simpler to give the entire table one name and identify individual numbers within the table by their table locations. That is precisely what an array does.

Conceptually, arrays are very simple. When you have two or more data items, instead of giving each data item a separate variable name, you give the collection of data items a single variable name. The collection is called an *array*, and its name is an *array name*. Individual data items are often called *array elements*. The elements in an array are numbered. You select an individual item using its position number, which is referred to as its *index*.

As an example of using an array, consider how a motel with ten rooms might keep track of who is staying in each of the rooms. There could be ten separate variable names for each room, say R1$, R2$, R3$, and so on (see Figure 7-5). The value of variable R1$ would be the name of the guest in Room 1, the value of R2$ would be the name of the guest in Room 2, and so on. Alternatively, there could be one array with ten elements, possibly named R$ (see Figure 7-6). In this case, the index after the array name specifies the room number, and the value of the corresponding array element is the name of the guest in that room.

Arrays in Applesoft can represent integer variables, real variables, or string variables; however, a single array variable can

Jones	Smith	Doe		Littke	Alton	Davis	Hanson	Shorten	
R1$	R2$	R3$	R4$	R5$	R6$	R7$	R8$	R9$	R10$

Figure 7-5. Using separate variable names

Jones	Smith	Doe		Littke	Alton	Davis	Hanson	Shorten	
R$(1)	R$(2)	R$(3)	R$(4)	R$(5)	R$(6)	R$(7)	R$(8)	R$(9)	R$(10)

Figure 7-6. Using an array

only represent one data type. In other words, a single variable cannot mix strings and numbers (except in the sense that a string can be a series of digits). Each type of array uses a different amount of memory; see Appendix H for details.

Integer BASIC does not allow string arrays, only numeric arrays.

Array Dimensions

If you plan to use arrays in your program, you may need to declare their maximum sizes, or dimensions, in a DIM statement or statements early in the program. A dimension statement can provide dimensions for any number of arrays, as long as the statement fits on a standard program line. The following example dimensions a string array of 11 elements and an integer array of 21 elements.

```
]DIM R$(10),R%(20)
```

The number following an array name in a DIM statement is equal to the largest index value that can occur in that particular index position. But remember that indexes begin at 0. Therefore R$(10) dimensions the variable R$( ) to have 11 values, not 10, since indexes 0, 1, 2, 3, 4, 5, 6, 7, 8, 9, and 10 will be allowed.

Applesoft arrays can have more than one dimension, in which case it takes more than one index to select an individual element. An array with a single dimension is equivalent to a table with just one row of numbers. The index identifies a number within the single row. An array with two dimensions yields an ordinary table of numbers with rows and columns; one index identifies the row, while the other identifies the column. You can visualize an array with three dimensions as a cube of numbers, or perhaps a stack of tables. Four or more dimensions yield an array that is hard to visualize, but no harder to use than an array with fewer dimensions.

We can create an example of a two-dimensional array by extending the previous example of the motel guest list. Consider an eight-story hotel with ten rooms on each floor. There are four options for keeping track of the 80 guests' names. First, each room could have its own variable. Second, the hotel could have one 80-element array. Third, each floor could have a separate ten-element array. Fourth, the hotel could have one two-dimensional array.

In the last case (shown in Figure 7-7), the first index of the two-dimensional array could be the floor number, and the second index could be the room number on that floor. That would make R$(3,2) the name of the guest in the second room on the third floor. The following example dimensions a two-dimensional array:

```
]15 DIM H$(8,10)
```

Applesoft arrays can have up to 88 dimensions. There is no specific limit on the number of elements in each dimension. The amount of memory available limits the total number of elements, of course, since each element requires a certain amount of memory space.

An Applesoft array does not have to appear in a DIM statement unless it has more than 11 indexes in any one dimension. If Applesoft encounters an array name for the first time somewhere other than in a DIM statement, it automatically dimensions the array with indexes 0 through 10 for each dimension used.

In Integer BASIC, you must dimension all arrays and all simple string variables too. Only one-dimensional numeric arrays are allowed—no string arrays or multidimensional arrays. The following example dimensions 2 strings of 5 and 25 characters,

H$(8,1)	H$(8,2)	H$(8,3)	H$(8,4)	H$(8,5)	H$(8,6)	H$(8,7)	H$(8,8)	H$(8,9)	H$(8,10)
H$(7,1)	H$(7,2)	H$(7,3)	H$(7,4)	H$(7,5)	H$(7,6)	H$(7,7)	H$(7,8)	H$(7,9)	H$(7,10)
H$(6,1)	H$(6,2)	H$(6,3)	H$(6,4)	H$(6,5)	H$(6,6)	H$(6,7)	H$(6,8)	H$(6,9)	H$(6,10)
H$(5,1)	H$(5,2)	H$(5,3)	H$(5,4)	H$(5,5)	H$(5,6)	H$(5,7)	H$(5,8)	H$(5,9)	H$(5,10)
H$(4,1)	H$(4,2)	H$(4,3)	H$(4,4)	H$(4,5)	H$(4,6)	H$(4,7)	H$(4,8)	H$(4,9)	H$(4,10)
H$(3,1)	H$(3,2)	H$(3,3)	H$(3,4)	H$(3,5)	H$(3,6)	H$(3,7)	H$(3,8)	H$(3,9)	H$(3,10)
H$(2,1)	H$(2,2)	H$(2,3)	H$(2,4)	H$(2,5)	H$(2,6)	H$(2,7)	H$(2,8)	H$(2,9)	H$(2,10)
H$(1,1)	H$(1,2)	H$(1,3)	H$(1,4)	H$(1,5)	H$(1,6)	H$(1,7)	H$(1,8)	H$(1,9)	H$(1,10)

Figure 7-7. Using a two-dimensional array

respectively, and a numeric array of 13 elements (0 through 12):

```
>10 DIM SI$(5),S2$(25),NB(12)
```

The number following a string variable name in an Integer BASIC DIM statement is the maximum length that string can have during the program. The number following a numeric array name is equal to the largest index value that you can use for that array.

Redimensioning Arrays

Once you have dimensioned an array variable, you cannot redimension it without rerunning the whole program. Subsequent references cannot use an index higher than the number of indexes you declared; each index must have a value between 0 and the number of indexes dimensioned.

EXPRESSIONS

You can combine the values of variables and constants by using *expressions.* We have already used expressions to calculate the value of simple arithmetic problems in immediate mode. Recall that the statement

```
]PRINT 4 + 6
```

tells the Apple II to add 4 and 6 and display the sum. The statement

```
]PRINT A + B
```

tells the Apple II to add the values of the two numeric variables A and B and display the sum.

The plus sign specifies addition. Standard computer jargon refers to the plus sign as an *operator*. The plus sign is an *arithmetic operator* because it specifies addition, which is an arithmetic operation.

Arithmetic operators are easy enough to understand; we all learn to add, subtract, multiply, and divide in early childhood. But there are other types of operators: *string operators*, *relational operators*, and *logical operators*. These are also easy to understand, but they take a little more explanation since they involve more abstract notions.

Each category of operators defines a type of expression. There are arithmetic expressions, string expressions, relational expressions, and logical expressions.

Precedence of Operators

Expressions can call for more than one operation to occur. For example, the following statement calls for both addition and division in the same expression:

```
]PRINT A + B/10
```

There is a standard scheme for determining in what order to evaluate an expression. We will go through these rules of precedence for each type of expression, starting with string concatenation, then integer, real, relational, logical, and mixed-type expressions. First, let's look at a way to override the standard rules of precedence.

Overriding Standard Precedence

You can change the order in which Applesoft and Integer BASIC evaluate expressions by using parentheses. Any operation within parentheses is performed first. When more than one set of parentheses is present, BASIC evaluates them from left to right.

When one set of parentheses is enclosed within another set, it is called *nesting*. In this case, BASIC evaluates the innermost set first, then the next innermost, and so on. Parentheses can be nested to any level. You may use them freely to clarify the order of operations being performed in an expression.

Here are some examples of the immediate mode arithmetic calculations using parentheses:

```
]PRINT (2 + 10) * 3
36

]PRINT ((2 + 10) * 3 + 31) * 10
670

]PRINT -(2 ^ (3 + 8/4))
32

]▒
```

String Concatenation

You can join strings together end to end to form one longer string. This is called *concatenation* (see Figure 7-8). With concatenation, you can develop strings up to 255 characters long.

Applesoft uses the plus sign as a concatenation operator. Here are some examples of string concatenation in Applesoft:

Before	After
"OVER" + "DUE"	becomes "OVERDUE"
"MONTHLY" + " " + "REPORT"	becomes "MONTHLY REPORT"
"WEEKLY" + R$	becomes the characters WEEKLY followed by the value of R$
A1$ + YA$ + C$(1)	becomes the value of A1$ followed by the value of YA$ followed by the value of C$(1)

Integer Expressions

Integer expressions are arithmetic expressions that involve only integer variables and integer constants. We will cover arithmetic expressions involving both integer and real values under the heading "Mixed-Type Expressions."

The operators for integer expressions are addition (+), subtraction (−), multiplication (*), division (/), and exponentiation (^). You can also use negation (–) to indicate a negative numeric value. Operations are performed in this order: negation first, followed by exponentiation; multiplication and division next; and

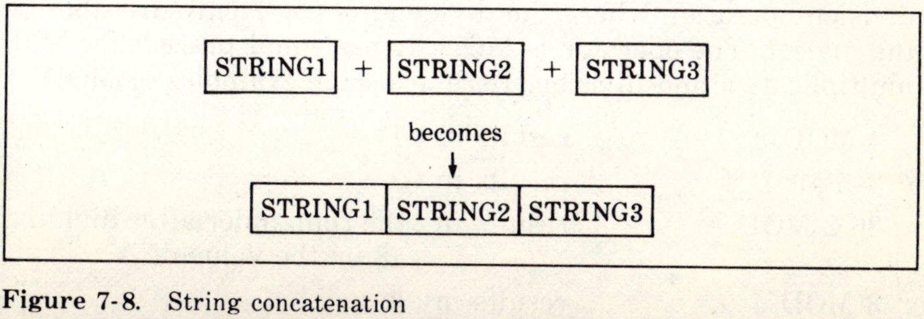

Figure 7-8. String concatenation

finally addition and subtraction. Operations of equal precedence are performed in order from left to right.

Here are some examples of integer expressions in Applesoft:

−120/2 + 100	results in	40
2^3*2	results in	16
N1%*N2%/N3%	results in	the value of N1% times the value of N2% and the product divided by N3%
AA%/AB%/AC%	results in	the value of AA% divided by the value of AB% and the quotient divided by the value of AC%
5/2*2	results in	5 (the quotient of 5/2 is not converted to an integer)

Here are some examples of integer expressions in Integer BASIC:

100 − 30*2	results in	40
−9^2	results in	81
A/B*C	results in	the value of A divided by the value of B and the integer value of the quotient multiplied by the value of C
D + X*3	results in	three times the value of X and the value of D added to that product
5/2*2	results in	4 (the quotient of 5/2 is converted to the integer 2)

Integer BASIC has one more operator you can use in integer expressions. It returns the remainder that is left over from a division operation where the dividend is not evenly divisible by the divisor. The operator is MOD. It has equal precedence with multiplication and division. Here are some examples of MOD:

4 MOD 3	results in	1
3*5 MOD 4	results in	3
36/2 MOD A	results in	the remainder after dividing 18 by the value of A
3 MOD 4	results in	3

Real Expressions

Applesoft has another type of arithmetic expression; it yields a real value. Its operators are the same as those in Applesoft integer expressions: addition (+), subtraction (−), multiplication (*), division (/), exponentiation (^), and negation (−). The precedence of operation is the same also: negation first, followed by exponentiation, multiplication and division, and finally addition and subtraction. Here are some examples of real expressions:

87.5 − 4.25*2	results in	79
1.5 ^ (3/2/2)	results in	1.35540301
A*(P − 3.1*C)	results in	the value of A times the result of subtracting the product of 3.1 times the value of C from the value of P
7.5*2/5	results in	3

Relational Expressions

Relational operators allow you to compare two values to see what relationship one bears to the other. You can compare whether the first is greater than, less than, equal to, not equal to, greater than or equal to, or less than or equal to the second value. The values you compare can be constants, variables, or any kind of expression. (There are some restrictions in Integer BASIC.) If the value on one side of a relational operator is a string, the value on the other side must also be a string. Otherwise, you can compare one type of value to another type using relational operators.

If the relationship is true, the relational expression has a numeric value of 1. If the relationship is false, the relational expression has the value 0.

The relational operators for Integer BASIC and Applesoft are much the same, as shown in Table 7-1. All relational operators have the same precedence; they are evaluated in order from left to right. Here are some examples of relational expressions:

1 = 5−4	results in	1 (true)
14 > 66	results in	0 (false)
15 > = 15	results in	1 (true)
"AA" > "AA"	results in	0 (false)

"ACE" < "ACME"   results in 1 (true)

(A = B) = (A$ > B$)   depends on the values of the variables. If the value of A is equal to the value of B and the value of A$ is greater than the value of B$, then this expression results in 1 (true).

The concept behind relational operators is easy enough to understand. The values 0 and 1 that BASIC arbitrarily assigns to false and true conditions can be used in integer and real expressions. This is not so easy to understand, since it is utterly arbitrary. For example, what meaning does the expression (1 = 1)*4 have? Outside of a BASIC program, such an expression would be meaningless, but within BASIC (1 = 1) is true and true equates to 1, so the expression is the same as 1*4, which results in 4. You can include relational expressions within other BASIC expressions. Here are some examples:

25 + (14 > 66)   is the same as 25 + 0
(A + (1 = 5−4)) * (15 >= 15) is the same as (A + 1) * 1

String Comparisons

Strings are compared one character at a time, starting with the leftmost character—the first character of one string with the

Table 7-1. Relational Operators

Integer BASIC Operator	Operation	Applesoft Operator
<	Less Than*	<
>	Greater Than*	>
=	Equal To	=
# or <>	Not Equal To	<> or ><
>=	Greater Than or Equal To*	>= or =>
<=	Less Than or Equal To*	<= or =<

*Not allowed with strings in Integer BASIC

first character of the other, the second character with the second character, third with the third, and so on until one of the strings is exhausted or a character mismatch occurs. The strings are equal only if they are the same length and no mismatches occur. Integer BASIC can only determine string equality or inequality.

Applesoft determines which of two unequal strings is larger according to the ASCII code numbers of the first mismatched characters it finds. The character with the higher code number is greater. Thus the letters of the alphabet have the order A<B, B<C, C<D. Digits that appear in strings have conventional ordering, namely 1<2, 2<3, and so on. For other characters such as +, −, $, and so on, look up the ASCII code numbers in Appendix E.

Logical Expressions

Logical operators give programs the ability to make logical decisions. There are four standard logical operators: AND, OR, Exclusive OR, and NOT. BASIC on the Apple II has three of these operators: AND, OR, and NOT.

If you do not understand logical operators, then a simple supermarket shopping analogy will illustrate the concepts. Suppose you are shopping for breakfast cereals with two children, Spike and Iola. The AND operator says you will buy a cereal if both children select that cereal. The OR operator says you will buy a cereal if either Spike or Iola selects it. The NOT operator generates an opposite. If Spike insists on disagreeing with Iola, then Spike's decision is always the NOT of Iola's decision.

Computers do not work with analogies; they work with numbers. Therefore BASIC reduces the values in a logical expression to 1 or 0 (true or false). Since logical operators work on the values 0 and 1, they are most often used with relational expressions (remember that relational expressions result in the value 0 or 1). Logical operators can work on other types of operands, as we will see in the next section.

Table 7-2 summarizes the way in which logical expressions are evaluated. This table is referred to as a *truth table*. Logical operators have equal precedence. If more than one logical operator is present in the same expression, they are evaluated from left to right. Here are some examples of logical expressions:

NOT ((3 + 4) > = 6)	results in 0 (false)
("AA" = "AB") OR ((8*2) = 4 ^ 2)	results in 1 (true)
NOT ("APPLE" = "ORANGE") AND (A$ = B$)	results in 1 (true) if A$ and B$ are equal; 0 (false) if not

Mixed-Type Expressions

Very often expressions involve values of more than one type; for example, an expression may involve real and integer values, or perhaps relational and logical values. You can mix types freely in any expression, but strings cannot be part of integer, real, or logical expressions. Strings can be present only in string and relational expressions. Here are some examples of mixed-type expressions:

Legal	Illegal
3.1416 * (R ^ 2)	1600 + "PENNSYLVANIA AVENUE"
A% > = B/3	ST$ < A%
43 AND 137	A$ AND B$
1 OR 4E + 10	NOT (A$) = B$
(A$ = B$) AND −6.25	NOT(A = B) OR C$

Table 7-2. Logical Expression Truth Table

First value	Oper-and	Second value		Value of expression
–	NOT	T	=	F
–	NOT	F	=	T
T	AND	T	=	T
T	AND	F	=	F
F	AND	T	=	F
F	AND	F	=	F
T	OR	T	=	T
T	OR	F	=	T
F	OR	T	=	T
F	OR	F	=	F

BASIC has several things to resolve when it evaluates a mixed-type expression. The first issue is the precedence of operators. Table 7-3 summarizes the operators for all types of expressions in order of precedence, from highest to lowest. This table shows that anything in parentheses is evaluated first. If there is more than one level of parentheses present, BASIC evaluates the innermost set first, then the next innermost, and so on. (You will recall that we covered this concept of nesting earlier.) Next, arithmetic expressions are evaluated. After that, relational expressions are evaluated. Finally, logical expressions are evaluated.

As we noted earlier, relational expressions return a value of 0 or 1 depending on whether the relationship being tested is false or true. Thus, a relational expression can exist as part of an integer or real expression.

You can also include numeric values in logical expressions. A numeric value is considered true if it is zero; otherwise it is considered false.

Table 7-3. Operators

	Precedence	Integer BASIC Operator	Applesoft Operator	Meaning
	1st	( )	( )	Parentheses denote order of evaluation
Arithmetic Operators	2nd	^	^	Exponentiation
	3rd	−	−	Unary Minus
	4th	*	*	Multiplication
	4th	/	/	Division
	4th	MOD	N/A	Division
	5th	+	+	Addition
	5th	—	−	Subtraction
Relational Operators	6th	=	=	Equal
	6th	#	<> or ><	Not equal
	6th	<	<	Less than
	6th	>	>	Greater than
	6th	<=	<= or =<	Less than or equal
	6th	>=	>= or =>	Greater than or equal
Logical Operators	7th	NOT	NOT	Logical complement
	8th	AND	AND	Logical AND
	9th	OR	OR	Logical OR

BASIC cannot automatically convert strings to numeric values, so strings are illegal in integer, real, and logical expressions, except as part of a relational expression.

In Applesoft, both integer and real values can be present in the same real, relational, or logical expression. Whenever they occur in a real expression, integer values are temporarily converted to real values in order to evaluate the expression. Applesoft converts the final result of such an expression to integer or real, depending on the context in which the expression occurs.

When a real value occurs in a context that requires an integer, it is converted by discarding the fractional part and using the next lower whole number. This is called *truncation*. Here are some examples of truncation:

1.1 becomes 1
1.9 becomes 1
−1.1 becomes −2
−1.9 becomes −2

ASSIGNING VALUES

Variables and arrays are not much good without values. The simplest way to assign a value to a variable is with a LET statement. Here is an example:

```
]90 REM INITIALIZE VARIABLE X
]100 LET X = 3
```

In statement 100, variable X is assigned the value 3. This same statement could be rewritten as follows:

```
]100 X = 3
```

The word LET is optional; it is usually omitted.

Here is a string variable assignment statement:

```
]215 A$ = "ALSO RAN"
```

The string variable A$ is assigned the two words ALSO RAN.

Here are three assignment statements that assign values to array variable R$( ), which you encountered earlier in the description of arrays:

```
]200 REM  R$() IS THE MOTEL GUEST LIST
]210 R$(1) = "JONES"
]220 R$(2) = "SMITH"
]230 R$(3) = "DOE"
```

Remember, you can put more than one statement on a single line; therefore, three R$ assignments could be placed on a single line as follows:

```
]200 REM  R$() IS THE MOTEL GUEST LIST
]210 R$(1) = "JONES": R$(2) = "SMITH": R$(3) =
     "DOE"
```

Recall that a colon must separate adjacent statements appearing on the same line.

Assignment statements can include any of the arithmetic or logical operators described earlier in this chapter. Here is an example of such an assignment statement:

```
]90 REM  THIS IS A DUMB WAY OF ASSIGNING A
    VALUE
]100 V = 33 + 7/9
```

The statement above assigns the value 33.7777778 to the real variable V. It is equivalent to these three statements:

```
]90 REM  X AND Y USED LATER
]100 X = 7
]110 Y = 9
]120 V = 33 + X/Y
```

which could be written on one line as follows:

```
]100 X = 7: Y = 9: V = 33 + X/Y
```

Here are assignment statements that perform the logical operations given earlier in this chapter:

```
]90 REM  THESE EXAMPLES WERE DESCRIBED EARLIER
    IN THE CHAPTER
]100 A = NOT ((3 + 4) >= 6)
]110 B = ("AA" + "AB") OR (8 * 2) = (4 ^ 2))
```

The following example shows how a string variable could have its value assigned using string concatenation in Applesoft:

```
]90 REM  R$(6) IS ASSIGNED THE VALUE "MR. ALTON"
]100 MR$ = "MR. "
]110 MS$ = "MS. "
]120 N$ = "ALTON"
]200 R$(6) = MR$ + N$
```

DATA and READ Statements

When a number of variables need value assignments in an Applesoft program, you can use the DATA and READ statements rather than the previous type of assignment statement. Consider the following example:

```
]5 REM   INITIALIZE ALL PROGRAM VARIABLES
]10 DATA 10, 20, -4, 300
]20 READ A,B,C,D
```

The statement on line 10 specifies four numeric data values. These four values are assigned to four numeric variables by the statement on line 20. After the statements on lines 10 and 20 have been executed, A = 10, B = 20, C = −4, and D = 300.

If you have one or more DATA statements in your program, then you can visualize them as building a column of values (Figure 7-9). For example, a DATA statement that contains a list of ten values would build a ten-entry column. Two DATA statements each specifying five of the ten data entries would build exactly the same column.

READ statements use a pointer to the column of DATA statement values. The pointer starts at the beginning of the column.

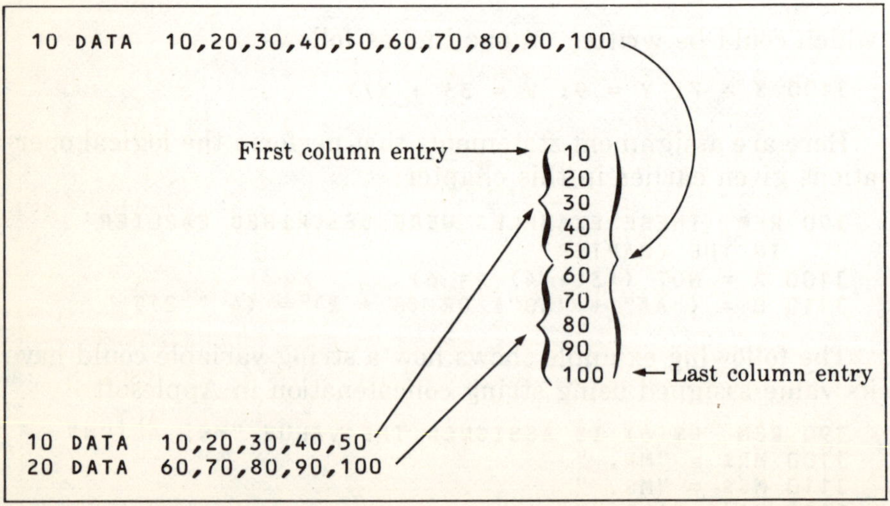

Figure 7-9. How DATA statements build a column of values

Each time a READ statement uses a value from the column, it moves the pointer down to the next value (Figure 7-10).

The first READ statement in the program starts at the first column entry and takes values sequentially, assigning them to variables named in the READ statement. The second and subsequent READ statements take values from the column, starting at the point where the previous READ statement left off.

The DATA column can contain both numeric and string values. When you assign the values to variables using a READ statement, each variable must be the same type (string or numeric) as the corresponding value it is assigned.

You can at any time send the pointer back to the beginning of the DATA column by executing a RESTORE statement in Applesoft (Figure 7-11).

Clearing Variables

Both Integer BASIC and Applesoft let you set every numeric variable and array element to zero and every string variable and array element to null, all at once.

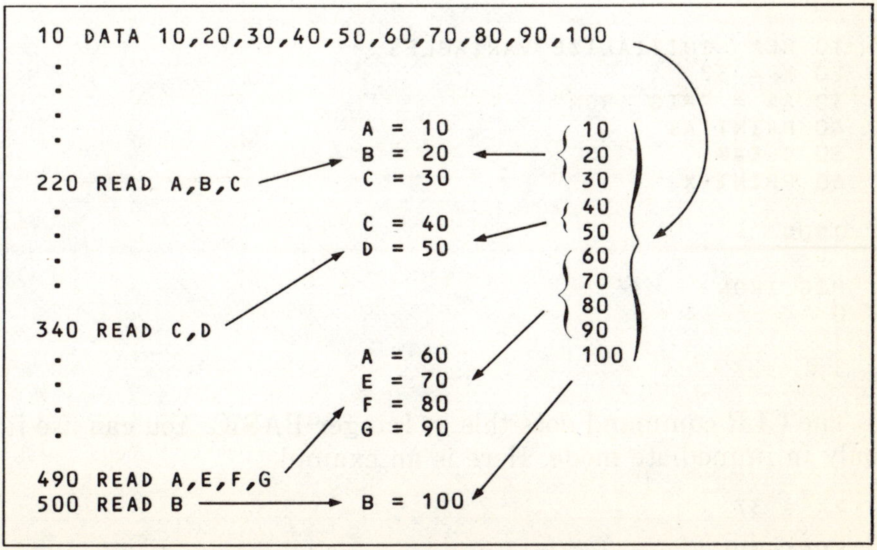

Figure 7-10. How READ statements assign values

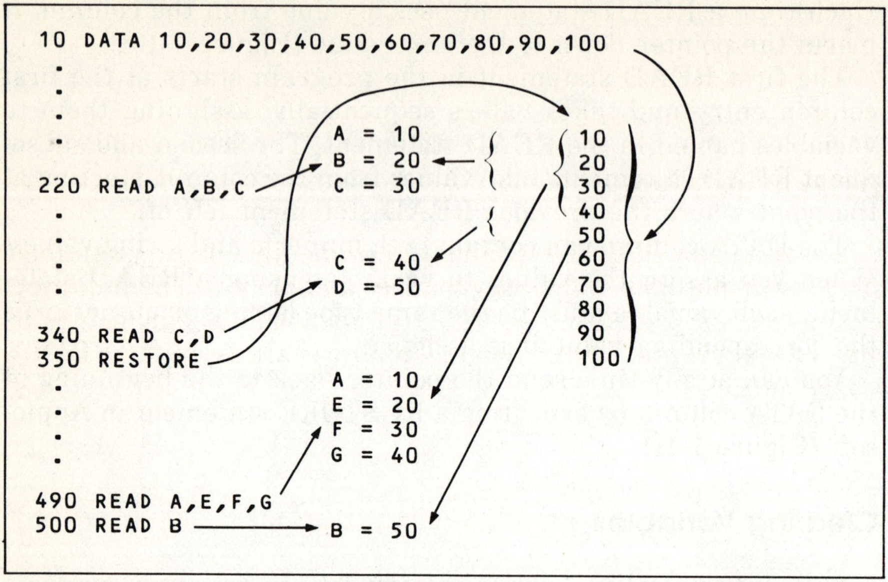

Figure 7-11. How a RESTORE statement affects READ statements

The CLEAR statement does this in Applesoft. Like RESTORE, it also resets the DATA column pointer. Here is an example:

```
]LIST

10 REM  INITIALIZE VARIABLES
20 X = 37
30 A$ = "PIG IRON"
40 PRINT A$
50 CLEAR
60 PRINT X

]RUN

PIG IRON
0

]▒
```

The CLR command does this in Integer BASIC. You can use it only in immediate mode. Here is an example:

```
>X = 37

>PRINT X
37
```

```
>CLR

>PRINT X
0

> ▒
```

DISPLAYING VALUES

You can use a PRINT statement in immediate or programmed mode to display the values of variables and arrays. The following example uses DATA and READ statements to assign values to several variables, then displays the values with PRINT statements:

```
]LIST

100 REM READ A NAME & ADDRESS
110 READ NA$,SR$,CI$,ST$,ZI
200 REM DISPLAY NAME & ADDRESS
210 PRINT "  NAME: ";NA$
220 PRINT "STREET: ";SR$
230 PRINT "  CITY: ";CI$
240 PRINT " STATE: ";ST$
250 PRINT "   ZIP: ";ZI
500 END
9990 REM NAME AND ADDRESS
10000 DATA FRANK N. STINE, 1 BLIND ALLEY,
    UPSTATE, NY, 10101

]RUN

  NAME: FRANK N. STINE
STREET: 1 BLIND ALLEY
  CITY: UPSTATE
 STATE: NY
   ZIP: 10101

] ▒
```

A single PRINT statement can display any mixture of constant and variable values. In the example above, each PRINT statement displays both a string constant and a variable. The following program illustrates another way to display the same variables:

```
]LIST

100 REM READ A NAME & ADDRESS
110 READ NA$,SR$,CI$,ST$,ZI
```

```
200 REM DISPLAY NAME & ADDRESS
210 PRINT NA$
220 PRINT SR$
230 PRINT CI$;", ";ST$;"  ";ZI
500 END
9990 REM NAME AND ADDRESS
10000 DATA FRANK N. STINE, 1 BLIND ALLEY,
    UPSTATE, NY, 10101

]RUN

FRANK N. STINE
1 BLIND ALLEY
UPSTATE, NY  10101

]▒
```

INPUTTING VALUES

The INPUT statement makes it possible for a program to request the value for a variable from its user, via the keyboard. When the computer executes an INPUT statement, it waits for input from the keyboard. Nothing happens until the computer receives the input.

In its simplest form, an INPUT statement begins with the word INPUT and is followed by a variable name. Data entered from the keyboard is assigned to the named variable. The variable name type determines the type of data that must be entered. A numeric variable name can be satisfied only by numeric input. To demonstrate numeric input, type in the following short program and run it (try entering some letters and see what happens):

```
]10 INPUT A
]20 PRINT A
]30 END
```

Upon executing an INPUT statement like the one on line 10 above, the computer displays a question mark, then waits for your entry. Each time you press a key, the corresponding character appears immediately on the screen at the location marked by the cursor. When you press the RETURN key to end the entry, the whole entry is displayed again. The first display occurs when the INPUT statement on line 10 is executed and you make an entry at the keyboard. The second display is in response to the PRINT statement on line 20.

An INPUT statement can input more than one value at a time. To do this, list all the variables for which you want to input values following the word INPUT. Separate the variables with commas. When such an INPUT statement is executed, you must respond with a separate value for each variable. Be sure each value is the same type as the variable it will be assigned to. The following example inputs two numeric values, then displays them:

```
]10 INPUT A,B
]20 PRINT A,B
]30 END
```

Run the program above and enter one number followed by a comma, then another number, and then press RETURN. Now try something a bit different. Enter one number and press RETURN; Applesoft reminds you to enter the next value by displaying a double question mark (Integer BASIC displays a single question mark). So enter another number and press RETURN. Thus, when an INPUT statement calls for more than one numeric value, you have a choice of entering all the values on one line or entering them on separate lines. Because you use commas to separate the values for different variables, you cannot use commas as punctuation in a single number; enter 1000, not 1,000.

The INPUT statement works somewhat differently with string variables in Integer BASIC. First of all, it does not display a question mark. Try this Integer BASIC example:

```
>10 DIM A$(19)
>20 INPUT A$
>30 PRINT A$
>40 END
```

When you run the program above, try entering a string of more than 19 characters. You will get a *** **STR OVFL ERR** message and the program will stop. The length of the string you enter cannot exceed the maximum length of the string variable used in the INPUT statement.

Integer BASIC forces you to enter each string value on a separate line. If an INPUT statement specifies a list of variables and there are string variables in the list, the associated string values must be entered on separate lines. This is because Integer

BASIC lets you include commas as part of a string value. You can prove this for yourself by running the example program above and entering the string value DOE, JOHN.

As we saw earlier, any real variable can have an integer value in Applesoft. Therefore you can input an integer value for a real variable. A real value entered for an integer variable is converted to an integer value according to the truncation rules presented in the "Mixed-Type Expressions" section of this chapter.

INPUT Statement Prompts

The INPUT statement is very fussy; its syntax is too demanding for any normal person. Upon encountering the types of error messages that can occur if one comma happens to be out of place, the person using the program is like to give up in despair. You should therefore do your best to write foolproof data entry programs. These programs watch out for every mistake that the program user can make when entering data. A foolproof program will cope with errors in a way that anyone can understand.

One simple trick is the INPUT statement's ability to display a short message that can describe the expected input. Such a message is called a *prompt message*. The message appears in the INPUT statement as a string value enclosed in quotation marks. The message will be displayed just ahead of the input request. This certainly beats sticking a bunch of variables into a single INPUT statement, with only your memory reminding you what to enter next.

In Applesoft, the prompt message should be placed immediately after the word INPUT. It is followed by a semicolon, which is in turn followed by the list of variables to be input. The existence of a prompt message suppresses the standard INPUT statement question mark. The prompt message is displayed only once, even if more than one line is required to enter all of the values requested by the variable list. Here is an Applesoft example:

```
]100 REM  INPUT NAME AND ADDRESS
]110 INPUT "  NAME? ";NA$
]120 INPUT "STREET? ";SR$
]130 INPUT "  CITY? ";CI$
]140 INPUT " STATE? ";ST$
]150 INPUT "   ZIP? ";ZI
```

```
]200 REM  DISPLAY NAME AND ADDRESS
]210 PRINT NA$
]220 PRINT SR$
]230 PRINT CI$;", ";ST$;"  ";ZI
]500 END
]RUN

   NAME? MARY GOLD
 STREET? 300 BLOSSOM LANE
   CITY? VERDANT VALLEY
  STATE? KY
    ZIP? ▒
```

In Integer BASIC, the prompt message should immediately follow the word INPUT. It is followed by a comma and then the list of variables to be input. When the list contains more than one variable, the prompt message is still displayed only once, on the first line of input. If the first variable on the list is numeric, a question mark is displayed immediately after the prompt message. If the first variable is a string, no such question mark is displayed. Here is an Integer BASIC example:

```
>DIM A$(10)
>20 INPUT "ENTER YOUR NAME AND AGE ",A$,A
>30 PRINT A$;" IS ";A
>40 END
```

FUNCTIONS

Another element of BASIC is the function. Functions act like expressions, but they look more like BASIC statements. The rest of this chapter shows you how to use selected functions, and later chapters explain how other functions work. Appendix A summarizes all 28 predefined BASIC functions.

Some functions calculate a numeric amount:

```
]10 A = SQR(B)
```

In this example, the variable A is set equal to the square root of the variable B. The reserved word SQR specifies the square root function.

Other functions generate a string value, as in the following example:

```
]20 HT$=STR$(IN/12)
```

The STR$ in the example above generates the same string of characters that would result if the expression in parentheses, IN/12, were displayed using a PRINT statement. In this case, though, the characters are not displayed. Instead they are assigned to variable HT$.

You specify a function with a reserved word (like SQR for the square root function or STR$ for the numeric-to-string conversion function). In this respect functions are similar to statements. But functions are always followed by an operand or operands enclosed in parentheses.

You can use a function anywhere you can use a variable or constant in a BASIC statement, except to the left of an equal sign. In other words, you can say that A = SQR(B), but you cannot say that SQR(A) = B.

Every function in a BASIC statement is reduced to a single numeric or string value before any other parts of the BASIC statement are evaluated. Function operands can be constants, variables, or expressions. So before the Apple II can perform the function, it may have to evaluate the function operand. Then it can apply the function to the operand, yielding the final numeric or string value.

Not until all functions in a given expression are evaluated is the expression itself evaluated. For example, consider this statement:

```
]10 B = 24.7 * (SQR(C) + 5) - SIN(0.2 + D)
```

In this example, the Apple II evaluates the SQR function as soon as it retrieves the value of variable C from memory. Then it evaluates the expression 0.2+D and applies the SIN function to it. Finally, it uses the function results in evaluating the entire expression. Suppose SQR(C)=6.72 and SIN(0.2+D)=0.625. The expression is first reduced to 24.7*(6.72+5)−0.625. Then this simpler expression is evaluated. Variable B ends up equaling 288.859.

Substring Functions

Three widely used Applesoft string functions each extract a portion of a larger string value, called a *substring*. You specify a source string and the number of characters to extract. The LEFT$ function starts with the first character, the RIGHT$

function starts with the last character, and the MID$ function takes a piece out of the middle. For the MID$ function, you must specify where to start extracting. The following Applesoft example illustrates substring functions:

```
]LIST

10 INPUT "TYPE SOMETHING! ";S$
20 PRINT "THE FIRST THREE CHARACTERS ARE: ":
   LEFT$(S$,3)
30 PRINT "THE MIDDLE THREE CHARACTERS ARE:";
   MID$(S$,(LEN(S$/2),3)
40 PRINT "THE LAST THREE CHARACTERS ARE: ";
   RIGHT$(S$,3)
50 END

]RUN

TYPE SOMETHING! COMPUTERS
THE FIRST THREE CHARACTERS ARE: COM
THE MIDDLE THREE CHARACTERS ARE:PUT
THE LAST THREE CHARACTERS ARE:  ERS

]▒
```

Although Integer BASIC has no functions that let you extract portions of a string, there is a way of doing it. You specify the starting position and the number of characters in the substring, as in the following example:

```
>10 DIM A$(20),B$(5)
>20 B$ = A$(1,4)
>30 END
```

In this example, B$ is set equal to the first four characters of A$. It may look to you as though B$ is being assigned the value of one of the elements of string array A$( ), but remember that Integer BASIC does not allow string arrays, much less two-dimensional string arrays. Instead, this notation refers to a substring. The first value in parentheses is the starting position of the substring, and the second value is the number of characters in the substring.

Integer BASIC String Concatenation

Unlike Applesoft, Integer BASIC has no string concatenation operator. However, the LEN function allows you to concatenate strings in Integer BASIC.

```
>10 DIM A$(10),B$(10),C$(10)
>20 A$ = "WIND"
>30 B$ = "PIPE"
>40 C$ = "LINE"
>50 A$(LEN(A$) + 1) = B$
>60 PRINT A$
>70 B$(LEN(B$) + 1) = C$
>80 PRINT B$
>90 END
>RUN
WINDPIPE
PIPELINE

>▒
```

ASCII Conversion Functions

In Applesoft, the CHR$ function translates a number into its ASCII character equivalent. For example, to generate a $ character, first find its ASCII code in Appendix E. Then use the code with CHR$, like this:

```
]PRINT CHR$(36);954.32
$954.32

]▒
```

Going the other way, the ASC function converts a string character to its ASCII code number. The following example illustrates this:

```
]PRINT ASC("A")
65

]▒
```

User-Defined Functions

In addition to the many functions that are a standard part of BASIC, you can define your own arithmetic functions in Applesoft, provided that they are not very complicated. User-defined string functions are not allowed. A DEF FN statement defines the function. You invoke the function with an FN statement. Next is a short program that uses a DEF FN statement.

```
]LIST

10 DEF FNR(X) = INT(X * 100 + 0.5)/100
100 INPUT "AMOUNT OF SALE? ";A
110 INPUT "SALES TAX RATE? ";R
120 T = FNR(A * R/100)
130 PRINT "AMOUNT OF SALE $";A
140 PRINT "     SALES TAX $";T;" (";R;"%)"
150 PRINT "                -----------"
160 PRINT "         TOTAL $";A + T

]RUN

AMOUNT OF SALE? 99.95
SALES TAX RATE? 6.5
AMOUNT OF SALE $99.95
     SALES TAX $6.5 (6.5%)
               -----------
         TOTAL $106.45

]▒
```

In this example, line 10 defines a function that rounds an amount to the nearest hundredth. On line 120, the program employs the function to round off a sales tax calculation to the nearest cent.

The function name follows the reserved words DEF FN. It consists of one or two characters that uniquely identify the function. The first character must be a letter. The second character, if present, can be either a letter or a digit.

The arithmetic expression in a DEF FN statement defines what the function does. It can be made up of any combination of constants, variables, array elements, and other functions. However, the expression cannot refer to itself, nor to any other function that in turn refers to it.

In a DEF FN statement, a single variable, enclosed in parentheses, must follow the function name. This variable name is local to the function definition; it is a dummy variable and has no effect outside of the DEF FN statement. You can use the same variable name elsewhere in the program without affecting the function, and the dummy variable will not affect any like-named variable elsewhere in the program.

To use a function you have defined with a DEF FN statement, start with the reserved word FN, then state the function name.

Following that, specify an operand in the form of a constant, variable, or expression enclosed in parentheses. When Applesoft encounters such a function reference, it uses the value of the operand everywhere the dummy variable appears in the DEF FN statement expression that defines the function.

Program Organization And Control 8

To use the full power of the Apple II, you must be able to control the execution path in your programs. That can be done in several ways. This chapter explains controlling program execution with branch statements, executing statements repeatedly with program loops, making decisions with conditional statements, and structuring programs with subroutine statements. It also describes how to halt and resume program execution, how to directly access and change the contents of individual memory cells, and how to track program execution.

BRANCHING

Normally, program execution begins with the first statement in the program and continues sequentially, as Figure 8-1 illustrates. Branch statements change this execution sequence by explicitly designating the line number of the next statement to be executed (see Figure 8-2).

The GOTO Statement

GOTO is the simplest branch statement; it allows you to specify the statement that will be executed next. In Figure 8-2, which illustrates unconditional branching, the statement on line 20 assigns a value to variable A. The next statement is a GOTO, which specifies that program execution must branch to line 70. Therefore, the instruction execution sequence surrounding this

```
 10  INPUT A
 20  INPUT B
 30  PRINT A*B
 40
 50
 60
 70
 80
 90
100  END
```

Figure 8-1. Normal program execution

part of the program will be as follows: line 20, then line 30, then line 70. Of course, some other statement must branch back to line 40; otherwise the statement on line 40 would never be executed by program logic, as illustrated in Figure 8-2.

You can branch to any line number, even if the line has nothing on it but a remark. However, the computer ignores the remark, so the effect is the same as branching to the next line. In Figure 8-2, for example, program execution branches from line 30 to line 70. Since there is nothing but a remark on line 70, the computer moves on to line 80, executing the statement on that line. Therefore, even though you can branch to a remark, you might as well branch to the next line. Attempting to branch to a nonexistent line number causes an error message.

```
20  A=4
30  GOTO 70
40
50
60
70  REM   THIS LINE CONTAINS ONLY A REMARK
80
90
```

Figure 8-2. Unconditional branching to a REM statement

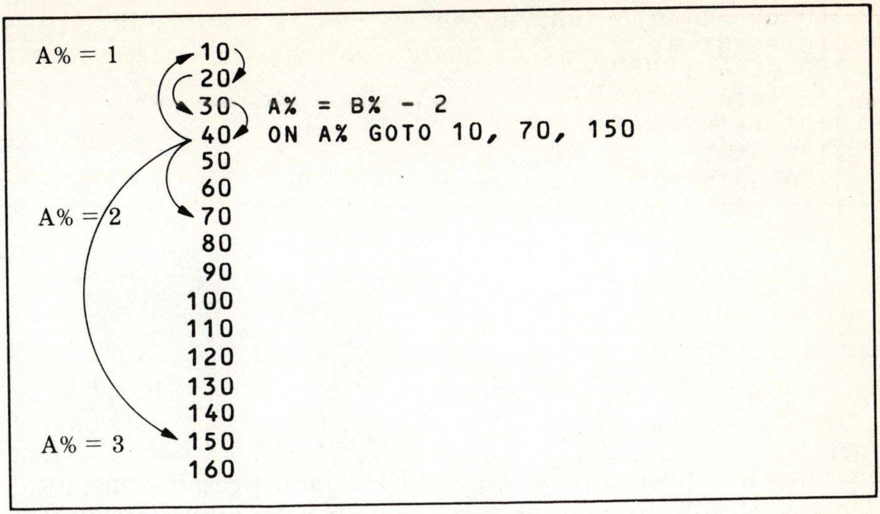

Figure 8-3. Computed GOTO in Applesoft

Computed GOTO Statement

Another type of GOTO statement lets program logic branch to one of two or more different line numbers, depending on the current value of a numeric expression. The statement on line 40 in Figure 8-3 is an Applesoft computed GOTO. When this statement is executed, program logic branches to statement 10 if variable A% = 1, to statement 70 if variable A% = 2, and to statement 150 if A% = 3. If A% has any value other than 1, 2, or 3, the program continues at statement 50.

The value of the expression in an Applesoft computed GOTO statement determines which line number to branch to from the computed GOTO statement's list of line numbers. If the value is 1, the first line number is used, if the value is 2, the second line number is used, and so on. If the value is 0 or exceeds the number of line numbers in the list, the program will go to the statement that follows the computed GOTO statement.

The following Applesoft program demonstrates how the computed GOTO statement works:

```
]10 B% = 4
]20 PRINT B%
]30 A% = B% - 2
```

```
]40  ON A% GOTO 180,70,150
]70  PRINT B%
]80  B% = 5
]90  GOTO 30
]150  PRINT B%
]160  B%=3
]170  GOTO 20
]180  END
]RUN

4
4
5
3

]▒
```

Execute this program by typing RUN and pressing RETURN. Can you account for the sequence in which the numbers are displayed (4, 4, 5, 3)? Try rewriting the program so that each number is displayed in the sequence 3, 4, 5.

Figure 8-4 shows a computed GOTO in Integer BASIC. When the statement on line 40 is executed, program logic branches to the statement number computed by evaluating the expression. In this example, it branches to statement 50 if variable A = 0, to statement 80 if A = 1, and to statement 110 if A = 2. If the computed line number does not exist in the program, a *** **BAD BRANCH ERR** message results. Notice that variable A is assigned a value in statement 30. The value assigned to A

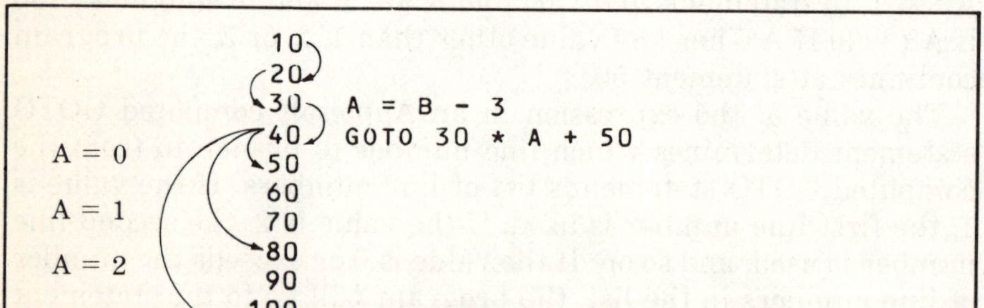

Figure 8-4. Computed GOTO in Integer BASIC

depends on the current value of variable B. The illustration does not show how variable B is computed; however, as long as B has a value of 3, 4, or 5, the statement on line 40 will cause a branch to occur.

LOOPS

GOTO and computed GOTO statements let you create any sequence of statement execution that your program logic may require. But suppose you want to reexecute an instruction (or a group of instructions) many times. For example, suppose that array variable A(I) has 100 elements and that each element needs to be assigned a value ranging from 0 to 99. Writing 100 assignment statements would be tedious. It is far simpler to reexecute one statement 100 times in a *program loop.*

FOR and NEXT Statements

You can create a loop using the FOR and NEXT statements, as follows:

```
]10 DIM A(99)
]20 FOR INDEX = 0 TO 99 STEP 1
]30 A(INDEX) = INDEX
]40 NEXT INDEX
]50 END
```

Statements between FOR and NEXT are executed repeatedly. In the example above, a single assignment statement appears between FOR and NEXT; therefore, this single statement is reexecuted repeatedly. This kind of program structure is called a FOR-NEXT loop.

So you can see the workings of a FOR-NEXT loop, the following program displays the values it assigns to array A( ) within the loop:

```
]10 DIM A(99)
]20 FOR INDEX = 0 TO 99 STEP 1
]30 A(INDEX) = INDEX
]35 PRINT A(INDEX)
]40 NEXT INDEX
]50 END
```

When you run this program, it displays 100 numbers, starting at 0 and ending at 99.

Statements between FOR and NEXT are reexecuted the number of times specified by the *index variable*, which appears directly after the word FOR. In the preceding example, this index variable is INDEX. Variable INDEX is specified as going from 0 to 99 in *steps* of 1. Variable INDEX also appears in the assignment statement on line 30. Therefore, the first time the assignment statement is executed, INDEX will equal 0, and the assignment statement will be executed as follows:

```
]30 A(0) = 0
```

Variable INDEX is increased by the step size, which is specified on line 20 as 1; INDEX therefore equals 1 the second time the assignment statement on line 30 is executed. The assignment statement has effectively become

```
]30 A(1) = 1
```

Variable INDEX continues to be incremented by the specified step until the maximum value of 99 is reached (or exceeded).

The step does not have to be 1; it can have any integer value. Change the step to 5 on line 20 and reexecute the program. Now the assignment statement is executed just 20 times, since incrementing INDEX 19 times by 5 will take it to 95; the 20th increment will take it to 100, which is more than the maximum value of 99. Keeping the step at 5, you could allow the assignment statement to be executed 100 times by increasing the maximum value of INDEX to 500. Try making this change. (Remember to change the DIM statement as well.)

The step size does not have to be positive. If the step size is negative, however, the initial value of the loop index must be larger than the final value of the loop index. For example, if the step size is −1 and you want to initialize 100 elements of array A( ) with values ranging from 0 to 99, you will have to rewrite the statement on line 20 as follows:

```
]10 DIM A(99)
]20 FOR INDEX = 99 TO 0 STEP -1
]30 A(INDEX) = INDEX
]35 PRINT A(INDEX)
]40 NEXT INDEX
]50 END
```

If the step size is 1 (and this is frequently the case), you do not have to specify a step size definition. In the absence of any definition, BASIC assumes a step size of 1.

You may specify the initial and final index values and the step size using expressions if you wish, but you should avoid doing so, since this unnecessarily complicates the program. If you must calculate one of these values, it is more efficient to do so in a separate statement ahead of the loop.

In an Applesoft program, you can use real values for the initial and final index values and for the step size. Also, Applesoft does not require an index variable in the NEXT statement. A plain NEXT statement matches the most recently executed FOR statement.

Nested Loops

Loops are frequently nested one inside the other like a set of mixing bowls. There can be any number of statements between FOR and NEXT. Often there are tens or even hundreds of statements, and within these tens or hundreds of statements additional loops may occur. Figure 8-5 illustrates a single level of nesting.

Complex loop structures appear frequently, even in relatively short programs. Figure 8-6 shows an example with the FOR and NEXT statements, but none of the intermediate statements. In this example the outermost loop uses index variable I; it contains

```
10 DIM A(99)
20 FOR INDEX = 0 TO 99 STEP 1
30 A(INDEX) = INDEX
40 REM DISPLAY ALL VALUES OF A() ASSIGNED
   THUS FAR
50 FOR COUNTER = 0 TO INDEX
60 PRINT A(COUNTER)
70 NEXT COUNTER
80 NEXT INDEX
90 END
```

Figure 8-5. Single-level FOR-NEXT loop nesting

```
50   FOR I = 1 TO 10
60   FOR X = 25 TO 347 STEP 3
     .
     .
     .
100  FOR A = 9 TO 0 STEP -1
     .
     .
     .
140  NEXT A
200  FOR B = 25 TO 100 STEP 5
     .
     .
     .
280  NEXT B
300  NEXT X
     .
     .
     .
500  FOR Y = 1 TO 20 STEP 2
     .
     .
     .
600  FOR P = 10 TO 20
     .
     .
     .
650  NEXT P
700  NEXT Y
     .
     .
     .
1000 FOR Z = 1 TO 10
     .
     .
     .
1090 NEXT Z
     .
     .
     .
1200 NEXT I
```

Figure 8-6. Complex FOR-NEXT loop nesting (intermediate program steps omitted for clarity)

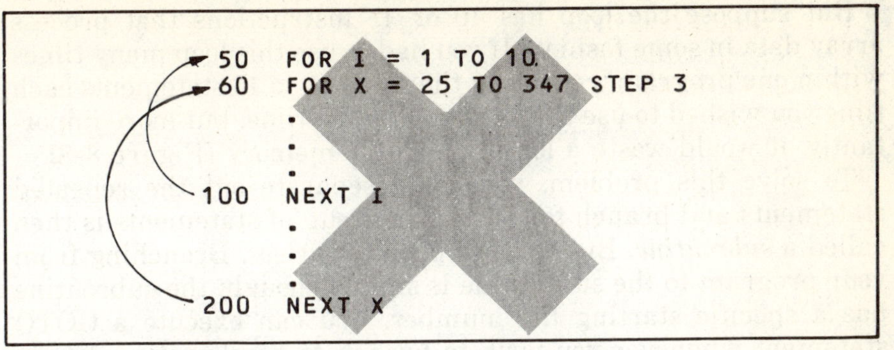

Figure 8-7. Illegal FOR-NEXT loop nesting

three nested loops that use indexes X, Y, and Z. The X loop contains two additional loops that use indexes A and B. The Y loop contains one nested loop using index P. The Z loop contains no nested loops.

Loop structures are easy to visualize and use. There is only one common error that you must avoid: do not terminate an outer loop before you terminate an inner loop (see Figure 8-7).

Every program must have the same number of FOR and NEXT statements, since every loop must begin with a FOR statement and end with a NEXT statement. For example, suppose your program has one FOR statement but two NEXT statements. The first NEXT statement terminates a FOR statement, so the loop executes correctly. But the second NEXT statement has no FOR statement, which causes an error.

SUBROUTINES

Once you start writing programs that are more than a few statements long, you will quickly find short sections that are used repeatedly. For example, suppose you have an array variable, such as A( ), that is reinitialized frequently at different points in your program. Would you simply repeat the three instructions that constitute the FOR-NEXT loop described earlier? Since there are just three instructions, you may as well do so.

But suppose the loop has 10 or 11 instructions that process array data in some fashion. If you had to use this loop many times within one program, rewriting the same 10 to 15 statements each time you wished to use the loop would take time, but more importantly, it would waste a lot of computer memory (Figure 8-8).

To solve this problem, you could separate out the repeated statements and branch to them. The group of statements is then called a *subroutine*. But another problem arises. Branching from your program to the subroutine is simple enough; the subroutine has a specific starting line number. You can execute a GOTO statement whenever you wish to branch to a subroutine, but to what line would the program return at the end of the subroutine, as in Figure 8-9? If two or more GOTO statements branch to the subroutine, there are two or more different places to which the program may have to return when the subroutine has completed execution. The solution is to use special subroutine statements. Instead of branching to the subroutine using a GOTO, you should use a GOSUB statement.

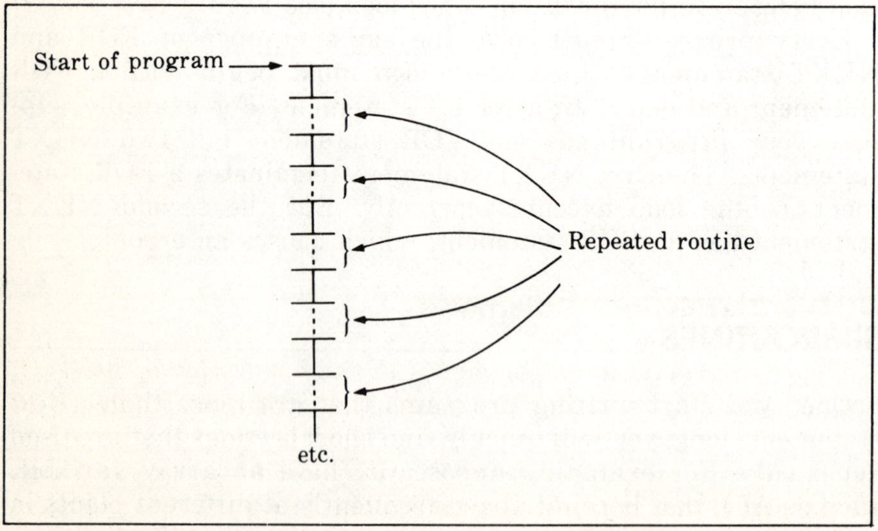

Figure 8-8. Duplicate routines waste memory

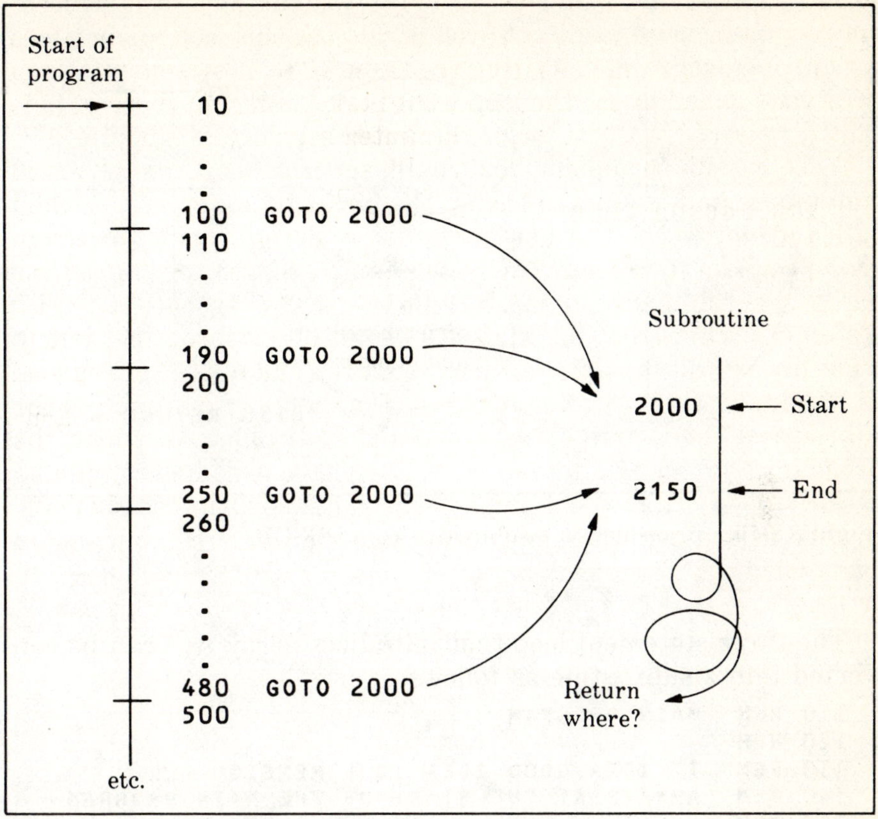

Figure 8-9. Branching to a subroutine with GOTO

GOSUB and RETURN Statements

The GOSUB statement branches in the same way as a GOTO, but in addition it remembers where to return, as Figure 8-10 shows. In computer jargon, we say GOSUB *calls* a subroutine. You must end the subroutine with a RETURN statement, which causes a branch back to the statement following the GOSUB statement. If the GOSUB is the last statement on the line, the program returns to the first statement on the next line.

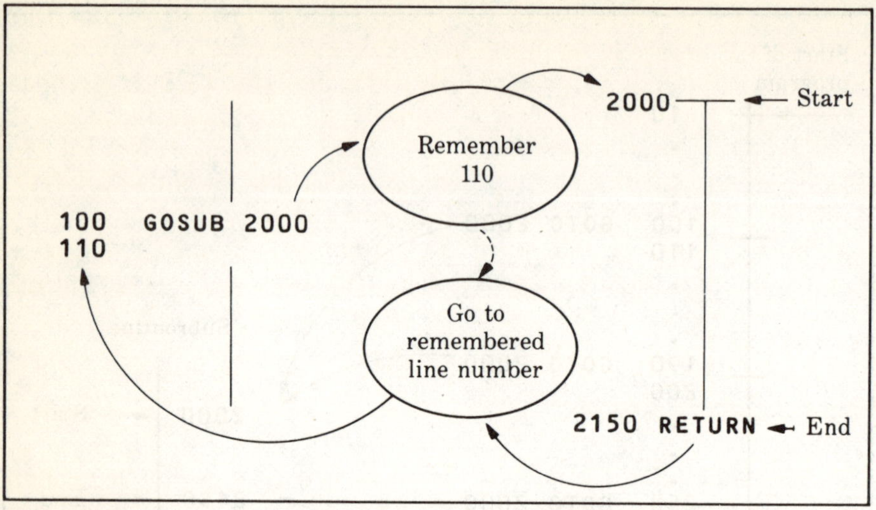

Figure 8-10. Branching to a subroutine with GOSUB

The three-statement loop that initializes array A( ) can be converted into a subroutine as follows:

```
]10 REM   MAIN PROGRAM
]20 REM
]30 REM   IT IS A GOOD IDEA TO DIMENSION ALL
]40 REM   ARRAYS AT THE START OF THE MAIN PROGRAM
]50 REM
]60 DIM A(99)
]70 PRINT "INITIALIZING...";
]80 GOSUB 2000: REM INITIALIZE A()
]90 PRINT "COMPLETE"
]100 END
]1985 REM
]1990 REM INITIALIZATION SUBROUTINE
]1995 REM
]2000 FOR INDEX = 0 TO 99
]2010 A(INDEX) = INDEX
]2020 PRINT A(INDEX)
]2030 NEXT INDEX
]2040 RETURN
```

The POP Statement

Under some circumstances you will not want a subroutine to return to the statement following the GOSUB statement. You might be tempted to use a GOTO statement to return, but that can cause a problem because BASIC is still remembering where it should return to. In cases like this, use the POP statement. Otherwise you risk an error caused by the accumulation of unused RETURN statements. All POP does is make BASIC forget the most recent return location. You can then use a GOTO statement to branch somewhere else in the program.

Bypass the RETURN statement sparingly. Using POP excessively to enable branching out of subroutines with GOTO statements leads to tangled, confusing programs.

Nested Subroutines

Subroutines can be nested. That is to say, a subroutine can itself call another subroutine, which in turn can call a third subroutine, and so on. You do not have to do anything special in order to use nested subroutines. Simply branch to the subroutine using a GOSUB statement and end the subroutine with a RETURN statement. BASIC will remember the line number for each nested return.

The following program illustrates nested subroutines:

```
]10 REM  MAIN PROGRAM
]20 REM
]30 REM  IT IS A GOOD IDEA TO DIMENSION ALL
]40 REM  ARRAYS AT THE START OF THE MAIN PROGRAM
]50 REM
]60 DIM A(99)
]70 PRINT "INITIALIZING...";
]80 GOSUB 2000: REM INITIALIZE A()
]90 PRINT "COMPLETE"
]100 END
]1985 REM
]1990 REM INITIALIZATION SUBROUTINE
]1995 REM
]2000 FOR INDEX = 0 TO 99
]2010 A(INDEX) = INDEX
]2020 GOSUB 3000: REM PRINT VALUES
]2030 NEXT INDEX
]2040 RETURN
]2985 REM
]2990 REM PRINT-VALUES SUBROUTINE
]2995 REM
]3000 PRINT A(INDEX)
]3010 RETURN
```

This program moves the PRINT A(INDEX) statement out of the subroutine at line 2000 and puts it into a nested subroutine at line 3000. Nothing else changes.

While it is perfectly acceptable and even desirable for one subroutine to call another, a subroutine cannot call itself. Neither can a subroutine call another subroutine that in turn calls the first subroutine. This is called *recursion* and is not allowed in Applesoft or Integer BASIC.

Computed GOSUB Statement

There is a computed GOSUB statement that is akin to the computed GOTO statement. The computed GOSUB statement allows you to branch to one of two or more subroutines depending on the value of a numeric expression. The computed GOSUB statement remembers where to return. It does not matter which of the subroutines is called; the called subroutine's RETURN statement causes a branch back to the remembered line number. You can nest subroutines using computed GOSUB statements, just as you can nest them using standard GOSUB statements.

Consider the following Applesoft statements:

```
]100 ON A GOSUB 1000,500,5000,2300
]110 REM
```

If A = 1 when the statement on line 100 is executed, the subroutine beginning at line 1000 is called. If A = 2 the subroutine beginning at line 500 is called. If A = 3 the subroutine beginning at line 5000 is called. If A = 4 the subroutine beginning at line 2300 is called. If A has any value other than 1, 2, 3, or 4, program execution falls through to line 110, and no subroutine is called.

The Integer BASIC version of the computed GOSUB statement works in a manner similar to the Integer BASIC computed GOTO statement.

CONDITIONAL EXECUTION

The computed GOTO and computed GOSUB statements are conditional statements. That is, the exact flow of program execution depends on the values of one or more variables that can change as the program is running. The exact program flow depends on the condition of the variables.

IF-THEN Statements

Another conditional statement is the IF-THEN statement. It has the following general form:

IF *expression* THEN *statement*

If the expression is true (that is, reduces to a value of 1), then the statement is executed. Relational and logical expressions are most common with IF-THEN statements, but arithmetic expressions can be used as well. This gives a BASIC program real decision-making capabilities. Here are three simple examples of IF-THEN statements:

```
]10 IF A = B + 5 THEN PRINT MSG$
]40 IF CC$ = "M" THEN IN = 0
]50 IF Q < 14 AND M < M1 THEN GOTO 66
```

The statement on line 10 causes a PRINT statement to be executed if the value of variable A is five more than the value of variable B. The PRINT MSG$ statement will not be executed otherwise. The statement on line 40 sets numeric variable IN to 0 if string variable CC$ is the letter M. The statement on line 50 causes program execution to branch to line 66 if variable Q is less than 14 and variable M is less than variable M1. Otherwise, program execution will continue with the statement on the next line. If you do not understand the evaluation of expressions following IF, refer to the discussion of expressions in Chapter 7.

An IF-THEN statement can be followed by other statements on the same program line. Integer BASIC and Applesoft handle this situation somewhat differently. Applesoft executes statements that follow an IF-THEN statement on the same line only if the expression in the IF-THEN statement is true. If the expression is false, program execution drops down to the first statement on the next program line. This may be illustrated as follows:

```
]10 IF V > 100 THEN PRINT "DEWEY WINS": GOSUB 2000
]20 T = T + V: PRINT T
```

In the example above, the program will print the message **DEWEY WINS** and call the subroutine at line 2000 only if the value of variable V is greater than 100. If V is less than or equal to 100, the program will not print the message or call the subroutine, but will instead proceed directly to the first statement on line 20.

In Integer BASIC, only the statement that immediately follows THEN is conditionally executed. Any later statements on the same program line are always executed, regardless of whether the expression in the IF-THEN statement is true or false. If the example above were in Integer BASIC, the program would print the message **DEWEY WINS** only if the value of variable V were greater than 100. The program would call the subroutine at line 2000 no matter what the value of V was.

There is a special form of the IF-THEN statement available in Applesoft. Whenever the conditionally executed statement is a GOTO statement, you can omit the word THEN or the word GOTO if you wish. The following three statements are equivalent:

```
]10 IF MM$ = DD$ THEN GOTO 100
]10 IF MM$ = DD$ THEN 100
]10 IF MM$ = DD$ GOTO 100
```

HALTING AND RESUMING EXECUTION

If a program is running and you want to stop it, press CONTROL-C. If the program is waiting for keyboard input from an INPUT statement, you will have to press RETURN after you press CONTROL-C.

In Applesoft, you will see the message **BREAK IN** followed by the line number at which program execution halted when you pressed CONTROL-C. You can continue program execution by typing the command CONT.

In Integer BASIC, you will see the message **STOPPED AT** and then the line number at which program execution halted. You can resume program execution by typing the command CON.

The RESET Key

You can interrupt your program at any time by pressing CONTROL-RESET (RESET alone on a standard Apple II).

On the Apple IIe, the Apple II Plus, and on a standard Apple II with a Language Card installed, CONTROL-RESET has the same effect as CONTROL-C. However, after CONTROL-RESET the CONT command (CON in Integer BASIC) does not work and the 80-column adapter is deactivated.

On some standard Apple II machines, pressing RESET causes the Machine Language Monitor command prompt (an asterisk) to appear. If you were using Integer BASIC or if your Apple II has an Applesoft ROM accessory card, press CONTROL-C and then RETURN to get back to BASIC. However, if you had loaded Applesoft from cassette, you return to Applesoft by typing 0G and then pressing RETURN. If you use the wrong procedure when trying to recover from an accidental reset, you will lose your BASIC program.

The END Statement

As described earlier in this chapter, the program stops running when it encounters an END statement. The Applesoft command CONT works after an END statement, but the Integer BASIC command CON does not.

The STOP Statement

The Applesoft STOP statement halts program execution. When Applesoft executes a STOP statement, it displays the message **BREAK IN** along with the line number where program execution stopped. You can continue program execution with the CONT command.

The WAIT Statement

The Applesoft WAIT statement causes program execution to pause until a memory location that you specify has a value that you specify. You can, for example, make your program pause until someone presses the button on game control number 1 (or on an Apple IIe, until someone presses the SOLID APPLE key). This is how:

```
]10 REM  WAIT FOR BUTTON ON GAME CONTROL NO. 1
]20 REM    OR THE SOLID APPLE KEY.
]30 REM
]40 PRINT "PLEASE PRESS THE BUTTON ON "
]50 PRINT "GAME CONTROL ONE,"
]60 PRINT "OR THE SOLID APPLE KEY."
]70 WAIT -16286,128
]80 PRINT "THANKS.  THAT FEELS MUCH BETTER."
]90 END
```

See Appendix A for a more complete description of the WAIT statement.

DIRECT ACCESS AND CONTROL

A number of statements give you direct access to the Apple II. There are many things you can do only by using these statements, such as sensing the game controls and operating the speaker.

Memory and Addressing

The Apple IIe can have two banks of memory, each with 65,536 individually addressable memory locations, for a total of 131,072 memory locations. The Apple II Plus and standard Apple II have one memory bank, with up to 65,536 memory locations. Each location can store a number ranging between 0 and 255. All programs and data are converted into sequences of numbers—each between 0 and 255—that are stored in this memory.

You must specify the numeric address of a memory location for each of the BASIC statements covered in this section. You can specify the address with a number, a variable, or an expression, as long as the value is a legitimate address. There are two legitimate addresses for each memory location. One is positive and is a number between 0 and 65535. The other is negative and can be derived by subtracting 65536 from the positive address. For example, −32768 and 32768 address the same memory location. Another memory location is addressed by either −1 or 65535. When you remember that the largest integer value allowed is 32767, you can see the utility of using negative numbers for addressing the higher memory locations.

PEEK and POKE

The PEEK function lets you read the value stored in any memory location. Consider the following statement:

```
]10 A = PEEK(222)
```

This statement assigns the content of memory location 222 to variable A.

The POKE statement puts a value into a memory location. For example, the statement

```
]]10 POKE 768,A
```

takes the value of variable A and stores it in memory location 768. A POKE statement stores any number, variable, or expression with a value between 0 and 255 in a memory location.

You can use PEEK with read/write memory (RAM) or read-only memory (ROM), but you can use POKE only with read/write memory. This is self-evident; read-only memory, as its name implies, can have its contents read but cannot be written into.

It takes two consecutive memory locations to store values greater than 255. In this case, the total value of both cells equals the value of the first location, plus 256 times the value of the second. For example, the expression PEEK(218)+PEEK(219)*256 reports the value that is stored in the pair of memory cells at locations 218 and 219. Conversely, the two statements POKE 232, SA-INT(SA/256)*256 and POKE 233, INT(SA/256) will store the value of variable SA, which may range between 0 and 65535, in the pair of memory cells at locations 232 and 233.

The CALL Statement

You can transfer control from BASIC to an assembly language program or subroutine with the CALL instruction. Look at this sample CALL statement:

```
] 100 CALL A1
```

Control is transferred to a machine language program that starts at the memory location specified by variable A1.

The assembly language subroutine or program can be one that is permanently resident in the Apple II (in ROM), or it can be one you provide. Appendix G has a complete list of built-in subroutines. In addition, you may refer to Chapter 12 for more coverage of the machine language Monitor and assembly language.

DEBUGGING: TRACING EXECUTION

A new program never seems to work quite the way you expect it to. Even if there are no errors in the BASIC syntax, there are likely to be errors in the program logic. Either kind of error is called a *bug*. The process of finding and eliminating program errors is called *debugging*.

The computer will catch and announce some errors for you. Those are the easy ones. The insidious errors require careful detective work that always includes tracing the flow of program execution. You must make sure that program statements are being executed in the order you expect and that the values of variables are being assigned as you expect. If you have carefully designed and written your program but it still doesn't work properly, there are some BASIC statements you can use to trace what happens after you type RUN.

The PRINT Statement

Surprisingly, the PRINT statement is a very useful debugging tool. You can temporarily put extra PRINT statements in your program at strategic points to display messages telling you that the program has reached a certain point without failing and to print out intermediate values of variables. This way you can trace the flow of program execution and check the results of intermediate calculations.

The TRACE Statement

The TRACE statement lives up to its name; it traces the flow of program execution by displaying the line number of each statement as it is executed. To see how it works, type in the following program, then enter TRACE followed by RUN.

```
]100 PRINT "ENTER A NUMBER FROM 1 TO 5
     (6 TO END)";
]110 INPUT N
]120 IF N = 1 THEN PRINT "UNO";
]130 IF N = 2 THEN PRINT "DOS";
]140 IF N = 3 THEN PRINT "TRES";
]150 IF N = 4 THEN PRINT "CUATRO";
]160 IF N = 5 THEN PRINT "CINCO";
]170 IF N > 5 THEN END
]180 FOR X = 1 TO N
]190 PRINT " *";: REM PRINT N ASTERISKS
]200 NEXT X
]210 PRINT
]220 GOTO 100
```

To cancel TRACE mode and return to normal, execute the statement NOTRACE.

The DSP Statement

There is another useful debugging statement available in Integer BASIC: the DSP statement. Here is an example:

```
>10 DSP COUNT
```

Once this particular DSP statement has been executed, Integer BASIC notifies you each time the value of variable COUNT changes and tells you at which line number the change occurred. Since the RUN command disables any previously executed DSP statements, you must either use GOTO to start the program or put your DSP statements in program lines.

You can also turn off DSP mode for a variable with a NODSP statement. Here is an example:

```
>300 NODSP NAME$
```

Once this statement has been executed, Integer BASIC ceases to notify you each time the value of variable NAME$ changes.

Screen Output And Data Entry 9

The most inexperienced programmer quickly discovers that the input and output sections of a program are its trickiest parts. Input and output are perhaps the most important program features as far as the user is concerned, so it is worth spending some time to make your programs clear and easy to use. People will get far less out of a program that simply displays its results with several unplanned PRINT statements than from a program with carefully designed output. And nearly every program uses data that must be entered at the keyboard. Will a few INPUT statements suffice? In most cases the answer is no. What if the program user accidentally presses the wrong key? Or worse, what if the user discovers that he or she input the wrong data—after entering two or three data items? A usable program must assume that its user is human and therefore likely to make mistakes. This chapter explores some ways of arranging information on the display screen for best readability. It also discusses ways to minimize data-entry errors and techniques for correcting those that do occur.

CLEARING THE DISPLAY SCREEN

The statement CALL −936 clears the display screen and moves the cursor to the home position (the upper-left corner of the screen). In Applesoft, the HOME statement does the same thing. Either statement works in immediate mode as well as programmed mode.

Display-Screen Line Length

An Apple II with an 80-column adapter can display up to 80 characters per screen line. Initially, the adapter is not active, and the display line length is limited to 40 characters. In immediate mode, you activate the adapter when you type the PR#3 command. This same command works from within a BASIC program.

The PR#3 command is actually a command to the operating system (ProDOS or DOS 3.3). To issue any operating system command from within a BASIC program, you put it in a PRINT statement, prefixed with the character whose ASCII code is 4. Here is an example:

```
]10 PRINT: PRINT CHR$(4);"PR#3": REM ..Activate
    80-col. adapter
```

Warning: The operating system prefix character (ASCII code 4) must be the first character printed by the PRINT statement. Furthermore, the PRINT statement executed most recently (if any) must not end with a semicolon. If you violate either of these restrictions, you may disconnect the operating system, forcing you to restart the Apple II and causing you to lose your BASIC program in the process.

In the example above, the second PRINT statement contains the operating system command. It uses the CHR$ function to generate the required operating system prefix character and then lists the operating system command between quotes. The first PRINT statement ensures that the most recent PRINT statement did not end with a semicolon.

When the operating system receives a PR#3 command, it activates the accessory card installed in slot 3, or on an Apple IIe, the adapter card installed in the auxiliary slot. If the 80-column adapter is installed in a different slot, use that slot number instead of the 3 in the PR# command. If you use the PR# command with the wrong slot number, the computer will behave unpredictably, and may even lock up, forcing you to restart it.

Many Applesoft programmers assign a string variable to the value CHR$(4) and then use that variable in PRINT statements. The following example shows how:

```
]10 D$=CHR$(4): REM ..Prefix for op. sys. commands
]20 PRINT: PRINT D$;"PR#3": REM ..Activate 80-col.
```

Integer BASIC does not allow the CHR$ function. You can create the operating system prefix by typing CONTROL-D between quotes instead. This example illustrates:

```
>10 D$="": REM ..CONTROL-D prefix for DOS 3.3
    commands
>20 PRINT: PRINT D$;"PR#3": REM ..Activate 80-col.
```

Activating an 80-column adapter automatically sets the display width to 80, but you can switch to 40 by printing CHR$(17) and back to 80 by printing CHR$(18). There is no need to activate the 80-column adapter each time, for once it is active, it remains so until deactivated. You can deactivate the 80-column adapter by printing CHR$(21).

You can tell whether the 80-column adapter is active or not by looking at the cursor's design. Table 9-1 shows the different forms of the cursor.

Table 9-1. Standard Apple II Cursor Designs

Cursor		80-Column Adapter	Line Width	Escape Mode
Design	**Blinking**			
	Yes	Inactive	40	*
	Yes	Inactive	40	*
	No	Active	80	No
	No	Active	40	No
	No	Active	80	Yes
	No	Active	40	Yes

*With 80-column adapter inactive, the cursor does not indicate escape mode status.

FORMATTED OUTPUT

Formatting is the process of arranging information on a display screen so that the information is easy to understand or pleasing to the eye. The basic tool for displaying information is the PRINT statement. We used it in Chapter 5 to print numeric and string data.

The key to formatting output on the display screen is cursor control. Printed output starts wherever the cursor is located. Each character displayed on the screen moves the cursor. In most cases, after a character is displayed the cursor moves one column to the right. A few characters move the cursor in other directions. The PRINT statement may end by forcing the cursor to the beginning of the next display line. As in typewriter terminology, this is called a *carriage return.*

Carriage Return

When you press the RETURN key, the cursor advances to the beginning of the next display line. The RETURN key generates an invisible character that causes a carriage return. The PRINT statement also generates the carriage return character.

Normally, a PRINT statement outputs a carriage return character as its last action. That explains why the cursor advances to the next display line at the end of a PRINT statement. For example, the following program displays a column of 20 Z's in the first position of each display line:

```
]200  C$="Z"
]210 FOR N = 1 TO 20
]220 PRINT C$
]230 NEXT N
]240 PRINT "PHEW!"
]250 END
```

Of course a semicolon at the end of a PRINT statement will suppress the carriage return. Or will it? Try this variation on the last program:

```
]200  C$="Z"
]210 FOR N = 1 TO 800
]220 PRINT C$;
]230 NEXT N
]240 PRINT "PHEW!"
]250 END
```

Assuming that the screen displays 40 characters per line, the screen fills with 20 lines of Z's, and the word PHEW! appears at the beginning of the twenty-first line. Where did those 20 carriage return characters come from? The semicolon at the end of the PRINT statement on line 220 is supposed to suppress the carriage return character. However, it doesn't seem to work at the end of a display line.

Whenever anything is displayed in the last column of any display line, it triggers a carriage return. This is a feature of the display screen. Rather than lose the characters off the screen to the right, the display screen generates a carriage return character and continues the same output line on the next display line.

Suppose you display something in the last column of the last line on the screen. A carriage return occurs, but there is no next line for the cursor to advance to. However, the computer forces the first line off the top of the screen so the cursor will have somewhere to go. The following program illustrates this with a line width of 40:

```
]300 PRINT "FIRST LINE"
]310 REM  Skip down to bottom line
]320 FOR N = 1 TO 22
]330 PRINT
]340 NEXT N
]350 REM  Space over to last character
]360 PRINT "WATCH TOP LINE AS CHARACTER
     APPEARS--->";
]370 REM  Ring the bell awhile
]380 FOR N = 1 TO 25
]390  PRINT CHR$(7);
]400 NEXT N
]410 REM  Display last col., last line
]420 PRINT "@";
]430 REM  Pause until RETURN pressed
]440 INPUT A$
]450 END
```

This program first displays the **FIRST LINE** message (line 300). Then it outputs 22 carriage returns, moving the **FIRST LINE** message to the top of the screen and leaving the cursor at the beginning of the bottom line of the screen (lines 320-340). Next it displays a message that moves the cursor to the penultimate column of the last row (line 360). After that, it sounds the console speaker for a few seconds (lines 380-400). This gives you a chance to watch the top line carefully. Finally, the program displays a character in the last column of the bottom line (line 420);

a carriage return occurs. The **FIRST LINE** message is instantly pushed off the top of the screen so the cursor can advance to the next display line. The program waits for some keyboard entry before ending (line 440). To use the example above in Integer BASIC, you must eliminate the CHR$ function in line 380 and in its place type a quotation mark, press CONTROL-G, and type another quotation mark.

Were you surprised that sounding the speaker did not cause a carriage return? After all, the PRINT statement on line 390 looks as if it should display a character in the last column of the bottom line. It doesn't, however, because the bell character, ASCII code 7, is an invisible character. It does not affect the cursor's position.

Columnar Output

A list of items is easy to scan if it is aligned in columns. Applesoft provides two ways to output information in columns. One is to use commas between values in PRINT statements, and the other is to use the TAB and SPC functions. The TAB and SPC functions are not available in Integer BASIC.

If the computer finds a comma after a PRINT statement value, it moves the cursor to the right after displaying the value, putting blank spaces between the end of the value and the next tab stop. Integer BASIC tab stops on a 40-column screen are eight columns apart, at columns 1, 9, 17, 25, and 33. Applesoft has three tab stops on a 40-column screen, at columns 1, 17, and 33. The following Applesoft program uses commas to align equivalent Celsius and Fahrenheit temperatures in two columns:

```
]10 INPUT "LOWEST CELSIUS TEMPERATURE? ";L
]20 PRINT "CELSIUS","FAHRENHEIT"
]30 FOR C = L TO L + 20
]40 F = C * 9 / 5 + 32: REM FAHRENHEIT
]50 F = INT ( ABS (F) + .5) * SGN (F): REM ROUND
]60 PRINT C,F
]70 NEXT C
]80 END
```

Instead of using semicolons between PRINT statement items, the program uses commas (lines 20 and 60). When BASIC encounters a comma in a PRINT statement, it advances the cursor to the next active tab stop before it displays the next value, thereby aligning the display in columns (see Figure 9-1). The

```
CELSIUS                FAHRENHEIT
10                     50
11                     52
12                     54
13                     55
14                     57
15                     59
16                     61
17                     63
18                     64
19                     66
20                     68
21                     70
22                     72
23                     73
24                     75
25                     77
26                     79
27                     81
28                     82
29                     84
30                     86

]
```

Figure 9-1. Columnar output generated by using commas in PRINT statements

program also uses the INT, ABS, and SGN functions to round the converted temperature to the nearest whole degree (line 50).

There is a catch to using commas, however. At least one blank space must be left just ahead of a tab stop (except the first tab stop), or that stop will be deactivated for the current display line. Except on an Enhanced Apple IIE, Applesoft will also deactivate the tab stop in column 33 if anything is displayed in columns 24 through 32 (see Figure 9-2).

On older Apple II machines, tabbing with commas in PRINT statements has little value when the display line width is 80. There are essentially only two tab stops, the first at column 1 and the second at column 9 in Integer BASIC or column 17 in Applesoft. Every comma in a PRINT statement (except those enclosed in quotes) sends the cursor to that second tab stop, which means values will be displayed on top of each other. However, on an Enhanced Apple IIe, tabbing with commas works correctly on an 80-column screen.

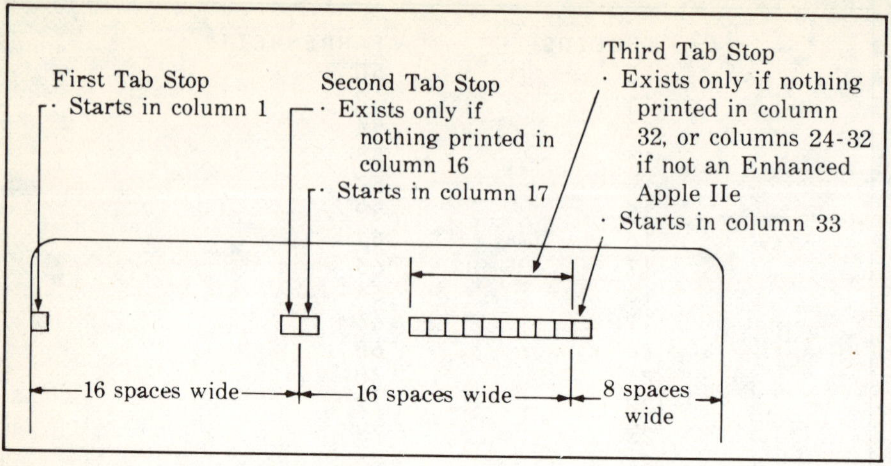

Figure 9-2. Applesoft tab stops set on a 40-column screen by PRINT statement with commas

The TAB Function

Suppose you want to align information in columns, but not the columns set by PRINT statement commas. In an Applesoft program, you can use the TAB function in PRINT statements to advance the cursor to any column you specify. For this purpose, columns on the display screen are numbered from 1 to 40. Compare the following example to the previous program:

```
]10 INPUT "LOWEST CELSIUS TEMPERATURE? ";L
]20 PRINT TAB( 7);"CELSIUS"; TAB( 15);"FAHRENHEIT"
]30 FOR C = L TO L + 20
]40 PRINT TAB( 9);C;
]50 F = C * 9 / 5 + 32: REM FAHRENHEIT
]60 F = INT ( ABS (F) + .5) * SGN (F): REM ROUND
]70 PRINT TAB( 19);F
]80 NEXT C
]90 END
```

This program uses the TAB function to align its output in two columns down the center of the screen (see Figure 9-3). Notice that it uses semicolons to separate adjacent items in PRINT statements (lines 20, 40, and 70), including the TAB functions.

The TAB function works with any column number from 1 to 80. However, TAB is erratic with column numbers 41-80 on any machine except an Enhanced Apple IIe.

```
          CELSIUS FAHRENHEIT
            20        68
            21        70
            22        72
            23        73
            24        75
            25        77
            26        79
            27        81
            28        82
            29        84
            30        86
            31        88
            32        90
            33        91
            34        93
            35        95
            36        97
            37        99
            38        100
            39        102
            40        104

     ]
```

Figure 9-3. Columnar output generated by the TAB function

Right-Justified Output

Both of Applesoft's methods for aligning output in columns line up values on the left, leaving a ragged right edge. This is called *left-justified* output and is fine for words and other alphabetic strings. Numbers, on the other hand, are easier to read if they line up on the right. The Applesoft functions SPC, STR$, and LEN make right-justified output easy. To use them you must know the width of the widest value (see Figure 9-4). The following program is a further modification of the previous two examples:

```
]10 INPUT "LOWEST CELSIUS TEMPERATURE? ";L
]20 PRINT TAB( 7);"CELSIUS"; TAB( 15);"FAHRENHEIT"
]30 FOR C = L TO L + 20
]40 W = LEN ( STR$ (C)): REM CELSIUS WIDTH
```

```
]50 PRINT TAB( 7); SPC( 6 - W + 1);C;
]60 F = C * 9 / 5 + 32: REM FAHRENHEIT
]70 F = INT ( ABS (F) + .5) * SGN (F): REM ROUND
]80 W = LEN ( STR$ (F)): REM FAHR. WIDTH
]90 PRINT TAB( 18); SPC( 6 - W + 1);F
]100 NEXT C
]110 END
```

This program converts numeric values to strings so it can use the LEN function to determine their lengths (lines 40 and 80). It uses a TAB function to arrive at a predetermined column, and then it uses the SPC function to move far enough over to align the string values on the right (lines 50 and 90). The program allows six spaces per number: five for digits and one for a possible minus sign. The right-justified output in Figure 9-5 is a definite improvement over the original output (Figure 9-1). As an exercise, try changing the program so it right-justifies the output without using the SPC function.

Decimal-Aligned Output

Columns of numbers with decimal points are easy to read if the numbers line up on the decimal point. Aligning decimals is almost the same as right-justifying numbers, but in this case the numbers are right-justified on the decimal point instead of the last digit. Therefore, the program must figure out where the decimal point is. This is easy enough to determine by applying the LEN function to a string version of the integer part of the

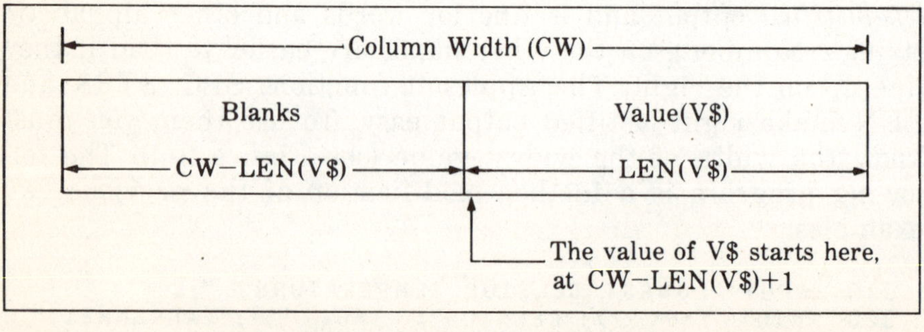

Figure 9-4. Right-justifying a string value (convert numeric values to strings with STR$)

```
            CELSIUS  FAHRENHEIT
                 30          86
                 31          88
                 32          90
                 33          91
                 34          93
                 35          95
                 36          97
                 37          99
                 38         100
                 39         102
                 40         104
                 41         106
                 42         108
                 43         109
                 44         111
                 45         113
                 46         115
                 47         117
                 48         118
                 49         120
                 50         122

]
```

Figure 9-5. Right-justified column output

number. The number will be wider with its decimal point and post-decimal digits, so you must plan for this when determining the starting point for each number.

As an example, consider a program that converts from whole degrees in Fahrenheit to the nearest tenth of a degree in Celsius. The following program aligns the Celsius temperatures on their decimal points, making them easy to read. The results are shown in Figure 9-6.

```
]10 INPUT "LOWEST FAHRENHEIT TEMPERATURE? ";L
]20 PRINT TAB( 7);"FAHRENHEIT"; TAB( 20);"CELSIUS"
]30 FOR F = L TO L + 20
]40 W = LEN ( STR$ (F)): REM FAHR. WIDTH
]50 PRINT TAB( 10); SPC( 6 - W + 1);F;
]60 C = 5 / 9 * (F - 32): REM CELSIUS
]70 C = INT ( ABS (C) * 10 + .5) / 10 * SGN (C):
    REM ROUND
```

```
]80 W = LEN ( STR$ ( INT (C))): REM CELSIUS WIDTH
]90 PRINT TAB( 18); SPC( 6 - W + 1);C
]100 NEXT F
]110 END
```

After converting a temperature to Celsius, the program rounds it to the nearest tenth of a degree (lines 60 and 70). Then, for the Celsius temperatures, the TAB function advances to the predetermined leftmost column, which is two columns farther left than in earlier examples, in order to allow for the decimal point and fractional digit (line 90). From there the SPC function right-justifies based on the integer portion of the value, and the entire value—including its fractional part—is displayed (line 90). This program aligns Celsius temperatures 0.6 and −0.6 (Fahrenheit 31 and 33) incorrectly. See if you can figure out how to fix that.

```
          FAHRENHEIT   CELSIUS
                  40       4.4
                  41       5
                  42       5.6
                  43       6.1
                  44       6.7
                  45       7.2
                  46       7.8
                  47       8.3
                  48       8.9
                  49       9.4
                  50      10
                  51      10.6
                  52      11.1
                  53      11.7
                  54      12.2
                  55      12.8
                  56      13.3
                  57      13.9
                  58      14.4
                  59      15
                  60      15.6

]▒
```

Figure 9-6. Decimal-aligned output

CURSOR CONTROL

Semicolons, commas, and the TAB and SPC functions are fine for formatting simple tables like those you've seen so far. More complicated displays demand more cursor control. Applesoft offers two ways of directly controlling the cursor. One is to program cursor movement characters with the CHR$ function. The other is to use the VTAB and HTAB statements. Integer BASIC also recognizes the VTAB statement, and has a TAB statement equivalent to HTAB.

When used together, VTAB and HTAB (TAB in Integer BASIC) allow you to move the cursor to any position on the screen. VTAB moves the cursor vertically and HTAB moves the cursor horizontally. You must specify the row number for VTAB and the column number for HTAB. The following Applesoft program uses these two statements to position the cursor and display an asterisk at that location.

```
]80 HOME
]90 VTAB 1: HTAB 1
]100  INPUT "Row?";R
]110  INPUT "Column?";C
]120 VTAB R: HTAB C
]130 PRINT "*";
]140 GOTO 90
```

The VTAB statement works with row numbers 1 through 24. Row 1 is at the top of the screen and row 24 is at the bottom. A number outside that range causes an error.

When the screen width is 40, the HTAB (or TAB) statement works with column numbers 1 through 40. Column 1 is at the left edge of the screen and column 40 is at the right edge. A row number less than 0 causes an error, but a row number larger than 40 wraps around to the beginning of the next lower line and keeps on going. For example, HTAB 50 is the same as HTAB 10 on the next line down.

Except on an Enhanced Apple IIe, you cannot use an HTAB statement to position the cursor in a column between 41 and 80 on an 80-column display. Instead, you must use a POKE statement with memory location 36. However, column numbers for the POKE statement range between 0 and 79 (instead of 1 and 80). Column 0 is at the left edge of the screen and column 79 is at the right edge. Another variation of the last example works on an 80-column screen.

```
]10 PRINT CHR$ (4);"PR#3": REM ..Activate 80-column
    adapter
]80 HOME
]90 VTAB 1: HTAB 1
]100  INPUT "Row?";R
]110  INPUT "Column?";C
]120  VTAB R: POKE 36,C - 1
]130  PRINT "*"
]140  GOTO 90
```

Warning: Do not put a value greater than the current width of the screen (40 or 80) in memory location 36. The results are unpredictable and may destroy your program or even force you to restart the Apple II.

An Applesoft program can move the cursor left or down by displaying the ← or ↓ characters; their ASCII codes are 8 and 10 respectively. These cursor movement characters do not erase any other characters they pass over. To program one of the cursor movement characters, use the CHR$ function with the appropriate ASCII code. For example, CHR$(8) will backspace the cursor.

Determining Cursor Position

The Applesoft function POS reports the column in which the cursor is located. POS requires a single numeric operand but does not use it for anything. Here is an example:

```
]10  PRINT "123456789";
]20  C = POS (0) + 1
]30  PRINT
]40  PRINT "LAST LINE ENDED AT COLUMN ";C
]50  END
```

If you run this example, it will report that the message displayed by line 10 ended at column 10. Line 20 adds 1 to the column number that POS reports because the POS function numbers columns from 0 to 39, unlike the TAB function and the HTAB (TAB in Integer BASIC) statement.

You can also use PEEK(36) to learn the current cursor column (0 to 39 or 0 to 79). In fact, this is the only way to get the current column position on an 80-column screen.

To determine the current cursor row, use PEEK(37). It reports a number between 0 (top of screen) and 23 (bottom of screen).

SPECIAL EFFECTS

The Apple II actually has two sets of characters. It uses its standard set when the 80-column adapter is not active (the cursor is a blinking checkered square), and its alternate set when the 80-column adapter is active (the cursor is a solid white box). Both sets have a full complement of uppercase and lowercase letters, numbers, and symbols. They differ in the styles in which the characters can be displayed.

The character styles available are *normal*, *inverse*, and *flashing*. Normal characters are white (or green or orange, depending on your monitor) on a black screen. Inverse characters are black on a white (or green or orange) screen. Flashing characters alternate between normal and inverse several times a second.

The standard character set (80-column adapter not active) can display all characters in normal style. Lowercase letters are not available in inverse or flashing style, however. The alternate character set (80-column adapter active) can display all characters in both normal and inverse style but does not display in flashing style. On an Enhanced Apple IIe, the alternate character set can also display 33 special graphics symbols called *Mousetext*.

You can control the speed at which characters appear on the screen with either character set and in any character style.

The INVERSE Statement

Applesoft can reverse the black and white parts of characters on the display screen with the INVERSE statement. Once the INVERSE statement is executed, everything displayed by PRINT statements appears in inverse style. However, inverse lowercase letters are only available when the 80-column adapter is active. The Apple II returns to normal style when Applesoft executes a NORMAL statement. To see how these two statements work, try the following example. The shaded characters will be in inverse style.

```
]INVERSE

]?"BLACK ON WHITE"
BLACK ON WHITE

]NORMAL
```

```
]?"WHITE ON BLACK"
WHITE ON BLACK

]▒
```

The FLASH Statement

When the 80-column adapter is *not* active, everything displayed after an Applesoft FLASH statement alternates between normal and inverse style. Remember, though, that flashing style does not work with lowercase letters. Here again, a NORMAL statement causes the Apple II to revert to normal style. In the next example, the shaded areas will be flashing:

```
]FLASH

]?"FLASH IN THE PAN"
FLASH IN THE PAN

]NORMAL

]?"STEADY AS RAIN"
STEADY AS RAIN

]▒
```

The SPEED Statement

The rate at which characters display on the screen is variable. You can slow down the display speed with an Applesoft SPEED statement. The following program illustrates how SPEED works:

```
]100 INPUT "SPEED=";SP
]110 SPEED= SP
]120 FOR CT = 1 TO 3
]130 PRINT "HIC"
]140 NEXT
]150 PRINT "HICCUP"
]160 SPEED= 255
]170 END
```

The value of SP on line 110 adjusts the display speed; 0 is slowest and 255 is fastest. SPEED also affects the rate at which characters are sent to other devices, not just the display screen.

Mousetext

When the 80-column adapter is active, the Enhanced Apple IIe can display 33 graphics characters called *Mousetext*. Table 9-2 identifies the Mousetext characters. The screen display depicted in Figure 9-7 gives you some idea of how they can be used. The program listed in Figure 9-8 generates the display in Figure 9-7. (To quit the program listed in Figure 9-8, press any key.) On other Apple II machines, inverse uppercase letters and punctuation replace the Mousetext characters.

To display Mousetext, a program must:

- Activate the 80-column adapter with the statement PRINT CHR$(4); "PR#3", or its equivalent.
- Set inverse style (with an INVERSE statement).
- Turn on Mousetext by using CHR$(27) or its equivalent to print the invisible character whose ASCII code is 27.
- Display the appropriate uppercase letters and punctuation marks (see Table 9-2).

Table 9-2. Mousetext Graphics Characters

Mousetext Character	Regular Character	Mousetext Character	Regular Character	Mousetext Character	Regular Character
🍎	@	↑	K	▒	V [2]
⌘	A	‾	L	▒	W [2]
➤	B	↵	M	⊏	X
⌛	C	█	N	⊐	Y
✓	D	⇞	O	|	Z [3]
☑	E	⇟	P	◆	[
▶	F [1]	◂	Q	═	\
◀	G [1]	▸	R	⁜	]
←	H	—	S	⊡	^ [3]
…	I	└	T	|	—
↓	J	→	U		

[1] Combine F and G to make a runner.
[2] Combine V and W to make a continuous gray line.
[3] Combine Z and ^ to make a boxed dot.

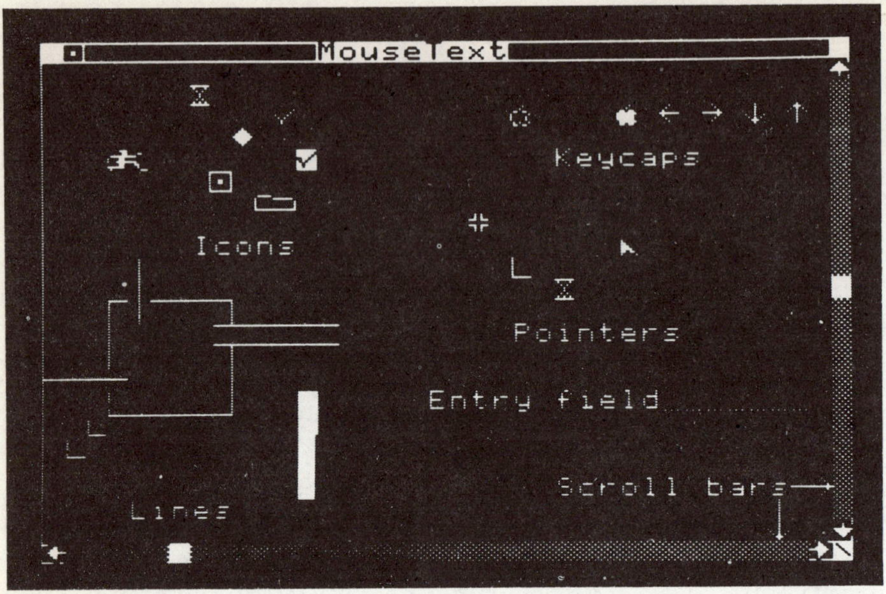

Figure 9-7. Mousetext characters demonstration

To display inverse uppercase letters or symbols again, a program must turn off Mousetext by using CHR$(24) or its equivalent to print the invisible character whose ASCII code is 24. To display normal characters again, a program must turn off Mousetext with CHR$(24) and set normal style (with a NORMAL statement).

```
100  REM ...Set variables...
110 MT$ =  CHR$ (27):
    REM ..Mousetext on
120 RT$ =  CHR$ (24):
    REM ..Regular text on
130 D$ =  CHR$ (4): REM ..ProDOS command prefix
```

Figure 9-8. Mousetext demonstration program (Enhanced Apple IIe only; see Figure 9-7 for sample output)

```
140 W4$ =  CHR$ (17):
     REM ..Display width 40
1000  PRINT : PRINT D$;"PR#3":
     REM ..Enhanced video on
1010  PRINT : PRINT W4$;:
     REM ..Screen width 40
1100 TI$ = "Mousetext"
1110  GOSUB 10000: REM ..Display title bar
1120  GOSUB 10100: REM ..Display left border
1130 TR = 12: REM ..Vertical thumb row
1140  GOSUB 10200: REM ..Display vertical
     scroll bar
1150 TC = 8: REM ..Horizontal thumb column
1160  GOSUB 10320: REM ..Display horizontal
     scroll bar
1200  REM ...Display Icons...
1210  INVERSE : PRINT MT$;:
     REM ..Mousetext on
1220  VTAB 3: HTAB 9: PRINT "C":
     REM ..Hourglass
1230  VTAB 4: HTAB 13: PRINT "D":
     REM ..Check
1240  VTAB 5: HTAB 11: PRINT "]":
     REM ..Crosshairs
1250  VTAB 7: HTAB 10: PRINT "T":
     REM ..Text
1260  VTAB 8: HTAB 12: PRINT "B":
     REM ..Arrow
1270  NORMAL : PRINT RT$;:
     REM ..Mousetext off
1280  VTAB 10: HTAB 9: PRINT "Cursors";
1300  REM ...Keycaps...
1310  INVERSE : PRINT MT$;:
     REM ..Mousetext on
1320  VTAB 4: HTAB 24: PRINT "A":
     REM ..Open apple
1330  VTAB 4: HTAB 29: PRINT "@";:
     REM ..Solid apple
1340  VTAB 4: HTAB 31: PRINT "H";:
     REM ..Left arrow
1350  VTAB 4: HTAB 33: PRINT "U";:
     REM ..Right arrow
1360  VTAB 4: HTAB 35: PRINT "J";:
     REM ..Down arrow
```

Figure 9-8. Mousetext demonstration program (Enhanced Apple IIe only; see Figure 9-7 for sample output) (*continued*)

```
1370  VTAB 4: HTAB 37: PRINT "K";:
      REM ..Up arrow
1380  NORMAL : PRINT RT$;:
      REM ..Mousetext off
1390  VTAB 6: HTAB 26: PRINT "Keycaps";
1400  REM ...Icons...
1410  INVERSE : PRINT MT$;:
      REM ..Mousetext on
1420  VTAB 9: HTAB 23: PRINT "XY";:
      REM ..Folder
1430  VTAB 10: HTAB 29: PRINT "[";:
      REM ..Diamond
1440  VTAB 11: HTAB 24: PRINT "Z^";:
      REM ..Close box
1450  VTAB 12: HTAB 27: PRINT "FG";:
      REM ..Runner
1460  NORMAL : PRINT RT$;:
      REM ..Mousetext off
1470  VTAB 14: HTAB 24: PRINT "Icons";
1500  REM ...Lines...
1510  VTAB 12: HTAB 5: PRINT "______"
1520  INVERSE : PRINT MT$;: REM ..Mousetext on
1530  VTAB 18: HTAB 5: PRINT "LLLLLL"
1540  FOR ROW = 13 TO 17
1550  VTAB ROW: HTAB 5: PRINT "_";
1560  HTAB 10: PRINT "Z";
1570  NEXT ROW
1580  VTAB 16: HTAB 2: PRINT "SSSS";
1590  VTAB 14: HTAB 10: PRINT "\\\\\\"
1600 VTAB 19: HTAB 14: PRINT "N"
1610 HTAB 14: PRINT "N"
1620 HTAB 14: PRINT "N"
1630 VTAB 18: HTAB 4: PRINT "T"
1640 HTAB 3: PRINT "T"
1650 VTAB 17: HTAB 14: PRINT " "
1660 HTAB 14: PRINT " "
1670 NORMAL : PRINT RT$;: VTAB 11
1680 FOR ROW = 11 TO 13
1690 HTAB 6: PRINT "|"
1700 NEXT ROW
1710 VTAB 22: HTAB 6: PRINT "Lines"
1800 VTAB 17: HTAB 20: PRINT "Entry field";
1810 INVERSE : PRINT MT$;"IIIIII";RT$: NORMAL
1900 VTAB 21: HTAB 26: PRINT "Scroll bars"
1910 HTAB 36: PRINT "|";
```

Figure 9-8. Mousetext demonstration program (Enhanced Apple IIe only; see Figure 9-7 for sample output) (*continued*)

```
1920 INVERSE : VTAB 21: HTAB 37: PRINT MT$;"SU"
1930 VTAB 23: HTAB 36: PRINT "J";RT$: NORMAL
2000 GET A $
2010 END
9989 REM
9990 REM ...Title Bar Subroutine...
9991 REM
10000 INVERSE
10010 VTAB 1: HTAB 2
10020 PRINT " ";MT$;
      "^\\\\\\\\\\\\\\\\\\\\\\\\\\\\\\\\\\\\\";RT$;
      " ";
10030 VTAB 1: HTAB (40 - LEN (TI$)) / 2
10040 PRINT TI$;
10050 NORMAL : RETURN
10089 REM
10090 REM ...Print Left Border Subroutine...
10100 INVERSE : PRINT MT$;: REM ..Mousetext on
10110 FOR ROW = 1 TO 24
10120 VTAB ROW: HTAB 1
10130 PRINT "Z";
10140 NEXT ROW
10150 NORMAL : PRINT RT$;: REM ..Mousetext off
10160 RETURN
10189 REM
10190 REM ...Vertical Scroll Bar Subroutine...
10191 REM
10200 INVERSE : VTAB 2: HTAB 39
10210 PRINT MT$;"R": REM ..Up-arrow
10220 FOR ROW = 3 TO 22
10230 HTAB 39: PRINT "V": REM ..Gray area
10240 NEXT ROW
10250 HTAB 39: PRINT "Q": REM ..Down-arrow
10260 HTAB 39: PRINT RT$;"\";: REM ..Corner box
10270 VTAB TR: HTAB 39: PRINT " ": REM ..Thumb
10280 NORMAL : RETURN
10290 REM
10300 REM ... Horizontal Scroll Bar Subroutine...
10310 REM
10320 INVERSE : VTAB 24: HTAB 2
10330 PRINT MT$;
      "OVWVWVWVWVWVWVWVWVWVWVWVWVWVWVWVWVWVP";RT$;
      "\";
10340 VTAB 24: HTAB TC: PRINT " ";: REM ..Thumb
10350 NORMAL : RETURN
```

Figure 9-8. Mousetext demonstration program (Enhanced Apple IIe only; see Figure 9-7 for sample output) (*continued*)

Control Characters

Some of the example programs in this chapter have used the CHR$ function with ASCII codes between 0 and 31. You may have noticed that characters with those codes are invisible. For example, when the 80-column adapter is active, CHR$(17) sets the display width to 40 and CHR$(18) sets the display width to 80. Such characters are called *control characters* because they control special effects, display format, cursor movement, and the like. Most control characters are effective only when the 80-column adapter is active. Table 9-3 lists the ASCII code numbers of all control characters for the display screen.

Table 9-3. Display Screen Control Characters (Programmable With the CHR$ Function)

ASCII Code	Effect with 80-column card: Active	Inactive
4*	Deactivate control characters except codes 5, 7, 8, 10, and 13	None
5*	Reactivate control characters	None
7	Sound console speaker	Same
8	Move cursor left	Same
10	Move cursor down	Same
11	Clear from cursor to end of text window	None
12	Clear text window	None
13	Carriage return	Same
14	Set normal video	None
15	Set inverse video	None
17	Set active-40 mode	None
18	Set active-80 mode	None
21	Deactivate 80-column adapter	None
22	Scroll down one line	None
23	Scroll up one line	None
24*	Deactivate Mousetext	None
25	Move cursor home	None
26	Clear cursor line	None
27*	Activate Moustext	None
28	Move cursor right	None
29	Clear from cursor to end of display line	None

*Only on Enhanced Apple IIe.

CONTROLLING KEYBOARD INPUT

Nearly every program requires some kind of input from the person using it. The goal of any program should be to minimize input errors and make it easy for someone using the program to spot and correct errors that do occur. There are ways to organize input that tend to minimize input errors. This section discusses the following methods:

- Displaying helpful messages
- Checking inputs for reasonableness and range
- Anticipating errors and handling them smoothly
- Grouping inputs logically
- Allowing review and modification of grouped inputs.

Prompt Messages

Prompt messages were introduced in Chapter 7 and have been used since then in the example programs. As the examples have illustrated, prompt messages should be succinct. Space on the display screen is usually at a premium, so verbosity is a luxury. Keep the prompt brief and try to leave enough room on the same line for the entire input response. When this is impossible, put the prompt message on one line and the response on the next.

Checking Input Responses

No matter how carefully you design your input requests, you can't be sure how people will respond. If incorrect input could cause a problem, the program should check for it. Are string entries too long? Are numeric entries within range? Does the entry make sense in context? Will it cause an error later in the program? If you want to write a thorough program, you will make every effort to anticipate errors that a user might make. Your program should catch entry errors and force the user to reenter values that would cause the program to halt abnormally.

BASIC will catch some kinds of data-entry errors for you. For example, it will not accept alphabetic entry when inputting a numeric value with a statement like INPUT A. If you try to enter letters in response to such a statement, an error message appears and you must reenter the value.

Built-in error-checking capabilities are limited, though. It is entirely possible to enter the right kind of value, numeric or string, which will nevertheless cause a program error farther down the line. Here is a short program that illustrates the problem:

```
]100 INPUT X
]200 PRINT 100/X
]300 END
```

If you enter 0 in response to the INPUT statement, the program will fail when it tries to divide by 0 in the PRINT statement. It is easy enough to avoid this. The following lines will check the input to make sure it is not 0, and will request reentry if it is 0:

```
]110 IF X <> 0 THEN 200
]120 PRINT "NOT ALLOWED...RE-ENTER"
]130 GOTO 100
```

By extending the principle illustrated in this example, you can see how easy it is to check an entered value for the correct range. Depending on the circumstances, it may make sense to do range checking with ON-GOTO or ON-GOSUB statements, rather than a series of IF-THEN statements.

Sometimes checking for errors is expensive. It can take a lot of programming time, program space, and execution time. Consider a typical yes-or-no question, for example. The program should allow any of the correct natural responses: yes, no, Yes, No, YES, NO, y, n, Y, or N. There are ten answers in all, which is quite a few for a program to have to check. You can easily reduce the number of input tests: simply check the first character input. If the response is not allowed, the program repeats the input request. The following program fragment illustrates this:

```
]200 PRINT
]210 PRINT "ENTER ANOTHER BILL";
]220 INPUT R$:R$ = LEFT$ (R$,1)
]230 IF R$ = "Y" OR R$ = "y" THEN 90
]240 IF R$ = "N" OR R$ = "n" THEN END
]250 GOTO 210
```

This Applesoft program fragment uses the LEFT$ function to discard all characters input except the first one (line 220). That reduces the number of checks it has to make to ensure that a response is acceptable.

The GET Statement

For even more control over input in an Applesoft program, use the GET statement. GET accepts a single character from the keyboard. The entry is treated as a string or numeric value, depending on the type of variable following the command word GET.

```
]30010 GET C$
```

The program waits until you enter a character and then proceeds. You do not press the RETURN key after typing the character.

The GET statement does not display your keystroke on the screen; it simply inputs the character that the keystroke generates. If you want to display the keystroke, you can always do so with a PRINT statement. But before displaying the keystroke, check for undesirable characters. Your program can simply reject any characters that would adversely affect the display. The following short Applesoft program shows one approach:

```
]10 PRINT "Type anything: ";
]20 GET C$
]30 IF ASC(C$)>31 AND ASC(C$)<128 THEN PRINT C$;
]40 GOTO 20
```

Control characters, whose ASCII code numbers are less than 32, are the ones that wreak havoc on a display. For purposes of keyboard input, the code numbers above 127 are meaningless also. The previous program avoids trouble by ignoring any keystroke that generates a code less than 32 or more than 127 (line 30). Note, however, that you must press CONTROL-RESET to stop the program because it ignores the RETURN key (code number 13) and CONTROL-C (code 3).

Indicating Entry Fields

Neither the INPUT nor the GET statement tells the program user much about the number of characters allowed, information that would make the user's job easier. The program can indicate the number of characters allowed by displaying an entry field template just before it requests keyboard entry. The following example illustrates this.

```
9 REM ...Set Variable Values...
10 D$ = CHR$ (4): REM ..ProDOS/DOS 3.3 prefix
20 W4$ = CHR$ (17): REM ..Display width 40
30 FOR X1 = 1 TO 40:EF$ = EF$ + ".": NEXT X1:
   REM ..Entry field chars.
989 REM
990 REM ...Start Main Program...
991 REM
1000 PRINT: PRINT D$;"PR#3": REM ..Activate
     80-col. card
1010 PRINT W4$;: REM ..Set display width to 40
1020 VTAB 12: HTAB 5: PRINT "Type anything: ";
1030 GOSUB 20000
1040 VTAB 22: HTAB 1: PRINT NTRY$
1050 END
19990 REM
20000 REM ...GetEntry...
20001 REM
20010 NTRY$ = "": REM ..Empty entry
20020 CL% = LEN (NTRY$): REM ..Current entry length
20030 HTAB 20: PRINT NTRY$;
20040 IF 10 > CL% THEN PRINT
      LEFT$ (EF$,10 - CL%);:
      REM ..Fill unused entry field
20050 HTAB 20 + CL%: GET C$: REM ..Get one character
20090 IF C$ = CHR$ (13) THEN: RETURN:
      REM ..Return means done
20100 IF C$ > = " " AND C$ < = "~" AND CL% < 10
      THEN NTRY$ = NTRY$ + C$:
      REM ..Add valid characters if room
20110 GOTO 20020: REM ..Get another keystroke
```

This example adds several features to the previous one. It begins by assigning control character values to two variables and entry field template characters to another variable (lines 10-30). Next, it activates the 80-column adapter and sets the display width to 40 (lines 1000 and 1010). After that, it displays a prompt message (line 1020) and then calls a subroutine to input a value up to ten characters long (line 1030). After calling the subroutine, the program displays the entered value near the bottom of the screen and ends.

The entry subroutine begins by clearing the variable that will contain the entry (line 20010); then it prints the current entry, which is empty at this point (line 20030). The subroutine next fills the remaining space in the entry field with periods (line 20040). After setting up the entry field, the subroutine uses a GET statement to wait for a keystroke.

When a keystroke occurs, the entry subroutine checks to see if the RETURN key (ASCII code 13) was pressed. If so, the subroutine returns to the main program (line 20090). If not, the subroutine checks for troublesome keystrokes (those with code numbers below 32 or above 127) and adds a valid character to the entry value (line 20100). After processing one keystroke, the subroutine goes back to display the current entry value again (line 20030) and to wait for another keystroke.

Multiple Entries

A program that requires a good deal of keyboard input is usually easier to write and use if the user's input is organized in some fashion. Rather than having the user enter values in a running stream, the program can display a form that identifies the fields to be entered and leaves blank spaces for the user to fill in. The program can then request a value for each field in turn and allow changes or corrections to any field.

A sheet of graph paper turned sideways is handy for designing entry forms for the screen. Let each square on the paper correspond to one character position on the screen. Write the column numbers across the top of the paper and the row numbers down the side for reference (See Appendix I for a 40-column form). Write in the description for each entry field and mark off the space the entry itself will occupy. Designing a form on paper first will save time in the long run; it's much faster to rearrange entry items or reword descriptions on paper than it is to reprogram them again and again.

For example, Figure 9-9 shows the entry form for a program that inputs names and addresses for a mailing list. Notice the program title is centered at the top of the form and specific instructions appear on three lines near the bottom of the form. the mailing-list entry form has seven numbered fields. The user can select any of the seven fields by typing its number or pressing the ↑ or ↓ key. The currently selected field is highlighted by bracketing it and changing its description to all capital letters. However, nothing else happens unless the user presses the RETURN key to confirm the current selection. If the user chooses one of the first five fields, an entry field template made of periods appears on the form to define the maximum entry length. While entering the field value, the user can backspace by pressing the

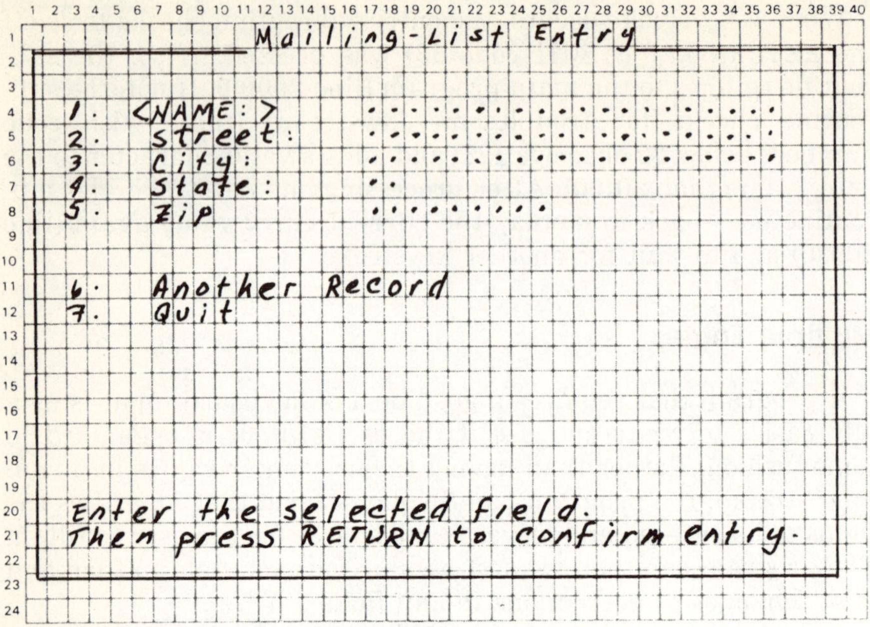

Figure 9-9. Designing a mailing-list entry form

DELETE key or cancel and restart the entry by pressing CONTROL-X. Pressing the RETURN key confirms the entry. If the user chooses field 6 or 7, a yes-or-no question appears in a box that temporarily overlays the main display. The answer choices (yes or no) are displayed inside the box and can be selected by typing Y or N in uppercase or lowercase, or by pressing ← or →.

Figure 9-10 lists a Mailing-List Entry program that creates the form and enters values for each field. Table 9-4 lists the variables the program uses. Figures 9-11, 9-12, and 9-13 show what the screen looks like while making an entry, selecting a field, and answering a yes-or-no question.

The Mailing-List Entry program starts by calling a subroutine to initialize eight variables and three arrays (line 1000). Then the program activates the 80-column adapter, sets the screen width to 40, and displays the entry form (lines 1010-1060).

```
1000 GOSUB 10000: REM ..Initialize variables
1010 PRINT: PRINT D$;"PR#3": REM ..Activate
     80-col. card
1020 PRINT W4$;: REM ..Set display width to 40
1030 GOSUB 11000: REM ..DisplayEntryWindow
1040 FOR X1 = 1 TO LF%
1050 FIELD% = X1: GOSUB 23500: REM ..Display
     field description
1060 NEXT X1
1070 FOR X1 = 1 TO 5: REM ..Enter all fields
1080 FIELD% = X1
1090 GOSUB 23000: GOSUB 12000: GOSUB 23500:
     REM ..SelectField:EnterField:DeselectField
1100 NEXT X1
1110 FIELD% = 6: GOSUB 23000: REM ..SelectField
1120 GOSUB 22000: REM ..GetFieldNumber
1130 IF FIELD% = 6 THEN FR% = 4:LR% = 8:
     GOSUB 30100: GOSUB 23500: GOTO 1040:
     REM ..If field=6, blank last entries,
     deselect and get another
1140 IF FIELD% < LF% THEN GOSUB 12000: GOTO 1120:
     REM ..EnterField
1150 REM ...Quit?...
1160 T% = 12:L% = 4:B% = 17:R% = 37: GOSUB 30200:
     REM ..DisplayBox
1170 VTAB 14: HTAB 5: PRINT BEEP$;"Are you sure
     you want to quit?";
1180 VTAB 16: HTAB 8:C$ = "Y": GOSUB 21000:
     REM ..GetYesNo
1190 IF NTRY$ = "NO" THEN FR% = 12:LR% = 17:
     GOSUB 30100: GOSUB 23000: GOTO 1120:
     REM ..If no, erase box, restore field,
     and get another field
1200 HOME: END: REM if yes, then quit
9989 REM
9990 REM ...InitializeVariables...
9991 REM
10000 D$ = CHR$ (4): REM ..ProDOS/DOS 3.3 prefix
10010 W4$ = CHR$ (17): REM ..Display width 40
10020 BEEP$ = CHR$ (07): REM ..Beep char.
10030 FOR X1 = 1 TO 40
10040 EF$ = EF$ + ".": REM ..Entry field chars.
10050 TL$ = TL$ + "‾": REM ..Top line chars.
10060 BL$ = BL$ + "_": REM ..Bottom line chars.
10070 NEXT X1
10080 SL$ = "|": REM ..Side line chars.
10090 LF% = 7: REM ..Last field number
```

Figure 9-10. Mailing-List Entry program

```
10100 DIM FR%(2,LF%),FC%(2,LF%),FD$(2,LF%)
10110 FOR X1 = 1 TO LF%: REM ..Read field
     locations and descriptions
10120 READ FR%(1,X1),FC%(1,X1),FD$(1,X1)
10130 READ FR%(2,X1),FC%(2,X1),FD$(2,X1)
10140 NEXT X1
10150 RETURN
10489 REM
10490 REM ...Field Descriptions and Locations...
10491 REM
10500 DATA 4,3," 1. <NAME:>  "
10510 DATA 4,3," 1.  Name:   "
10520 DATA 5,3," 2. <STREET:>"
10530 DATA 5,3," 2.  Street: "
10540 DATA 6,3," 3. <CITY:>  "
10550 DATA 6,3," 3.  City:   "
10560 DATA 7,3," 4. <STATE:> "
10570 DATA 7,3," 4.  State:  "
10580 DATA 8,3," 5. <ZIP:>   "
10590 DATA 8,3," 5.  Zip:    "
10600 DATA 11,3," 6. <ANOTHER RECORD>"
10610 DATA 11,3," 6.  Another Record "
10620 DATA 12,3," 7. <QUIT>"
10630 DATA 12,3," 7.  Quit "
10989 REM
10990 REM ...DisplayEntryWindow...
10991 REM
11000 HOME
11010 T% = 1:L% = 1:B% = 22:R% = 39: GOSUB 30200:
      REM ..DisplayBox
11020 TITLE$ = "Mailing List Entry"
11030 INVERSE: VTAB 1:
      HTAB (40 - LEN (TITLE$)) / 2:
      PRINT TITLE$;: NORMAL: REM ..Display title
11040 RETURN
11989 REM
11990 REM ...EnterField...
11991 REM
12000 VTAB 20: HTAB 3: PRINT "Enter the
      selected field."
12010 HTAB 3: PRINT "Then press RETURN to confirm
      entry.";
12020 ON FIELD% GOSUB 13100,13200,13300,
      13400,13500
12030 FR% = 19:LR% = 21: GOSUB 30100:
      REM ..ClearDisplayLines
12040 RETURN
```

Figure 9-10. Mailing-List Entry program (*continued*)

```
13089 REM
13090 REM ...EnterName...
13100 ML% = 20: VTAB 4: HTAB 17: GOSUB 20000
13110 NAME$ = NTRY$: RETURN
13189 REM
13190 REM ...EnterStreet...
13200 ML% = 20: VTAB 5: HTAB 17: GOSUB 20000
13210 STREET$ = NTRY$: RETURN
13289 REM
13290 REM ...EnterCity...
13300 ML% = 20: VTAB 6: HTAB 17: GOSUB 20000
13310 CITY$ = NTRY$: RETURN
13389 REM
13390 REM ...EnterState...
13400 ML% = 2: VTAB 7: HTAB 17: GOSUB 20000
13410 SE$ = NTRY$: RETURN
13489 REM
13490 REM ...EnterZip...
13500 ML% = 9: VTAB 8: HTAB 17: GOSUB 20000
13510 ZIP$ = NTRY$: RETURN
19989 REM
19990 REM ...GetEntry...
19991 REM
20000 HT% = PEEK (36) + 1: REM ..Cursor column
20010 NTRY$ = "": REM ..Empty entry
20020 CL% = LEN (NTRY$): REM ..Current entry
      length
20030 HTAB HT%: PRINT NTRY$;
20040 IF ML% > CL% THEN PRINT
      LEFT$ (EF$,ML% - CL%);:
      REM ..Fill unused entry field
20050 HTAB HT% + CL%: GOSUB 30000: REM ..Get one
      character
20060 IF C$ = CHR$ (127) AND CL% < = 1 THEN 20010:
      REM ..Delete key with empty entry?
20070 IF C$ = CHR$ (127) THEN NTRY$ =
      LEFT$ (NTRY$,CL% - 1): GOTO 20020:
      REM ..Delete key?
20080 IF C$ = CHR$ (24) THEN 20010:
      REM ..Control-X means cancel
20090 IF C$ = CHR$ (13) THEN
      PRINT SPC( ML% - CL%);:
      RETURN: REM ..Return means done
20100 IF C$ > = " " AND C$ < = "~" AND CL% < ML%
      THEN NTRY$ = NTRY$ + C$: REM ..Add valid
      characters if room
20110 GOTO 20020: REM ..Get another keystroke
```

Figure 9-10. Mailing-List Entry program (*continued*)

```
20989 REM
20990  REM ...GetYesNo...
20991 REM
21000 HT% = PEEK (36) + 1:VT% = PEEK (37) + 1:
      REM ..Cursor position
21010 IF C$ = "Y" OR C$ = "y" OR (C$ = CHR$ (8)
      AND NTRY$ = "NO") THEN VTAB VT%: HTAB HT%:
      PRINT "<YES>  No ";:NTRY$ = "YES"
21020 IF C$ = "N" OR C$ = "n" OR (C$ = CHR$ (21)
      AND NTRY$ = "YES") THEN VTAB VT%: HTAB HT%:
      PRINT " Yes  <NO>";:NTRY$ = "NO"
21030 VTAB 19: HTAB 3: PRINT "Type Y for Yes or N
      for No,"
21040 HTAB 3: PRINT "or press <-- or --> to
      change."
21050 HTAB 3: PRINT "Then press RETURN.  ";
21060 GOSUB 30000: REM ..GetChar
21070 IF C$ = " " THEN C$ = CHR$ (21):
      REM ..Accommodate 80-col. card
      "feature"
21080 IF C$ < > CHR$ (13) THEN 21010:
      REM ..Only RETURN confirms
21090 FR% = 19:LR% = 21: GOSUB 30100:
      REM ..ClearDisplayLines
21100 RETURN
21989 REM
21990  REM ...GetFieldNumber...
21991 REM
22000 VTAB 19: HTAB 3: PRINT "To select a field,
      type a number or "
22010 HTAB 3: PRINT "press UP-ARROW or
      DOWN-ARROW."
22020 HTAB 3: PRINT "Then press RETURN. ";
22030 GOSUB 30000: REM ..GetChar
22040 IF C$ = CHR$ (10) AND FIELD% < LF% THEN
      GOSUB 23500:FIELD% = FIELD% + 1: GOSUB
      23000: REM ..Down-arrow key
22050 IF C$ = CHR$ (11) AND FIELD% > 1 THEN GOSUB
      23500:FIELD% = FIELD% - 1: GOSUB 23000:
      REM ..Up-arrow key
22060 IF C$ > = "1" AND C$ < = STR$ (LF%) THEN
      GOSUB 23500:FIELD% = VAL (C$): GOSUB 23000:
      REM ..Digit key
22070 IF C$ < > CHR$ (13) THEN 22030:
      REM ..Only RETURN confirms
22080 FR% = 19:LR% = 21: GOSUB 30100:
      REM ..ClearDisplayLines
```

Figure 9-10. Mailing-List Entry program (*continued*)

```
22090 RETURN
22989 REM
22990 REM ...SelectField...
22991 REM
23000 VT% = PEEK (37) + 1:HT% = PEEK (36) + 1:
      REM ..Cursor location
23010 VTAB FR%(1,FIELD%): HTAB FC%(1,FIELD%):
      PRINT FD$(1,FIELD%);:
      REM ..Display selected description
23020 VTAB VT%: HTAB HT%: REM ..Reset cursor
23030 RETURN
23489 REM
23490 REM ...DeselectField...
23491 REM
23500 VT% = PEEK (37) + 1:HT% = PEEK (36) + 1:
      REM ..Cursor location
23510 VTAB FR%(2,FIELD%): HTAB FC%(2,FIELD%):
      PRINT FD$(2,FIELD%);: REM ..Display
      deselected description
23520 VTAB VT%: HTAB HT%: REM ..Reset cursor
23530 RETURN
29989 REM
29990 REM ...GetCharacter...
29991 REM
30000 GET C$: REM ..Wait for keystroke
30010 RETURN
30089 REM
30090 REM ...ClearDisplayLines...
30091 REM
30100 FOR ROW = FR% TO LR%
30110 VTAB ROW: HTAB 2: PRINT SPC( 37);
30120 NEXT ROW
30130 RETURN
30189 REM
30190 REM ...DisplayBox...
30191 REM
30200 VTAB T%: HTAB L% + 1
30210 PRINT LEFT$ (TL$,R% - L% - 1);: REM ..Top
      line
30220 FOR ROW = T% + 1 TO B%: REM ..Side lines
30230 VTAB ROW: HTAB L%: PRINT SL$;
30240 HTAB R%: PRINT SL$
30250 NEXT ROW
30260 VTAB B%: HTAB L% + 1: PRINT
      LEFT$ (BL$,R% - L% - 1);: REM ..Bottom line
30270 RETURN
```

Figure 9-10. Mailing-List Entry program (*continued*)

Table 9-4. Mailing-List Entry With Mouse Program Variables

Variable	Purpose	Used on lines:
B%	Bottom row of box	1160, 11010, 30220, 30260
BEEP$	Sound console speaker	1170, 10020
BL$	Characters for bottom edge of box	10060, 30260
C$	Keystroke	1180, 20060, 20070, 20080, 20090, 20100, 21010, 21020, 21070, 21080, 22040, 22050, 22060, 22070, 30000
CITY$	Value of City field	13310
CL%	Current entry length	20020, 20040, 20050, 20060, 20070, 20090, 20100
D$	ProDOS or DOS 3.3 command prefix	1010, 10000
EF$	Characters for entry field indicator	10040, 20040
FC%()	Field columns	10100, 10120, 10130, 23010, 23510
FD$()	Field descriptions	10100, 10120, 10130, 23010, 23510
FIELD%	Current field number	1050, 1080, 1110, 1130, 1140, 12020, 22040, 22050, 22060, 23010, 23510
FR%	First row to clear	1130, 1190, 12030, 21090, 22080, 30100
FR%()	Field rows	10100, 10120, 10130, 23010, 23510
HT%	Current horizontal tab position	20000, 20030, 20050, 21000, 21010, 21020, 23000, 23020, 23500, 23520
L%	Left column of box	1160, 11010, 30200, 30210, 30230, 30260
LF%	Last field number	1040, 1140, 10090, 10100, 10110, 22040, 22060
LR%	Last row to clear	1130, 1190, 12030, 21090, 22080, 30100
ML%	Maximum entry length	13100, 13200, 13300, 13400, 13500, 20040, 20090, 20100
NAME$	Value of Name field	13110
NTRY$	Current entry value	1190, 13110, 13210, 13310, 13410, 13510, 20010, 20020, 20030, 20070, 20100, 21010, 21020

Table 9-4. Mailing-List Entry With Mouse Program Variables (*continued*)

Variable	Purpose	Used on lines:
R%	Right column of box	1160, 11010, 30210, 30240, 30260
ROW	Row counter	30100, 30110, 30120, 30220, 30230, 30250
SE$	Value of State field	13410
SL$	Character for side lines of box	10080, 30230, 30240
STREET$	Value of Street field	13210
T%	Top row of box	1160, 11010, 30200, 30220
TITLE$	Title of window	11020, 11030
TL$	Characters for top edge of box	10050, 30210
VT%	Current vertical tab position	21000, 21010, 21020, 23000, 23020, 23500, 23520
W4$	Code for screen width of 40	1020, 10010
X1	Loop counter	1040, 1050, 1060, 1070, 1080, 1100, 10030, 10070, 10110, 10120, 10130, 10140
ZIP$	Value for ZIP field	13510

Next, the program has the user provide the information for one complete name and address in the first five fields (lines 1070-1100). When the user finishes, the program selects field 6 and waits (lines 1110-1120).

The user now has three options:

- Change any of the first five fields
- Go on to enter another name and address
- Quit the program.

To choose one of these options, the user selects the appropriate field by typing its number or by pressing the ↑ or ↓ key, and then presses the RETURN key to choose the selection. The program has preselected field 6, so the user can choose to enter a new name and address merely by pressing RETURN.

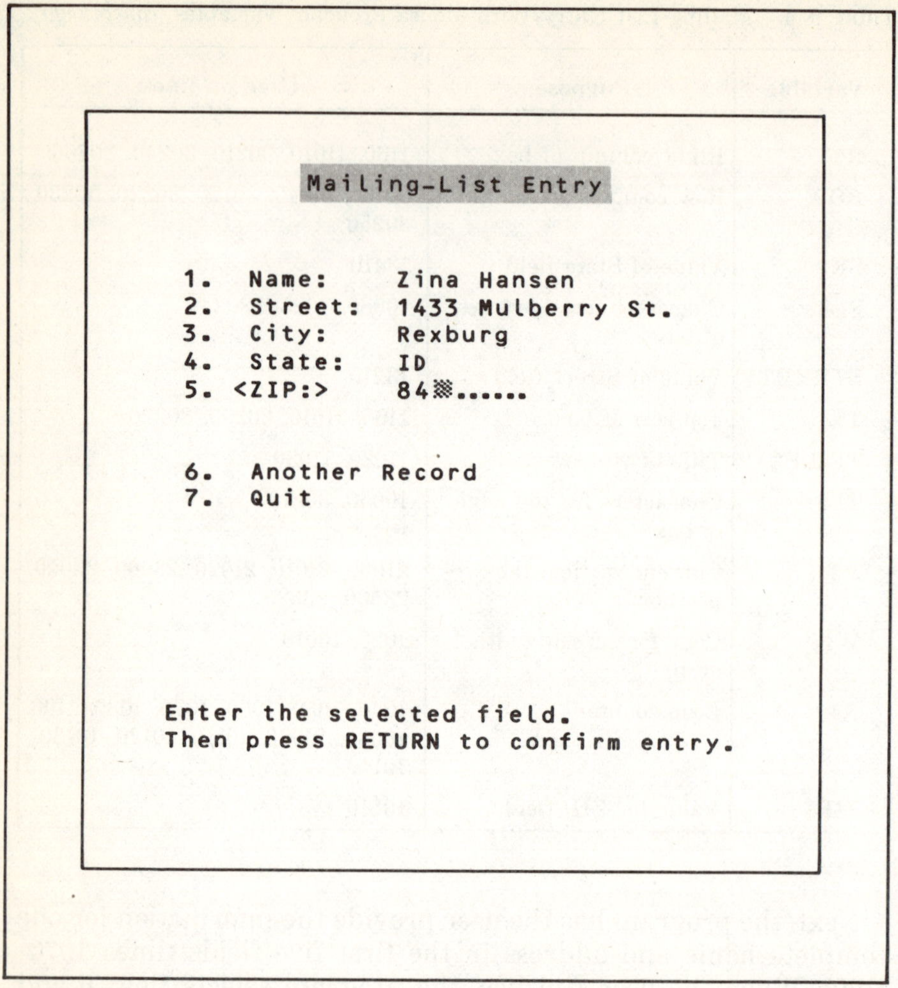

Figure 9-11. Filling in blanks in the Mailing-List Entry program

If the user chooses field 6, the program erases the first five fields, removes "selected" status from field 6, and branches to the first field to begin entering another name and address (line 1130). If the user instead chooses a field from 1 through 5, the program calls the subroutine that inputs the selected field (line 1140 and then 1120). If the user chooses field 7, the program displays a dialog box in which it asks the user to verify quitting the program (lines 1160-1200).

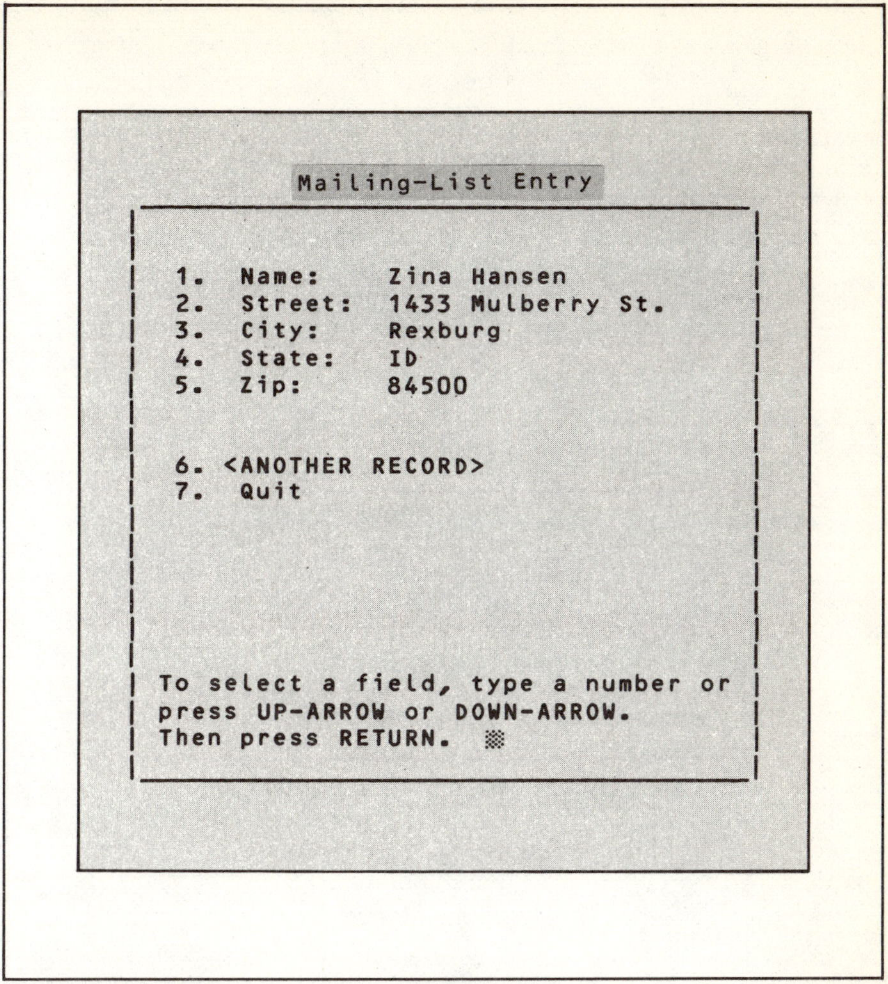

Figure 9-12. Selecting a field in the Mailing-List Entry program

The program uses 16 subroutines in all. The first eight are very specific to this program (lines 10000-13510). The next five are more general-purpose; they might be used in any program that inputs several values (lines 20000-23530). The last three subroutines could be used in almost any program, whether an entry program or some other kind (lines 30000-30270).

The InitializeVariables subroutine (line 10000) assigns values to variables and arrays used by the main program and by other

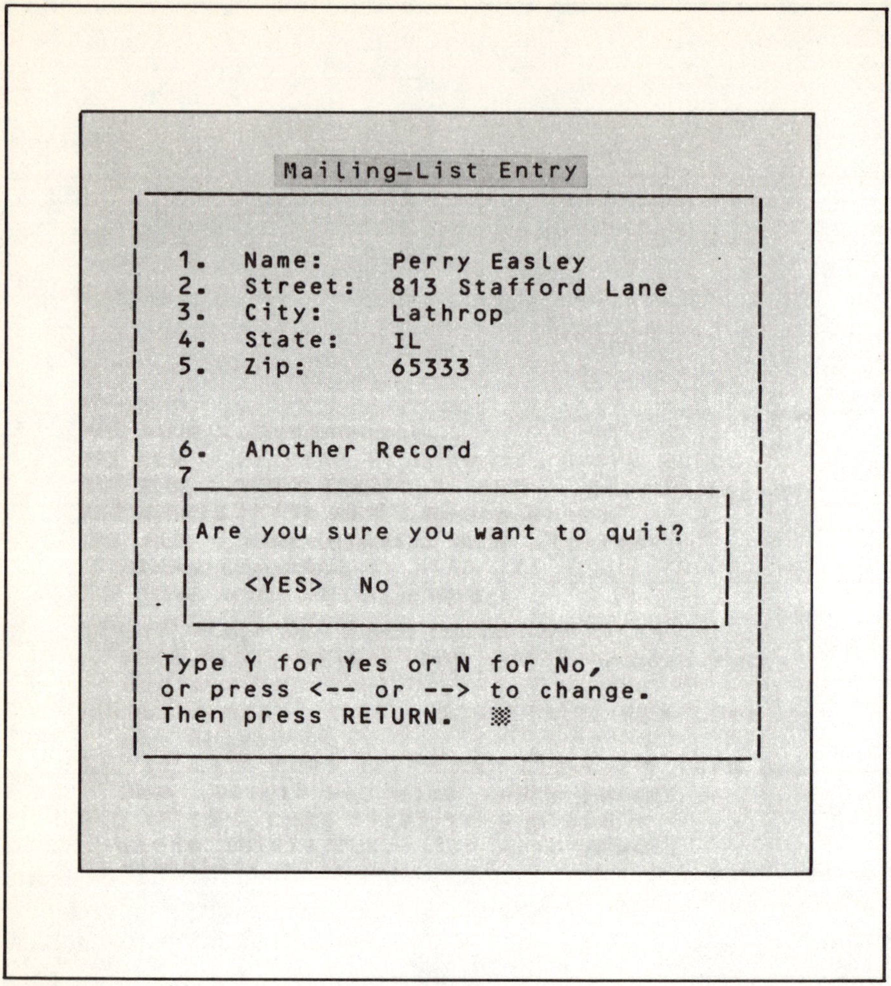

Figure 9-13. Answering a yes-no question in the Mailing-List Entry program

subroutines. The subroutine includes DATA statements that specify the field descriptions and their locations on the screen. There are two versions of each description, one to show a field is selected (all uppercase letters) and the other to show the field is not selected.

The DisplayEntryWindow subroutine (line 11000) calls another subroutine to display a screen-sized box and then displays a title centered above the box.

The EnterField subroutine (line 12000) displays instructions at the bottom of the screen for entering values in the fields. Then it calls one of five other subroutines (described in the next paragraph) to enter the currently selected field. After the field has been entered, the EnterField subroutine clears its instructions from the bottom of the screen.

The subroutines that enter individual fields include EnterName (line 13100), EnterStreet (line 13200), EnterCity (line 13300), EnterState (line 13400), and EnterZip (line 13500). Each sets the maximum entry length, positions the cursor, calls a subroutine to enter a value, and assigns the entered value to a dedicated field variable.

The GetEntry subroutine (line 20000) is very similar to the entry subroutine in the previous example program. This new version allows the calling program or subroutine to establish the screen location for entry and to set the maximum entry length. It also allows the user to correct typographical errors with the DELETE and CONTROL-X keys.

The GetYesNo subroutine (line 21000) requests a yes-or-no answer from the user. It assumes a prompt message has already been displayed and the cursor set to a location at least ten spaces from the right edge of the screen. Variable C$, which must be set to "y" or "n" before calling the subroutine, determines which response will be proposed initially. The subroutine displays instructions near the bottom of the screen and waits for input there. It allows the user to select a response in one of two ways: pressing Y selects Yes and pressing N selects No (shifted or not); alternatively, pressing ← selects Yes, and pressing → selects No. When the 80-column adapter is active, pressing the → key copies the character displayed at the position of the cursor—in this case, a blank space. Therefore the subroutine treats pressing the SPACEBAR the same as pressing the → key (line 21070). Pressing RETURN confirms the currently selected response. Just before ending, the subroutine clears its instructions from the bottom of the screen.

The GetFieldNumber subroutine (line 22000) allows the user to select a field. The subroutine displays instructions at the bottom of the screen and waits for a response. The user can select a field in one of two ways: typing a number selects a field directly; pressing ↓ moves the selection down and pressing ↑ moves the selection up. Pressing RETURN confirms the selection. As the subroutine ends, it clears its instructions from the screen.

The SelectField subroutine (line 23000) and DeselectField subroutine (line 23500) are very similar. SelectField displays the version of a field description that indicates the field is currently selected. The DeselectField displays the version of a field description that indicates the field is not currently selected. In both cases, variable FIELD% determines which description is displayed and where it is displayed. After displaying the description, the subroutine moves the cursor back to where it was when the subroutine was called.

The GetCharacter subroutine (line 30000) waits for a keystroke.

The ClearDisplayLines subroutine (lines 30100-30130) erases lines on the screen by displaying blank spaces. Variable FR% is the first line to erase; variable LR% is the last line to erase.

The DisplayBox subroutine (lines 30200-30270) draws a rectangle. Variable T% establishes the top edge, L% the left edge, B% the bottom edge, and R% the right edge.

To use the subroutines in Figure 9-10 with entry forms that span an 80-column screen, you will have to replace the HTAB statements with POKE statements to memory location 36. Also, variables EF$, TL$, and BL$ must be initialized to lengths of 80, not 40 (lines 10030-10070). Naturally, you will change subroutines DisplayEntryWindow and EnterField, since they display specific details of the mailing-list entry form (lines 11010, 11020, and 12000-12030). You may also want to recast the instructions displayed by the GetYesNo subroutine (lines 21030-21050) and the GetFieldNumber subroutine (lines 22000-22020).

The Apple II Plus and standard Apple II have no ↓ and ↑ keys. Change the GetFieldNumber subroutine to recognize the I key instead of ↑ and the M key instead of ↓ (lines 22010, 22040, and 22050).

To use the Mailing-List Entry program on an Apple II without an 80-column adapter, omit lines 1010 and 1020. Also, do not use lowercase letters for the program title, since it is displayed in inverse style (line 11030).

PROGRAMMING THE MOUSE II

The Apple Mouse II is a small device generally used as the remote control for a pointer displayed on the screen. Sliding the mouse with your hand on a flat surface moves the pointer on the screen. Slide the mouse in any direction—up, down, sideways, or diagonally—and the pointer moves the same distance in the same direction. If the mouse bumps into an obstacle before the pointer arrives at its destination, you can lift the mouse straight up, set it back down in a clear area, and start sliding it again. The pointer does not move when the mouse is in midair.

Moving the mouse moves the pointer, but pressing the button on top of the mouse makes things happen. For example, you might choose an option from a displayed list by pointing at it and pressing the mouse button. Or you might draw a line by pressing and holding the mouse button while you drag the displayed pointer around the screen by sliding the mouse.

Simply plugging in a mouse does not make a pointer appear on the screen, however. A program has to display the pointer. Even then, sliding the mouse affects the pointer only if the program realizes the mouse has moved and responds by redisplaying the pointer in the new location. Furthermore, pressing the mouse button does nothing until the program senses that the button has been pressed and takes appropriate action. The following five program examples show how to program the mouse. They can be combined to make a small program that draws on the screen in response to the movements of the mouse. Figure 9-14 lists the complete program, and Figure 9-15 shows a sample of its output.

```
10 D$ = CHR$ (4): REM ..ProDOS/DOS command prefix
20 PTR$ = "+": REM ..Pointer shape
30 CR = 1:CC = 1: REM ..Initialize pointer's
   current row and col.
40 PRINT CHR$ (21);: REM ..Deactivate 80-col. card
100 PRINT: PRINT D$;"PR#4": PRINT CHR$ (1):
    REM ..Activate mouse
110 PRINT: PRINT D$;"PR#0": REM ..Switch back to
    screen output
120 PRINT: PRINT D$;"IN#4": REM ..Switch to
    input from mouse
130 HOME
140 VTAB CR: HTAB CC: PRINT PTR$;:
    REM ..Display pointer
150 VTAB 23: HTAB 39: REM ..Accomodate INPUT
    "feature"
```

Figure 9-14. Mouse Drawing program

```
160 INPUT "";CC,CR,MS: REM ..Read mouse pos. and
    status
170 CC = CC / 25.6 + 1: REM ..Compute current
    column no.
180 CR = CR / 42.667 + 1: REM ..Compute current
    row no.
190 IF ABS (MS) < 4 THEN 130: REM ..Clear screen
    if mouse is down
200 IF MS > 0 THEN 140: REM ..Keep pointing until
    keystroke
210 PRINT: PRINT D$;"IN#0": REM ..Switch back to
    keyboard input
220 PRINT: PRINT D$;"PR#4": PRINT CHR$ (0):
    REM  ..Deactivate mouse
230 PRINT: PRINT D$;"PR#0": REM ..Switch back to
    screen output
240 POKE - 16368,0: REM ..Clear keyboard
250 END
```

Figure 9-14. Mouse Drawing program (*continued*)

```
        ++ +
         +++
         ++
    ++ +++
 +++++ +++ ++
++++++ +++++++
++  ++++++++  ++
    +++++++
     +++++
 +++   +++
 +++   +++      +
  ++   +++++++++
  ++  ++++++
   +++++++++
   ++++++
    +++++
      +++
      +++
      +++
      +++++
    +++++++++
```

Figure 9-15. Sample output from Mouse Drawing program

Activating the Mouse

You can monitor the mouse's position and the button's status from within a BASIC program. The first step is to activate the mouse with statements like these:

```
]10 D$ = CHR$ (4): REM ..ProDOS/DOS command prefix
]40 PRINT CHR$ (21);: REM ..Deactivate
    80-col. card
]100 PRINT: PRINT D$;"PR#4": PRINT CHR$ (1):
    REM ..Activate mouse
]110 PRINT: PRINT D$;"PR#0": REM ..Switch back to
    screen output
]120 PRINT: PRINT D$;"IN#4": REM ..Switch to input
    from mouse
```

Activating the mouse will partially deactivate an 80-column adapter, which may result in a crazy display, so the PRINT CHR$(21) statement on line 40 completely deactivates the 80-column adapter. In line 100, a PR#4 command switches output from the screen to the mouse. The next statement outputs a single control character (ASCII code 1) to activate the mouse. No further output to the mouse is required, so a PR#0 command switches output back to the screen. You can reactivate the 80-column adapter by using a PR#3 command instead of PR#0, but PR#3 has the side effect of clearing the display screen.

The IN#4 statement on line 120 switches input from the keyboard to the mouse. The next INPUT statement will read the mouse position and button status. (The program excerpt above won't work by itself because it doesn't include such an INPUT statement.)

The PR#4, PR#0, and IN#4 commands, like the PR#3 command that activates the 80-column adapter, are operating system commands. In programmed mode, they must be used from within PRINT statements and prefixed by the operating system prefix (ASCII code 4).

Warning: The PRINT D$;"PR#4" and the PRINT CHR$(1) statements must be on the same program line, as shown on line 100. Otherwise the mouse will not work and you will have to press CONTROL-RESET to regain control of the Apple II.

Displaying a Pointer

Before reading the mouse's position and the button's status for the first time, the program should display the pointer at its starting position. The following example illustrates this:

```
]20 PTR$ = "+": REM ..Pointer shape
]30 CR = 1:CC = 1: REM ..Initialize pointer's
     current row and col.
]130 HOME
]140 VTAB CR: HTAB CC: PRINT PTR$;:
     REM ..Display pointer
```

These program lines display a cross-shaped pointer (that is, a plus sign) in the upper-left corner of a blank screen. Activating the mouse initially puts the pointer at that spot. The text cursor is presently at the same spot, though only by coincidence. The mouse's position is not directly linked to the cursor's position.

Reading the Mouse

Having displayed the pointer, the program immediately needs to see whether the mouse has moved and find out what's happening with the button and the keyboard. It's time for an INPUT statement, as follows:

```
]150 VTAB 23: HTAB 39: REM ..Accommodate INPUT
     "feature"
]160 INPUT "";CC,CR,MS: REM ..Read mouse pos.
     and status
```

After executing the INPUT statement, variables CC and CR report the horizontal and vertical positions of the mouse, and variable MS reports the status of the mouse button and the keyboard. The empty prompt string on line 160 suppresses an undesirable feature of the INPUT statement: a question mark would otherwise appear on the screen at the current cursor location as if input were expected from the keyboard. The empty string eliminates this problem. The VTAB and HTAB statements on line 150 eliminate another INPUT statement quirk: when reading from the mouse, the INPUT statement usually erases the display from the current cursor position to the end of the line the cursor is on. It doesn't always erase, but most of the time it does. There is no way to suppress this feature, but its effects can be minimized by repositioning the cursor at the spot where the least damage will be done. Note that moving the cursor has no effect on the position reported by the mouse.

The mouse position is measured from the upper-left corner of

Table 9-5. Mouse Status Values

Value	Current INPUT	Last INPUT	Key Pressed*
+1	Pressed	Pressed	No
−1	Pressed	Pressed	Yes
+2	Pressed	Released	No
−2	Pressed	Released	Yes
+3	Released	Pressed	No
−3	Released	Pressed	Yes
+4	Released	Released	No
−4	Released	Released	Yes

*Since the keyboard was last reset with POKE −163680,0

the screen, the home position. The first variable input, CC in the previous example, reports how far the mouse is to the left of the home position. The second variable, CR, reports how far the mouse is below the home position. Both variables will have values between 0 and 1023, with 0 as the home position.

The third value input from the mouse, variable MS in the previous example, reports the status of the mouse button and the keyboard. It reports not only the current status of the button, but also the status during the last INPUT statement. If you press a key on the Apple II keyboard, the status value changes from positive to negative. The status value stays negative until the keyboard is reset with a POKE −16368,0 statement. Table 9-5 interprets the status values.

Moving the Pointer

Because there is no direct link between the mouse's position and the pointer's location, the program must establish one. It could use the mouse's position directly in VTAB and HTAB statements, but that would be asking for trouble. VTAB only allows rows 1 to 24; HTAB only works with columns 1 to 40. And as you know, the mouse's positions extend from 0 to 1023 both horizontally and vertically. A few simple calculations reduce the mouse's position to an acceptable range for the VTAB and HTAB statements as shown in the next example.

```
]170 CC = CC / 25.6 + 1: REM ..Compute current
     column no.
]180 CR = CR / 42.667 + 1: REM ..Compute current
     row no.
]190 IF ABS (MS) < 4 THEN 130: REM ..Clear screen
     if mouse is down
]200 IF MS > 0 THEN 140: REM ..Keep pointing
     until keystroke
```

The first two program lines, 170 and 180, scale the mouse's position to keep it within normal text-screen limits. The last two lines, 190 and 200, branch to an earlier part of the program to redisplay the pointer.

You may find that these scaling factors make the pointer unacceptably sluggish. If so, try smaller scaling factors. But if you do, make sure you add statements to guarantee that the variables stay within HTAB and VTAB limits. For example, putting the statement IF CC>40 THEN CC=40 on line 175 would keep the column number to 40 or less no matter where the mouse went.

If you want to use a screen width of 80, replace the HTAB CC statement on line 140 with a POKE 36,CC−1 statement, and change the horizontal scaling factor on line 170 from 25.6 to 12.8. In addition, change the HTAB 39 statement on line 150 to POKE 36,79.

Deactivating the Mouse

In order to accept input from the keyboard again, the program must turn off the mouse. The following statements do the job:

```
]210 PRINT: PRINT D$;"IN#0": REM ..Switch back to
     keyboard input
]220 PRINT: PRINT D$;"PR#4": PRINT CHR$ (0):
     REM ..Deactivate mouse
]230 PRINT: PRINT D$;"PR#0": REM ..Switch back
     to screen output
]240 POKE - 16368,0: REM ..Clear keyboard
]250 END
```

First, on line 210, an IN#0 command cancels the effect of the earlier IN#4 command, switching back to the keyboard for input. Next, a PR#4 command switches output to the mouse so a control character (ASCII code 0) can deactivate the mouse. A PR#0 command then switches back to the screen for output. Finally, on line 240, putting 0 in memory location −16368 with a POKE statement clears the keyboard, since you must have struck a key to end the program.

Using the Mouse

The mouse is well suited to making choices from a list of displayed options. As you may recall, this situation occurs in the Mailing-List Entry program (Figure 9-10) when it comes time to change an entry, enter another name and address, or quit the program. Making the choice is a two-step procedure:

1. Select a field by pressing the ↓ or ↑ key or by typing the field number (see Figure 9-11).
2. Press the RETURN key to choose the selected field.

You can replace this keyboard navigation with the mouse. You will select a field by pointing at it and choose the selection by pressing the mouse button. Figure 9-16 lists the new Mailing-List Entry With Mouse program; the lines that are different from the original Mailing-List Entry program are shaded. Table 9-6 lists the variables used by the new program.

```
1000 GOSUB 10000: REM ..Initialize variables
1010 PRINT CHR$ (21): REM ..Deactivate 80-col.
     card
1020 REM ..Display width is 40
1030 GOSUB 11000: REM ..DisplayEntryWindow
1040 FOR X1 = 1 TO LF%
1050 FIELD% = X1: GOSUB 23500:
     REM ..Display field description
1060 NEXT X1
1070 FOR X1 = 1 TO 5: REM ..Enter all fields
1080 FIELD% = X1
1090 GOSUB 23000: GOSUB 12000: GOSUB 23500:
     REM ..SelectField:EnterField:DeselectField
1100 NEXT X1
1110 FIELD% = 6: GOSUB 23000: REM ..SelectField
1120 GOSUB 22000: REM ..GetFieldNumber
1130 IF FIELD% = 6 THEN FR% = 4:LR% = 8:
     GOSUB 30100: GOSUB 23500: GOTO 1040:
```

Figure 9-16. Mailing-List Entry With Mouse Program

```
     REM ..If field=6, blank last entries,
     deselect and get another
1140 IF FIELD% < LF% THEN GOSUB 12000: GOTO 1120:
     REM ..EnterField
1150  REM ...Quit?...
1160 T% = 12:L% = 4:B% = 17:R% = 37:
     GOSUB 30200: REM ..DisplayBox
1170 VTAB 14: HTAB 5: PRINT BEEP$;"Are you
     sure you want to quit?";
1180 VTAB 16: HTAB 8:C$ = "Y": GOSUB 21000:
     REM ..GetYesNo
1190 IF NTRY$ = "NO" THEN FR% = 12:LR% = 17:
     GOSUB 30100: GOSUB 23000: GOTO 1120:
     REM ..If no, erase box, restore field,
     and get another field
1200 HOME: END: REM if yes, then quit
9989 REM
9990 REM ...InitializeVariables...
9991 REM
10000 D$ = CHR$ (4): REM ..ProDOS/DOS 3.3 prefix
10010 W4$ = CHR$ (17): REM ..Display width 40
10020 BEEP$ = CHR$ (07): REM ..Beep char.
10030 FOR X1 = 1 TO 40
10040 EF$ = EF$ + ".": REM ..Entry field chars.
10050 TL$ = TL$ + "_": REM ..Top line chars.
10060 BL$ = BL$ + "‾": REM ..Bottom line chars.
10070 NEXT X1
10080 SL$ = "|": REM ..Side line chars.
10090 LF% = 7: REM ..Last field number
10100 DIM FR%(2,LF%),FC%(2,LF%),FD$(2,LF%)
10110 FOR X1 = 1 TO LF%: REM ..Read field
      locations and descriptions
10120 READ FR%(1,X1),FC%(1,X1),FD$(1,X1)
10130 READ FR%(2,X1),FC%(2,X1),FD$(2,X1)
10140 NEXT X1
10150 PTR$ = "^": REM ..Pointer shape
10160 TRACK = 0.25: REM ..Mouse-pointer tracking
      factor
10170 RETURN
10489 REM
10490 REM ...Field Descriptions and Locations...
10491 REM
10500 DATA 4,3," 1. <NAME:>  "
10510 DATA 4,3," 1.  Name:   "
10520 DATA 5,3," 2. <STREET:>"
10530 DATA 5,3," 2.  Street: "
10540 DATA 6,3," 3. <CITY:>  "
```

Figure 9-16. Mailing-List Entry With Mouse program (*continued*)

```
10550 DATA 6,3," 3.  City:    "
10560 DATA 7,3," 4. <STATE:> "
10570 DATA 7,3," 4.  State:   "
10580 DATA 8,3," 5. <ZIP:>    "
10590 DATA 8,3," 5.  Zip:     "
10600 DATA 11,3," 6. <ANOTHER RECORD>"
10610 DATA 11,3," 6.  Another Record "
10620 DATA 12,3," 7. <QUIT>"
10630 DATA 12,3," 7.  Quit "
10989 REM
10990 REM ...DisplayEntryWindow...
10991 REM
11000 HOME
11010 T% = 1:L% = 1:B% = 22:R% = 39: GOSUB 30200:
      REM ..DisplayBox
11020 TITLE$ = "MAILING LIST ENTRY"
11030 INVERSE: VTAB 1:
      HTAB (40 - LEN (TITLE$)) / 2:
      PRINT TITLE$;: NORMAL: REM ..Display title
11040 RETURN
11989 REM
11990 REM ...EnterField...
11991 REM
12000 VTAB 19: HTAB 3: PRINT "Enter the
      selected field."
12010 HTAB 3: PRINT "Then press RETURN to
      confirm entry.";
12020 ON FIELD% GOSUB 13100,13200,13300,
      13400,13500
12030 FR% = 19:LR% = 21: GOSUB 30100:
      REM ..ClearDisplayLines
12040 RETURN
13089 REM
13090 REM ...EnterName...
13100 ML% = 20: VTAB 4: HTAB 17: GOSUB 20000
13110 NAME$ = NTRY$: RETURN
13189 REM
13190 REM ...EnterStreet...
13200 ML% = 20: VTAB 5: HTAB 17: GOSUB 20000
13210 STREET$ = NTRY$: RETURN
13289 REM
13290 REM ...EnterCity...
13300 ML% = 20: VTAB 6: HTAB 17: GOSUB 20000
13310 CITY$ = NTRY$: RETURN
13389 REM
13390 REM ...EnterState...
13400 ML% = 2: VTAB 7: HTAB 17: GOSUB 20000
```

Figure 9-16. Mailing-List Entry With Mouse program (*continued*)

```
13410 SE$ = NTRY$: RETURN
13489 REM
13490 REM ...EnterZip...
13500 ML% = 9: VTAB 8: HTAB 17: GOSUB 20000
13510 ZIP$ = NTRY$: RETURN
19989 REM
19990 REM ...GetEntry...
19991 REM
20000 HT% = PEEK (36) + 1: REM ..Cursor column
20010 NTRY$ = "": REM ..Empty entry
20020 CL% = LEN (NTRY$): REM ..Current entry length
20030 HTAB HT%: PRINT NTRY$;
20040 IF ML% > CL% THEN PRINT
      LEFT$ (EF$,ML% - CL%);:
      REM ..Fill unused entry field
20050 HTAB HT% + CL%: GOSUB 30000: REM ..Get one
      character
20060 IF C$ = CHR$ (127) AND CL% < = 1 THEN 20010:
      REM ..Delete key with empty entry?
20070 IF C$ = CHR$ (127) THEN NTRY$ =
      LEFT$ (NTRY$,CL% - 1): GOTO 20020:
      REM ..Delete key?
20080 IF C$ = CHR$ (24) THEN 20010:
      REM ..Control-X means cancel
20090 IF C$ = CHR$ (13) THEN
      PRINT SPC( ML% - CL%);:
      RETURN: REM ..Return means done
20100 IF C$ > = " " AND C$ < = "~" AND CL% < ML%
      THEN NTRY$ = NTRY$ + C$:
      REM ..Add valid characters if room
20110 GOTO 20020: REM ..Get another keystroke
20989 REM
20990 REM ...GetYesNo...
20991 REM
21000 HT% = PEEK (36) + 1:VT% = PEEK (37) + 1:
      REM ..Cursor position
21010 IF C$ = "Y" OR C$ = "y" OR (C$ =
      CHR$ (8) AND NTRY$ = "NO") THEN VTAB VT%:
      HTAB HT%: PRINT "<YES>  No ";:NTRY$ = "YES"
21020 IF C$ = "N" OR C$ = "n" OR (C$ =
      CHR$ (21) AND NTRY$ = "YES") THEN VTAB VT%:
      HTAB HT%: PRINT " Yes  <NO>";:NTRY$ = "NO"
21030 VTAB 19: HTAB 3: PRINT "Type Y for Yes or N
      for No,"
21040 HTAB 3: PRINT "or press <-- or --> to
      change."
21050 HTAB 3: PRINT "Then press RETURN.  ";
```

Figure 9-16. Mailing-List Entry With Mouse program (*continued*)

```
21060 GOSUB 30000: REM ..GetChar
21070 IF C$ = " " THEN C$ = CHR$ (21):
      REM ..Accommodate 80-col. card "feature"
21080 IF C$ < > CHR$ (13) THEN 21010:
      REM ..Only RETURN confirms
21090 FR% = 19:LR% = 21: GOSUB 30100:
      REM ..ClearDisplayLines
21100 RETURN
21989 REM
21990 REM ...GetFieldNumber...
21991 REM
22000 CR% = 1:CC% = 1: REM ..Initial pointer
      position
22010 VTAB 19: HTAB 3: PRINT "Point with the mouse
      to select a"
22020 HTAB 3: PRINT "field. Then click the mouse
      button.";
22030 GOSUB 30400: REM ..MouseOn
22040 GOSUB 30600: REM ..FollowMouse
22050 IF CR% = PR% THEN 22130: REM ..If no row
      change, skip selection change
22060 IF FIELD% < > 0 THEN GOSUB 23500:
      REM ..Deselect previous selection
22070 FIELD% = 0: REM ..Clear previous field
      selection
22080 FOR X1 = 1 TO LF%: REM ..Find current field
      selection
22090 IF CR% < > FR%(2,X1) THEN 22120: REM ..Is
      pointer on a field?
22100 FIELD% = X1: GOSUB 23000: REM ..Yes; select
      it
22110 X1 = LF%: REM ..and stop looking
22120 NEXT X1
22130 IF ABS (MS%) > 2 OR FIELD% = 0 THEN 22040:
      REM ..Keep polling until valid selection
22140 FR% = 19:LR% = 21: GOSUB 30100:
      REM ..ClearDisplayLines
22150 GOSUB 30500: REM ..MouseOff
22160 RETURN
22989 REM
22990 REM ...SelectField...
22991 REM
23000 VT% = PEEK (37) + 1:HT% = PEEK (36) + 1:
      REM ..Cursor location
23010 VTAB FR%(1,FIELD%): HTAB FC%(1,FIELD%):
      PRINT FD$(1,FIELD%);: REM ..Display selected
      description
```

Figure 9-16. Mailing-List Entry With Mouse program (*continued*)

```
23020 VTAB VT%: HTAB HT%: REM ..Reset cursor
23030 RETURN
23489 REM
23490 REM ...DeselectField...
23491 REM
23500 VT% = PEEK (37) + 1:HT% = PEEK (36) + 1:
      REM ..Cursor location
23510 VTAB FR%(2,FIELD%): HTAB FC%(2,FIELD%):
      PRINT FD$(2,FIELD%);: REM ..Display
      deselected description
23520 VTAB VT%: HTAB HT%: REM ..Reset cursor
23530 RETURN
29989 REM
29990 REM ...GetCharacter...
29991 REM
30000 GET C$: REM ..Wait for keystroke
30010 RETURN
30089 REM
30090 REM ...ClearDisplayLines...
30091 REM
30100 FOR ROW = FR% TO LR%
30110 VTAB ROW: HTAB 2: PRINT SPC( 37);
30120 NEXT ROW
30130 RETURN
30189 REM
30190 REM ...DisplayBox...
30191 REM
30200 VTAB T%: HTAB L% + 1
30210 PRINT LEFT$ (TL$,R% - L% - 1);: REM ..Top
      line
30220 FOR ROW = T% + 1 TO B%: REM ..Side lines
30230 VTAB ROW: HTAB L%: PRINT SL$;
30240 HTAB R%: PRINT SL$
30250 NEXT ROW
30260 VTAB B%: HTAB L% + 1: PRINT
      LEFT$ (BL$,R% - L% - 1);: REM ..Bottom line
30270 RETURN
30389 REM
30390 REM ...MouseOn...
30391 REM
30400 PRINT: PRINT D$;"PR#4": PRINT CHR$ (1):
      REM ..Turn mouse on
30410 PRINT: PRINT D$;"PR#0": REM ..Switch back
      to screen output
30420 PRINT: PRINT D$;"IN#4": REM ..Get input
      from mouse
30430 RETURN
```

Figure 9-16. Mailing-List Entry With Mouse program (*continued*)

```
30489 REM
30490 REM ...MouseOff...
30491 REM
30500 PRINT: PRINT D$;"IN#0": REM ..Switch back
      to keyboard input
30510 PRINT: PRINT D$;"PR#4": PRINT CHR$ (0):
      REM ..Turn mouse off
30520 PRINT: PRINT D$;"PR#0": REM ..Switch back to
      screen output
30530 POKE 49168,0: REM ..Clear keyboard
30540 RETURN
30589 REM
30590 REM ...FollowMouse...
30591 REM
30600 FCC% = SCRN( CC% - 1,2 * (CR% - 1)) + 16 *
      SCRN( CC% - 1,2 * (CR% - 1) + 1):
      REM  ..Former character's code
30610 VTAB CR%: HTAB CC%: PRINT PTR$;:
      REM ..Display pointer
30620 PC% = CC%:PR% = CR%: REM ..Previous pointer
      pos. = current pos.
30630 VTAB 23: HTAB 39: REM ..Accomodate INPUT
      "feature"
30640 INPUT "";CC%,CR%,MS%: REM ..Read mouse pos.
      and status
30650 CC% = CC% / 25.6 / TRACK + 1: REM ..Compute
      current column no.
30660 CR% = CR% / 42.667 / TRACK + 1:
      REM ..Compute current row no.
30670 IF CC% > 40 THEN CC% = 40: REM ..Restrict
      col. to 40 max.
30680 IF CR% > 24 THEN CR% = 24: REM ..Restrict
      row to 24 max.
30690 IF CR% = PR% AND CC% = PC% AND ABS (MS%) > 2
      THEN 30630: REM ..If mouse hasn't moved and
      button is up, read again
30700 VTAB PR%: HTAB PC%: REM ..If it has,
      redisplay prev. character
30710 IF FCC% > 127 THEN PRINT CHR$ (FCC%);: GOTO
      30740: REM ..Redisplay normal character
30720 IF FCC% < 32 THEN INVERSE:
      PRINT CHR$ (FCC% + 64);: NORMAL:
      GOTO 30740: REM ..Redisplay
      inverse uppercase
30730 INVERSE: PRINT CHR$ (FCC%);: NORMAL:
      REM ..Redisplay other inverse
30740 RETURN
```

Figure 9-16. Mailing-List Entry With Mouse program (*continued*)

Table 9-6. Mailing-List Entry With Mouse Program Variables

Variable	Purpose	Used on lines:
B%	Bottom row of box	1160, 11010, 30220, 30260
BEEP$	Sound console speaker	1170, 10020
BL$	Characters for bottom edge of box	10060, 30260
C$	Keystroke	1180, 20060, 20070, 20080, 20090, 20100, 21010, 21020, 21070, 21080, 30000
CC%	Current pointer column	22000, 30600, 30610, 30620, 30640, 30650, 30670, 30690
CITY$	Value of City field	13310
CL%	Current entry length	20020, 20040, 20050, 20060, 20070, 20090, 20100
CR%	Current pointer row	22000, 22050, 22090, 30600, 30610, 30620, 30640, 30660, 30680, 30690
D$	ProDOS or DOS 3.3 command prefix	10000, 30400, 30410, 30420, 30500, 30510, 30520
EF$	Characters for entry field indicator	10040, 20040
FCC%	Former character's screen code	30600, 30710, 30720, 30730
FC%()	Field columns	10100, 10120, 10130, 23010, 23510
FD$()	Field descriptions	10100, 10120, 10130, 23010, 23510
FIELD%	Current field number	1050, 1080, 1110, 1130, 1140, 12020, 22060, 22070, 22100, 22130, 23010, 23510
FR%	First row to clear	1130, 1190, 12030, 21090, 22140, 30100
FR%()	Field rows	10100, 10120, 10130, 22090, 23010, 23510
HT%	Current horizontal tab position	20000, 20030, 20050, 21000, 21010, 21020, 23000, 23020, 23500, 23520
L%	Left column of box	1160, 11010, 30200, 30210, 30230, 30260
LF%	Last field number	1040, 1140, 10090, 10100, 10110, 22080, 22110

Table 9-6. Mailing-List Entry With Mouse Program Variables (*continued*)

Variable	Purpose	Used on lines:
LR%	Last row to clear	1130, 1190, 12030, 21090, 22140, 30100
ML%	Maximum entry length	13100, 13200, 13300, 13400, 13500, 20040, 20090, 20100
MS%	Mouse button status	22130, 30640, 30690
NAME$	Value of Name field	13110
NTRY$	Current entry value	1190, 13110, 13210, 13310, 13410, 13510, 20010, 20020, 20030, 20070, 20100, 21010, 21020
PC%	Previous pointer column	30620, 30690, 30700
PR%	Previous pointer row	22050, 30620, 30690, 30700
PTR$	Pointer shape	10150, 30610
R%	Right column of box	1160, 11010, 30210, 30240, 30260
ROW	Row counter	30100, 30110, 30120, 30220, 30230, 30250
SE$	Value of State field	13410
SL$	Character for side lines of box	10080, 30230, 30240
STREET$	Value of Street field	13210
T%	Top row of box	1160, 11010, 30200, 30220
TITLE$	Title of window	11020, 11030
TL$	Characters for top edge of box	10050, 30210
TRACK	Mouse-pointer tracking factor	10160, 30650, 30660
VT%	Current vertical tab position	21000, 21010, 21020, 23000, 23020, 23500, 23520
W4$	Code for screen width of 40	10010
X1	Loop counter	1040, 1050, 1060, 1070, 1080, 1100, 10030, 10070, 10110, 10120, 10130, 10140, 22080, 22090, 22100, 22110, 22120
ZIP$	Value for ZIP field	13510

The main part of the mouse selection program in Figure 9-16 is identical with the main part of the original program in Figure 9-10 (lines 1000-1200), with one exception. The mouse version does not activate the 80-column adapter; in fact, it deactivates the adapter (lines 1010-1020). When using the mouse in a BASIC program, it's easier to keep the screen under control if the 80-column adapter is inactive.

There are some additional lines in the subroutine that initializes variables (lines 10150-10170). Variable PTR$ defines the shape of the mouse pointer. Variable TRACK establishes a mouse-pointer tracking factor; the smaller its value, the less you must move the mouse to move the pointer a given distance on the screen.

The standard subroutines from Figure 9-10 are used for specifying field descriptions and locations, displaying the entry form, entering a field value, inputting a value, and getting a yes-or-no response (lines 10500-21100). However, the program title is changed to all uppercase letters, since it will be displayed in inverse style (line 11020). Remember, lowercase letters are not available in inverse style unless the 80-column adapter is active.

More standard subroutines from Figure 9-10 select and deselect a field, get a single character from the keyboard, clear display lines, and draw a box on the screen (lines 23000-30270).

Subroutine GetFieldNumber is entirely new. It begins by setting the starting position for the pointer to the upper-left corner of the screen (line 22000). Next, it displays mouse instructions at the bottom of the entry window (lines 22010 and 22020). It then calls another new subroutine, MouseOn, to activate the mouse (line 22030). Yet another new subroutine, FollowMouse, is called to take care of moving the pointer (line 22040).

When the mouse moves or its button is pressed, the FollowMouse subroutine returns to the GetFieldNumber subroutine, which interprets the latest mouse activity. The GetFieldNumber subroutine ignores side-to-side movement (line 22050), but if the mouse has changed rows, it changes field selection according to the new position. First it deselects the currently selected field, if any (line 22060); then it finds out if the mouse is on the same line as a field description (lines 22070-22120). If so, it selects that field (line 22100). If not, it does nothing. This particular subroutine does not care whether a key has been struck.

After changing field selection as needed, the GetFieldNumber subroutine checks the reported status of the mouse button. If the button was up, or if no field is currently selected, the subroutine branches back to follow the mouse again (line 22130). If the button was pressed with the pointer over a field, the subroutine ends, clearing its instructions and deactivating the mouse on its way out (lines 22140-22160).

The new MouseOn subroutine activates the mouse as described earlier in this chapter (lines 30400-30430). The new MouseOff subroutine deactivates the mouse and clears the keyboard as described earlier (lines 30500-30540).

The last new subroutine, FollowMouse, displays the mouse pointer and waits until the mouse is moved or its button is pressed. The subroutine begins by determining the code number of the character at the spot where it is about to display the pointer, so it can restore the character after the pointer moves (line 30600). It determines the character code by a trick with the SCRN function, whose main purpose is to report the color of a dot on a graphics screen (see Chapter 12). Next it displays the pointer and calls its position the "previous" position (lines 30610 and 30620).

After displaying the pointer, the FollowMouse subroutine immediately reads the mouse, handling the undesirable INPUT statement features as described earlier (lines 30630 and 30640). Then it scales the new mouse position and keeps it within text-screen boundaries (lines 30650-30680). If the new position is the same as the previous position and the button is and was up, the subroutine branches back to read the mouse again (line 30690).

When the FollowMouse subroutine detects mouse movement or button activity, it restores the character that the pointer has been covering and returns (lines 30700-30740). Because of the way the Apple II displays inverse characters when the 80-column adapter is inactive, restoring the character when using the mouse is somewhat complicated.

On the screen, it turns out that all normal-style characters have code numbers 128 higher than their standard ASCII character codes. For example, the ASCII code for capital A is 65. But the code for a normal-style A on the screen is 193. The screen codes for uppercase inverse letters and a few special symbols are between 0 and 32. Screen codes for the other inverse punctuation and symbols are between 32 and 63. Screen codes 64 to 127 are for flashing characters. See Appendix E for a detailed comparison of screen and ASCII codes.

To display a normal-style character given its screen code, the program simply uses the CHR$ function, which automatically converts the screen code to the corresponding ASCII code.

For inverse characters, the program must use the INVERSE statement before restoring the character, and the NORMAL statement afterwards. For uppercase inverse, the program must also add 64 to the screen code in order to convert it to the proper ASCII code. For example, a capital A has a screen code of 1 and an ASCII code of 65.

The performance of the mouse is not very satisfactory in this program. By modifying the program, you may be able to make the pointer move a bit more smoothly and flicker slightly less, but only to a point. No matter how well written, BASIC programs simply cannot run fast enough for good mouse performance. What's more, BASIC provides access to only part of the mouse's capabilities. For the rest, and for more speed, you must program in assembly language.

Printer Output 10

When you turn on an Apple II, all of the text generated by statements such as PRINT and INPUT automatically appears on the display screen, as do error messages, disk directory listings, and program listings. It is easy to divert any of this text to a printer. All you have to know is the number of the slot that holds the accessory card your printer plugs into. This is usually slot 1. If you're not sure of the slot number, simply follow the cable from the printer to its destination inside the Apple II. The printer will connect to either an Apple II Parallel Interface Card, an Apple II Super Serial Card, an Apple II Serial Interface Card, an Apple II Communications Card, or the equivalent of one of those cards.

ACTIVATING THE PRINTER

The Apple II treats a printer as a substitute for the display screen. In order to create printer output, therefore, you must type a command that sends output meant for the display screen to the printer. The PR# command does this by switching output to a specified slot. The following command selects slot 1 for output:

```
]PR#1
```

This command activates a printer that is attached to an accessory card in slot 1. Everything you type will then be printed on the printer, as will the output of PRINT, INPUT, LIST, CATALOG, and other commands.

Activating a printer with a PR# command will partially deactivate an 80-column adapter. To avoid a garbled display, deactivate the 80-column adapter completely by pressing ESC and then CONTROL-Q.

If the PR#1 command does not activate your printer or if strange characters are printed, the fault could be due to one of the following conditions:

- Printer turned off.
- Printer "Select" or "Ready" light off.
- Printer covers are loose or missing.
- Printer out of paper, or nearly so.
- Printer ribbon broken or missing.
- PR# command mistyped (wrong slot specified).
- Switches set incorrectly on the accessory card or inside the printer.
- Wrong cable connecting printer and accessory card.
- Serial printer attached to parallel accessory card or vice versa.
- Malfunctioning accessory card, cable, or printer.

The occurrence of any of these problems may cause the Apple II to lock up until you correct the problem or press CONTROL-RESET. For specific advice on correcting printing problems on your system, consult your printer and accessory card manuals or talk to your dealer.

DISPLAYING AND PRINTING CONCURRENTLY

The serial and parallel accessory cards for printers may be set up initially so that output appears on the display screen and printer simultaneously. In this case, the length of a printed line is usually restricted to 40 characters. The Apple Super Serial Card has switches that control line length and determine whether output appears on the display screen. Both this card and the Apple Parallel Interface Card also respond to programmed commands to change these features.

You can instruct the Super Serial Card or Parallel Interface Card to stop the screen display and change the maximum line length. Output to the printer continues, however. The following example illustrates:

```
]PRINT CHR$(9);"80N"
```

Commands to the Super Serial Card and Parallel Interface Card start with the character whose ASCII code number is 9. In the example above, CHR$(9) generates that prefix, alerting the printer accessory card that a command follows, not just another character to be sent to the printer. You can also generate the prefix character by pressing CONTROL-I.

The example command, 80N, does two things: it blocks the flow of characters to the display screen, and it sets the maximum line width to 80. You can set the line width to anything between 1 and 255, but your printer imposes its own line width limit. There's no point in setting the line width past 80 at the Super Serial Card or Parallel Interface Card unless your printer can print wider lines.

Another command restarts the screen display and resets the maximum line width to 40. Here is an example:

```
]PRINT CHR$(9);"I"
```

In this example, CHR$(9) once again generates the prefix that signals a command to the Super Serial Card or Parallel Interface Card. The letter I, when prefixed by CHR$(9), is the command to start displaying and printing at the same time.

If CHR$(9) does not work with your Apple Super Serial Card, the card may be set to recognize a different prefix. In that case, try CHR$(1) where you see CHR$(9) in the examples above. If CHR$(1) works, use it wherever you see CHR$(9) throughout the rest of the chapter. Pressing CONTROL-A generates the same character as CHR$(1).

PRINTING A DISK DIRECTORY

To make a printed copy of a disk directory, first activate the printer as described earlier. Make sure the printer is turned on and ready to go, and then type a CAT or CATALOG command. The directory listing will be printed out. You can also specify a drive and slot number or ProDOS pathname with the CAT or CATALOG command, as explained in Chapter 6.

PRINTING A PROGRAM LISTING

If the printer is active when you type a LIST command, it will print the program lines in exactly the same format as they appear on the display screen. All of the LIST command options that affect which lines will be displayed also affect which lines will be printed; see Chapter 5 for details.

DEACTIVATING THE PRINTER

Yet another command to the Super Serial Card or Parallel Interface Card turns the card off, deactivating the printer. The following example illustrates:

```
]PRINT CHR$(9);"R"
```

All of the following actions also turn off the serial or parallel accessory card to deactivate the printer:

- Executing the command PR#0.
- Restarting the Apple II by pressing OPEN APPLE-CONTROL-RESET or switching the Apple II off and back on.
- Resetting the Apple II by pressing CONTROL-RESET.
- Activating the 80-column adapter with the PR#3 command.
- Deactivating the 80-column adapter by pressing ESC and CONTROL-Q or by sending CHR$(21) or its equivalent to the display screen.

PROGRAMMING PRINTER OUTPUT

Programming output on the printer is almost the same as programming output on the display screen. It is certainly no harder, although some differences do exist. For example, the printer has no cursor. The VTAB statement will move the cursor up and down on the display screen, but it cannot move a print head up and down on a piece of paper. Lines print sequentially, one line after another, one whole line at a time. On the screen, you can display the descriptions for a form (as in Figure 9-9); then you can go back and fill in values for each description. You cannot do that on the printer. Instead you must print the descriptions and values for one line before you go on to the next.

The PR# command works in programmed mode as well as in immediate mode. PR# is an operating system command, so in programmed mode you must use it from within a PRINT statement and prefix it with CHR$(4) (in Integer BASIC, press CONTROL-D between quotes). It's also a good idea to deactivate the 80-column adapter by printing CHR$(21) (or CONTROL-U in quotes) before activating the printer. Here is an example:

```
]11 PRINT CHR$(21): REM DEACTIVATE
     80-COLUMN ADAPTER
]12 PRINT: PRINT CHR$(4);"PR#1": REM SWITCH
     TO PRINTER
```

Perhaps you recall using this technique with the PR#4 command in Chapter 9 in order to activate the mouse.

Formatting Printer Output

Formatting output for the printer is similar to formatting output for the display screen. However, commas and TAB functions in PRINT statements do not work properly with the Super Serial Card or Parallel Interface Card. Fortunately, the SPC function does work reliably. For example, with a few changes and additions, the program from Chapter 9 that displays two columns of equivalent Celsius and Fahrenheit temperatures will print the same information in exactly the same format. Here is the new program:

```
]10 INPUT "LOWEST FAHRENHEIT TEMPERATURE? ";L
]11 PRINT CHR$(21): REM DEACTIVATE
     80-COLUMN ADAPTER
]12 PRINT: PRINT CHR$(4);"PR#1": REM SWITCH
     TO PRINTER
]13 PRINT CHR$(9); "40N": REM SET COLUMN WIDTH
]20 PRINT SPC( 6);"FAHRENHEIT"; SPC( 3);"CELSIUS"
]30 FOR F = L TO L + 20
]40 W = LEN ( STR$ (F)): REM FAHR. WIDTH
]50 PRINT SPC( 9 + 6 - W + 1);F;
]60 C = 5 / 9 * (F - 32): REM CELSIUS
]70 C = INT ( ABS (C) * 10 + .5) / 10 * SGN (C)
     : REM ROUND
]80 W = LEN ( STR$ ( INT (C))): REM CELSIUS WIDTH
]90 PRINT SPC( 1 + 6 - W + 1);C
]100 NEXT F
]101 PRINT CHR$(9);"R": REM SWITCH TO SCREEN
]110 END
```

As in the original program, this program starts by displaying a prompt message and by inputting the lowest Fahrenheit temperature (line 10). Three new program lines then deactivate the 80-column adapter (if any), switch output from the screen to the printer, set the line length to 40 characters, and turn off the display screen (lines 11-13). The program now uses SPC functions to position the column headings (line 20). It also uses SPC functions to position the column values (lines 50 and 90). Lines 50 and 90 could be simplified by combining the SPC function operands; they are separate in this example only for clarification.

You can use the HTAB statement in an Applesoft program (the TAB statement in Integer BASIC) to advance to a character position farther along the printed line. Except on an Enhanced Apple IIe, the HTAB statement only works with column numbers 1 through 40. For larger numbers, use the POKE statement with memory location 36 instead. For example, POKE 36,70 will advance to column 70. The printer ignores HTAB, TAB, and POKE statements that try to move to a column that the printer has already passed, so you cannot use them to back up along the printed line.

Paging

Most printers pay no attention to page length; they assume they are printing on an endless roll of paper with no page boundaries. You can print program listings page by page, however, by using a separate LIST statement to list one page-sized chunk at a time. Explicitly specify a starting and ending line number for each chunk, so that the program lines within that piece will fit on one page. Later in the chapter, we'll see a way to make the Apple Imagewriter page listings automatically.

Paging program output is much less tedious, because the program can count output lines for you. A special subroutine, shown in Figure 10-1, will do most of the work. Each time the program prints a line or group of lines, it increments the line count and calls the subroutine. The subroutine checks to see if the page is full (line 15000). If not, it does nothing. If the page is full, the subroutine prints enough blank lines to advance to the beginning of the next page (lines 15010 and 15020). There it prints a title and column headings (lines 15030-15050). Finally, it resets the line count (line 15060).

```
14989 REM
14990 REM ...TopPage...
14991 REM
15000 IF PL% < 55 THEN RETURN:
     REM ..Page full yet?
15010 FOR X1 = 1 TO (66 - PL%): REM ..Space to
     bottom of page
15020 PRINT: NEXT X1
15030 PRINT ,"TITLE": REM ..Print title here
15040 PRINT
15050 PRINT "COL1","COL2","COL3":
     REM ..Print column headings here
15060 PL% = 3: RETURN: REM ..Reset
     printed line counter
```

Figure 10-1. TopPage subroutine

Printed Mailing-List Program

Chapter 9 introduced a program to enter names and addresses for a mailing list (Figures 9-9 through 9-13). The Mailing-List Entry program would be much more useful if it printed the names and addresses you entered. The printed output could take any of several forms, as Figure 10-2 shows. It could be a simple list of names and addresses printed on plain paper, listing one name and address per line, with page and column headings; or the program could print mailing labels. With printers that allow it, the program could even print each name and address directly on an envelope.

The changes to the Mailing-List Entry program required for the first format—a list of names and addresses on plain paper—are quite simple. After each name and address is entered, the program needs to activate the printer, print the values just entered, and deactivate the printer. It can also use the TopPage subroutine to check for a full page. Figure 10-3 shows the improved program, with changes and additions to Figure 9-10 shaded.

The new program initializes variables, displays an entry window, and inputs values on the screen in much the same way as the

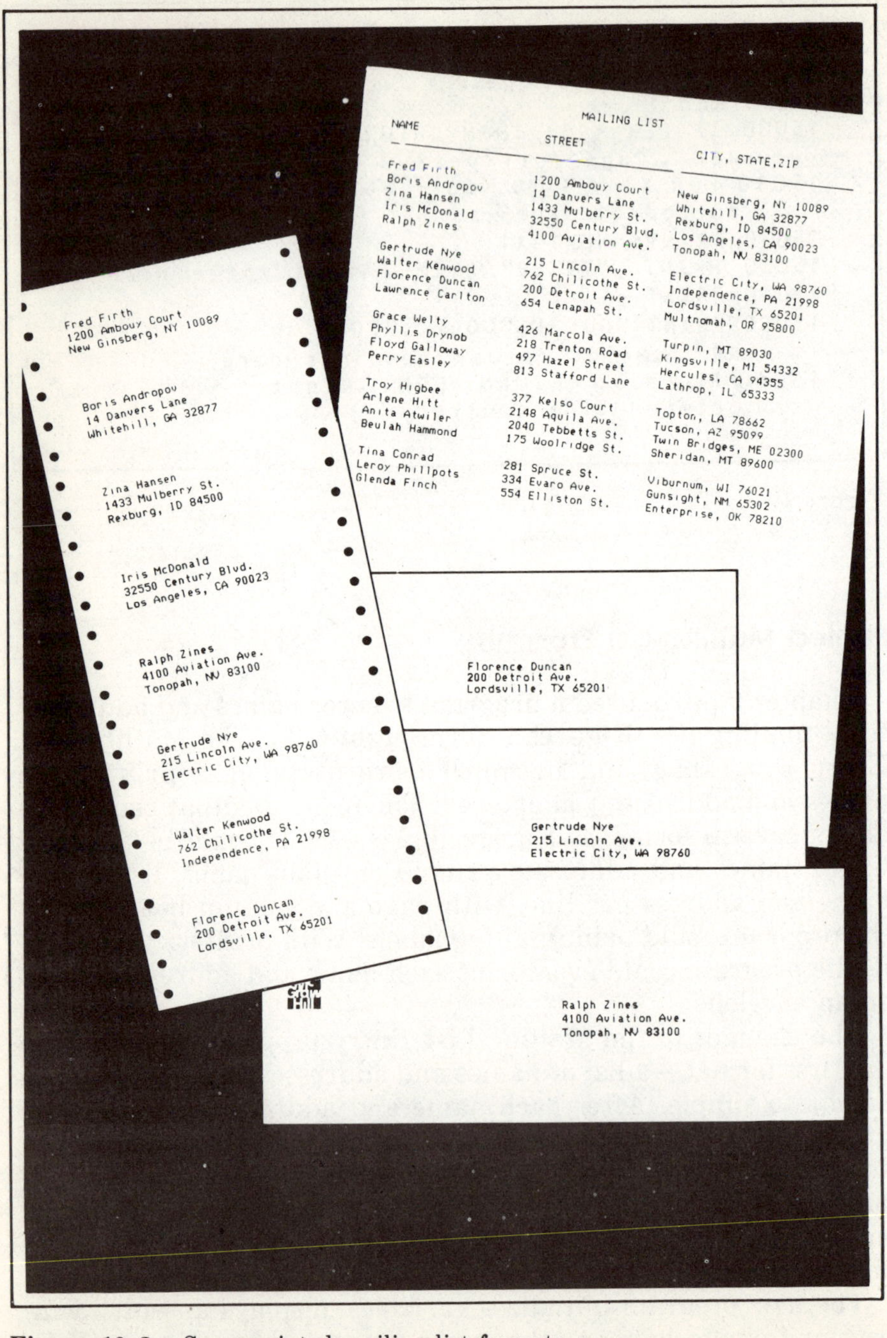

Figure 10-2. Some printed mailing list formats

```
1000 GOSUB 10000: REM ..Initialize variables
1010 PRINT CHR$ (21): REM ..Deactivate
     80-col. card
1020 REM ..Display width is 40
1030 GOSUB 11000: REM ..DisplayEntryWindow
1040 FOR X1 = 1 TO LF%
1050 FIELD% = X1: GOSUB 23500:
     REM ..Display field description
1060 NEXT X1
1070 FOR X1 = 1 TO 5: REM ..Enter all fields
1080 FIELD% = X1
1090 GOSUB 23000: GOSUB 12000: GOSUB 23500:
     REM ..SelectField:EnterField:DeselectField
1100 NEXT X1
1110 FIELD% = 6: GOSUB 23000: REM ..SelectField
1120 GOSUB 22000: REM ..GetFieldNumber
1130 IF FIELD% = 6 THEN GOSUB 14000:FR% = 4:
     LR% = 8: GOSUB 30100: GOSUB 23500: GOTO
     1040: REM ..If field=6, print, blank last
     entries, deselect, and get another
1140 IF FIELD% < LF% THEN GOSUB 12000: GOTO 1120:
     REM ..EnterField
1150 REM ...Quit?...
1160 T% = 12:L% = 4:B% = 17:R% = 37:
     GOSUB 30200: REM ..DisplayBox
1170 VTAB 14: HTAB 5: PRINT BEEP$;"Are you sure
     you want to quit?";
1180 VTAB 16: HTAB 8:C$ = "Y": GOSUB 21000:
     REM ..GetYesNo
1190 IF NTRY$ = "NO" THEN FR% = 12: LR% = 17:
     GOSUB 30100: GOSUB 23000: GOTO 1120:
     REM ..If no, erase box, restore field, and
     get another field
1200 GOSUB 14000: HOME: END: REM ..If yes, then
     print and quit
9989 REM
9990 REM ...InitializeVariables...
9991 REM
10000 D$ = CHR$ (4): REM ..ProDOS/DOS 3.3 prefix
10010 W4$ = CHR$ (17): REM ..Display width 40
10020 BEEP$ = CHR$ (07): REM ..Beep char.
10030 FOR X1 = 1 TO 40
10040 EF$ = EF$ + ".": REM ..Entry field chars.
10050 TL$ = TL$ + "_": REM ..Top line chars.
10060 BL$ = BL$ + "_": REM ..Bottom line chars.
10070 NEXT X1
```

Figure 10-3. Printed Mailing-List program

```
10080 SL$ = "|": REM ..Side line chars.
10090 LF% = 7: REM ..Last field number
10100 DIM FR%(2,LF%),FC%(2,LF%),FD$(2,LF%)
10110 FOR X1 = 1 TO LF%: REM ..Read field
    locations and descriptions
10120 READ FR%(1,X1),FC%(1,X1),FD$(1,X1)
10130 READ FR%(2,X1),FC%(2,X1),FD$(2,X1)
10140 NEXT X1
10150 PL% = 65: REM
10160 RETURN
10489 REM
10490 REM ...Field Descriptions and Locations...
10491 REM
10500 DATA 4,3," 1. <NAME:>   "
10510 DATA 4,3," 1.  Name:    "
10520 DATA 5,3," 2. <STREET:>"
10530 DATA 5,3," 2.  Street: "
10540 DATA 6,3," 3. <CITY:>   "
10550 DATA 6,3," 3.  City:    "
10560 DATA 7,3," 4. <STATE:> "
10570 DATA 7,3," 4.  State:   "
10580 DATA 8,3," 5. <ZIP:>    "
10590 DATA 8,3," 5.  Zip:     "
10600 DATA 11,3," 6. <ANOTHER RECORD>"
10610 DATA 11,3," 6.  Another Record "
10620 DATA 12,3," 7. <QUIT>"
10630 DATA 12,3," 7.  Quit "
10989 REM
10990 REM ...DisplayEntryWindow...
10991 REM
11000 HOME
11010 T% = 1:L% = 1:B% = 22:R% = 39: GOSUB 30200:
    REM ..DisplayBox
11020 TITLE$ = "MAILING LIST ENTRY"
11030 INVERSE: VTAB 1: HTAB (40 - LEN
    (TITLE$)) / 2: PRINT TITLE$;: NORMAL:
    REM ..Display title
11040 RETURN
11989 REM
11990 REM ...EnterField...
11991 REM
12000 VTAB 20: HTAB 3: PRINT "Enter the selected
    field."
12010 HTAB 3: PRINT "Then press RETURN to
    confirm entry.";
12020 ON FIELD% GOSUB 13100,13200,13300,
    13400,13500
```

Figure 10-3. Printed Mailing-List program (*continued*)

```
12030 FR% = 19:LR% = 21: GOSUB 30100:
     REM ..ClearDisplayLines
12040 RETURN
13089 REM
13090 REM ...EnterName...
13100 ML% = 20: VTAB 4: HTAB 17: GOSUB 20000
13110 NAME$ = NTRY$: RETURN
13189 REM
13190 REM ...EnterStreet...
13200 ML% = 20: VTAB 5: HTAB 17: GOSUB 20000
13210 STREET$ = NTRY$: RETURN
13289 REM
13290 REM ...EnterCity...
13300 ML% = 20: VTAB 6: HTAB 17: GOSUB 20000
13310 CITY$ = NTRY$: RETURN
13389 REM
13390 REM ...EnterState...
13400 ML% = 2: VTAB 7: HTAB 17: GOSUB 20000
13410 SE$ = NTRY$: RETURN
13489 REM
13490 REM ...EnterZip...
13500 ML% = 9: VTAB 8: HTAB 17: GOSUB 20000
13510 ZIP$ = NTRY$: RETURN
13989 REM
13990 REM ...PrintRecord...
13991 REM
14000 VTAB 21: HTAB 3: PRINT "Printing...";
14010 PRINT: PRINT D$;"PR#1": REM ..Switch
     to printer
14020 PRINT CHR$ (9);"80N";: REM ..Line width 80
14030 PL% = PL% + 1: GOSUB 15000: REM ..TopPage
14040 PRINT NAME$;
14050 HTAB 22: PRINT STREET$;
14060 POKE 36,42: PRINT CITY$;", ";SE$;" ";ZIP$
14070 IF PL% / 5 = INT (PL% / 5) THEN PRINT:
     PL% = PL% + 1: REM ..Print a blank line every
     5th address
14080 PRINT CHR$ (9);"R": REM ..Switch to screen
14090 VTAB 21: HTAB 2: PRINT SPC( 37);:
     REM ..Clear bottom line
14100 RETURN
14989 REM
14990 REM ...TopPage...
14991 REM
15000 IF PL% < 55 THEN RETURN:
     REM ..Page full yet?
```

Figure 10-3. Printed Mailing-List program (*continued*)

```
15010 FOR X1 = 1 TO (66 - PL%):
     REM ..Space to bottom of page
15020 PRINT: NEXT X1
15030 PRINT TAB( 28);"MAILING LIST"
15040 PRINT
15050 PRINT "NAME"; SPC( 18);"STREET";
     SPC( 16);"CITY, STATE,ZIP"
15060 PRINT "_____________________";
15070 PRINT "_____________________";
15080 PRINT "__________________________________"
15090 PRINT
15100 PL% = 6: RETURN: REM ...Reset
     printed line counter
19989 REM
19990 REM ...GetEntry...
19991 REM
20000 HT% = PEEK (36) + 1: REM ..Cursor column
20010 NTRY$ = "": REM ..Empty entry
20020 CL% = LEN (NTRY$): REM ..Current
     entry length
20030 HTAB HT%: PRINT NTRY$;
20040 IF ML% > CL% THEN PRINT LEFT$
     (EF$,ML% - CL%);: REM ..Fill unused entry
     field
20050 HTAB HT% + CL%: GOSUB 30000: REM ..Get
     one character
20060 IF C$ = CHR$ (127) AND CL% < = 1 THEN 20010:
     REM ..Delete key with empty entry?
20070 IF C$ = CHR$ (127) THEN NTRY$ =
     LEFT$ (NTRY$,CL% - 1): GOTO 20020:
     REM ..Delete key?
20080 IF C$ = CHR$ (24) THEN 20010: REM ..Control-
     X means cancel
20090 IF C$ = CHR$ (13) THEN PRINT
     SPC( ML% - CL%);: RETURN: REM ..Return means
     done
20100 IF C$ > = " " AND C$ < = "~" AND CL% < ML%
     THEN NTRY$ = NTRY$ + C$: REM ..Add valid
     characters if room
20110 GOTO 20020: REM ..Get another keystroke
20989 REM
20990 REM ...GetYesNo...
20991 REM
21000 HT% = PEEK (36) + 1:VT% = PEEK (37) + 1:
     REM ..Cursor position
```

Figure 10-3. Printed Mailing-List program (*continued*)

```
21010 IF C$ = "Y" OR C$ = "y" OR (C$ = CHR$ (8)
    AND NTRY$ = "NO") THEN VTAB VT%: HTAB HT%:
    PRINT "<YES>  No ";:NTRY$ = "YES"
21020 IF C$ = "N" OR C$ = "n" OR (C$ = CHR$ (21)
    AND NTRY$ = "YES") THEN VTAB VT%: HTAB HT%:
    PRINT " Yes  <NO>";:NTRY$ = "NO"
21030 VTAB 19: HTAB 3: PRINT "Type Y for Yes or N
    for No,"
21040 HTAB 3: PRINT "or press <-- or --> to
    change."
21050 HTAB 3: PRINT "Then press RETURN.  ";
21060 GOSUB 30000: REM ..GetChar
21070 IF C$ = " " THEN C$ = CHR$ (21):
    REM ..Accommodate 80-col. card "feature"
21080 IF C$ < > CHR$ (13) THEN 21010: REM ..Only
    RETURN confirms
21090 FR% = 19:LR% = 21: GOSUB 30100:
    REM ..ClearDisplayLines
21100 RETURN
21989 REM
21990 REM ...GetFieldNumber...
21991 REM
22000 VTAB 19: HTAB 3: PRINT "To select a field,
    type a number or "
22010 HTAB 3: PRINT "press UP-ARROW or
    DOWN-ARROW."
22020 HTAB 3: PRINT "Then press RETURN.  ";
22030 GOSUB 30000: REM ..GetChar
22040 IF C$ = CHR$ (10) AND FIELD% < LF% THEN
    GOSUB 23500:FIELD% = FIELD% + 1: GOSUB 23000:
    REM ..Down-arrow key
22050 IF C$ = CHR$ (11) AND FIELD% > 1 THEN GOSUB
    23500:FIELD% = FIELD% - 1: GOSUB 23000:
    REM .. Up-arrow key
22060 IF C$ > = "1" AND C$ < = STR$ (LF%) THEN
    GOSUB 23500:FIELD% = VAL (C$): GOSUB 23000:
    REM ..Digit key
22070 IF C$ < > CHR$ (13) THEN 22030: REM ..Only
    RETURN confirms
22080 FR% = 19:LR% = 21: GOSUB 30100:
    REM ..ClearDisplayLines
22090 RETURN
22989 REM
22990 REM ...SelectField...
22991 REM
```

Figure 10-3. Printed Mailing-List program (*continued*)

```
23000 VT% = PEEK (37) + 1:HT% = PEEK (36) + 1:
     REM ..Cursor location
23010 VTAB FR%(1,FIELD%): HTAB FC%(1,FIELD%):
     PRINT FD$(1,FIELD%);: REM ..Display selected
     description
23020 VTAB VT%: HTAB HT%: REM ..Reset cursor
23030 RETURN
23489 REM
23490 REM ...DeselectField...
23491 REM
23500 VT% = PEEK (37) + 1:HT% = PEEK (36) + 1:
     REM ..Cursor location
23510 VTAB FR%(2,FIELD%): HTAB FC%(2,FIELD%):
     PRINT FD$(2,FIELD%);: REM ..Display
     deselected description
23520 VTAB VT%: HTAB HT%: REM ..Reset cursor
23530 RETURN
29989 REM
29990 REM ...GetCharacter...
29991 REM
30000 GET C$: REM ..Wait for keystroke
30010 RETURN
30089 REM
30090 REM ...ClearDisplayLines...
30091 REM
30100 FOR ROW = FR% TO LR%
30110 VTAB ROW: HTAB 2: PRINT SPC( 37);
30120 NEXT ROW
30130 RETURN
30189 REM
30190 REM ...DisplayBox...
30191 REM
30200 VTAB T%: HTAB L% + 1
30210 PRINT LEFT$ (TL$,R% - L% - 1);:
     REM ..Top line
30220 FOR ROW = T% + 1 TO B%: REM ..Side lines
30230 VTAB ROW: HTAB L%: PRINT SL$;
30240 HTAB R%: PRINT SL$
30250 NEXT ROW
30260 VTAB B%: HTAB L% + 1: PRINT LEFT$
     (BL$,R% - L% - 1);: REM ..Bottom line
30270 RETURN
```

Figure 10-3. Printed Mailing-List program (*continued*)

original entry program in Figure 9-10 (lines 1000-13510). Both programs use the same subroutines to display the entry form, enter a field, get an entry, get a yes-or-no response, get a field number, select and deselect a field, get a single character, clear lines on the display, and draw a box (lines 20000-30270). Table 10-1 identifies the variables used in the new version of the program lines.

The first new line the Printed Mailing-List program executes is part of the variable initialization subroutine (line 10150). It sets the page-count variable (PL%) at a high value so that when the TopPage subroutine (beginning at line 15000) is called for the first time, it will print the page title and column headings on the first page.

Table 10-1. Printed Mailing-List Program Variables

Variable	Purpose	Used on lines:
B%	Bottom row of box	1160, 11010, 30220, 30260
BEEP$	Sound console speaker	1170, 10020
BL$	Characters for bottom edge of box	10060, 30260
C$	Keystroke	1180, 20060, 20070, 20080, 20090, 20100, 21010, 21020, 21070, 21080, 22040, 22050, 22060, 22070, 30000
CITY$	Value of City field	13310, 14060
CL%	Current entry length	20020, 20040, 20050, 20060, 20070, 20090, 20100
D$	ProDOS or DOS 3.3 command prefix	10000, 14010
EF$	Characters for entry field indicator	10040, 20040
FC%( )	Field columns	10100, 10120, 10130, 23010, 23510
FD$( )	Field descriptions	10100, 10120, 10130, 23010, 23510
FIELD%	Current field number	1050, 1080, 1110, 1130, 1140, 12020, 22040, 22050, 22060, 23010, 23510
FR%	First row to clear	1130, 1190, 12030, 21090, 22080, 30100

Table 10-1. Printed Mailing-List Program Variables (*continued*)

Variable	Purpose	Used on lines:
FR%( )	Field rows	10100, 10120, 10130, 23010, 23510
HT%	Current horizontal tab position	20000, 20030, 20050, 21000, 21010, 21020, 23000, 23020, 23500, 23520
L%	Left column of box	1160, 11010, 30200, 30210, 30230, 30260
LF%	Last field number	1040, 1140, 10090, 10100, 10110, 22040, 22060
LR%	Last row to clear	1130, 1190, 12030, 21090, 22080, 30100
ML%	Maximum entry length	13100, 13200, 13300, 13400, 13500, 20040, 20090, 20100
NAME$	Value of Name field	13110, 14040
NTRY$	Current entry value	1190, 13110, 13210, 13310, 13410, 13510, 20010, 20020, 20030, 20070, 20100, 21010, 21020
PL%	Page length counter	10150, 14030, 14070, 15000, 15010, 15100
R%	Right column of box	1160, 11010, 30210, 30240, 30260
ROW	Row counter	30100, 30110, 30120, 30220, 30230, 30250
SE$	Value of State field	13410, 14060
SL$	Character for side lines of box	10080, 30230, 30240
STREET$	Value of Street field	13210, 14050
T%	Top row of box	1160, 11010, 30200, 30220
TITLE$	Title of window	11020, 11030
TL$	Characters for top edge of box	10050, 30210
VT%	Current vertical tab position	21000, 21010, 21020, 23000, 23020, 23500, 23520
W4$	Code for screen width of 40	10010
X1	Loop counter	1040, 1050, 1060, 1070, 1080, 1100, 10030, 10070, 10110, 10120, 10130, 10140, 15010, 15020
ZIP$	Value for Zip field	13510, 14060

Unlike the original program, the new program deactivates the 80-column adapter (lines 1010-1020). Also, the program title is changed to all uppercase letters, since it will be displayed in inverse style (line 11020). Remember, lowercase letters are not available in inverse style unless the 80-column adapter is active.

In addition, the new program now prints the name and address whenever the user selects field 6 (Another Record) or 7 (Quit). This requires calling the PrintRecord subroutine, which prints a name and address.

The PrintRecord subroutine prints the currently displayed name and address (lines 14000-14100). It starts by displaying an advisory message at the bottom of the entry window (line 14000). With most printers the subroutine executes so quickly that the message just flashes on the screen. Note that if the printer is off or not ready, the message **Printing...** will display until the user corrects the printer problem.

The subroutine next switches output from the screen to the accessory card in slot 1 and sets the printer line width to 80 with no display-screen echo (lines 14010 and 14020). (This overrides a width and echo setting indicated by the switches on the accessory card.) The subroutine then increments the line counter variable by 1 (line 14030) in anticipation of the line about to be printed, and calls the TopPage subroutine in case the incremented line count exceeds the page limit. After that, the subroutine prints the name and address (lines 14040-14060). If the line counter value is divisible by 5, the subroutine prints a blank line to make the report more readable (line 14070). Finally, the subroutine switches from the Super Serial Card back to the display screen, clears the advisory it displayed, and returns to the main program (lines 14080-14100).

PRINTER COMMAND CHARACTERS

Most printers have a number of special features that are activated by command characters. The command characters themselves do not print, but they affect the way printing appears. The remainder of this chapter will illustrate the use of printer command characters by discussing those listed in Tables 10-2 and 10-3, which control some of the features available on the Apple Imagewriter printer. Command characters for more advanced

Table 10-2. Some Apple Imagewriter General Command Characters

<table>
<tr><th>Command Characters</th><th>Effect</th></tr>
<tr><td>CHR$(27) + "Lnnn"</td><td>Set left margin to position nnn</td></tr>
<tr><td>CHR$(27) + "Rnnn" + "c"</td><td>Repeat character c nnn times (nnn is 001 to 999)</td></tr>
<tr><td>CHR$(8) + "c"</td><td>Backspace one character before printing character c</td></tr>
<tr><td>CHR$(27) + "r"</td><td>Reverse line feed direction (subsequent line feeds back paper up)</td></tr>
<tr><td>CHR$(27) + "f"</td><td>Forward line feed direction (subsequent line feeds advance paper)</td></tr>
<tr><td>CHR$(10)</td><td>Feed paper one line (advance one line unless reverse direction set)</td></tr>
<tr><td>CHR$(31) + "c"</td><td>Feed paper from 1 to 15 lines (c is 1, 2, 3, 4, 5, 6, 7, 8, 9, :, ;, <, =, >, or ?)</td></tr>
<tr><td>CHR$(27) + "|1"</td><td>Automatic carriage return with subsequent line feed characters</td></tr>
<tr><td>CHR$(27) + "|0"</td><td>No automatic carriage return with subsequent line feed characters</td></tr>
<tr><td>CHR$(27) + "A"</td><td>Set line spacing to 6 lines per inch (line height is 24/144-inch)</td></tr>
<tr><td>CHR$(27) + "B"</td><td>Set line spacing to 8 lines per inch (line height is 18/144-inch)</td></tr>
<tr><td>CHR$(27) + "Tnn"</td><td>Set line height to nn/144-inch lines per inch (nn is 01 to 99); each dot is 1/72-inch tall</td></tr>
<tr><td>CHR$(12)</td><td>Advance the paper to the top of the next form</td></tr>
<tr><td>CHR$(27) + "v"</td><td>Set the top-of-form at the current position</td></tr>
<tr><td>CHR$(27) + ">"</td><td>Print going left-to-right only</td></tr>
<tr><td>CHR$(27) + "<"</td><td>Print going both directions</td></tr>
<tr><td>CHR$(27) + "O"</td><td>Keep printing if paper runs out</td></tr>
<tr><td>CHR$(27) + "o"</td><td>Stop printing 1 inch before paper runs out</td></tr>
<tr><td>CHR$(24)</td><td>Cancel all unprinted characters stored in Imagewriter's memory</td></tr>
<tr><td>CHR$(27) + "c"</td><td>Cancel special features; revert to internal switch settings</td></tr>
</table>

Table 10-3. Some Apple Imagewriter Type-Style Command Characters

Command Characters	Effect
CHR$(27) + "n"	Extended (9 characters per inch)
CHR$(27) + "N"	Pica (10 characters per inch)
CHR$(27) + "E"	Elite (12 characters per inch)
CHR$(27) + "p"	Pica proportional (144 dots per inch)
CHR$(27) + "P"	Elite proportional (160 dots per inch)
CHR$(27) + "e"	Semicondensed (13.4 characters per inch)
CHR$(27) + "q"	Condensed (15 characters per inch)
CHR$(27) + "Q"	Ultracondensed (17 characters per inch)
CHR$(27) + CHR$(*n*)	Set spacing between proportional characters to *n* (*n* is 1-9)
CHR$(27) + "s" + CHR$(*n*)	With elite proportional style only, add *n* dots of spacing between adjacent characters (*n* is 1-6)
CHR$(14)	Start headline style
CHR$(15)	End headline style
CHR$(27) + "X"	Start underline style
CHR$(27) + "Y"	End underline style
CHR$(27) + "!"	Start boldface style
CHR$(27) + CHR$(34)	End boldface style
CHR$(27) + "D" + CHR$(1) + CHR$(0)	Slash zeros
CHR$(27) + "Z" + CHR$(1) + CHR$(0)	Don't slash zeros
CHR$(27) + "c"	Cancel all special styles and sizes; revert to internal switch settings

features are also available; consult the Imagewriter manual for details.

You send the printer a command character the same way you send it any regular character: with a PRINT statement. The simplest way to generate many command characters is with the

CHR$ function. For example, you can instruct the printer to back up instead of advancing after printing a line. You do this by "printing" the pair of command characters CHR$(27) and CHR$(114) (or CHR$(27) + "r"). To go forward again, you "print" command characters CHR$(27) and CHR$(102) (or CHR$(27) + "f"). The following program uses this feature to strike a word through with hyphens.

```
]10 REV$ = CHR$ (27) + CHR$ (114):
    REM ..Reverse line feeding
]20 FWD$ = CHR$ (27) + CHR$ (102):
    REM ..Forward line feeding
]30 D$ = CHR$ (4): REM ..ProDOS/DOS command prefix
]40 SSC$ = CHR$ (9): REM ..Super Serial
    card command prefix
]100 PRINT D$;"PR#1": REM ..Switch to printer
]110 PRINT "This is a demonstration of strikeout"
]120 PRINT REV$: REM ..Back up a line
]130 PRINT "                                       ---------
    ";FWD$
]190 PRINT SSC$;"R": REM ..Switch to display
]200 END
```

Backing up the paper does have its problems, however. You cannot count on the pin-feed sprockets to reverse accurately. You must push the paper release lever to the friction feed (rear) position. Here are the results:

This is a demonstration of ~~strikeout~~

Other command characters enable you to use different type styles and sizes. Figure 10-4 shows some of the possibilities. Figure 10-5 lists the program that prints Figure 10-4.

Setting Page Length

Wouldn't it be great if the printer would automatically skip over the perforation between sheets of continuous paper? Long program listings would then have margins at the top and bottom of each page. This can be done on an Imagewriter by using several command characters (not listed in Tables 10-2 and 10-3) that

```
Imagewriter Type Samples

Extended prints 72 characters per eight-inch line.
Pica prints 80 characters per eight-inch line.
Elite prints 96 characters per eight-inch line.
Pica proportional prints different width characters at 1152 dots per eight-inch line.
Elite proportional prints different width characters at 1280 dots per eight-inch line.
Semicondensed prints 107 characters per eight-inch line.
Condensed prints 120 characters per eight-inch line.
Ultracondensed prints 136 characters per eight-inch line.

Extended Headline
Pica Headline
Elite Headline
Pica Proportional Headline
Elite Proportional Headline
Semicondensed Headline
Condensed Headline
Ultracondensed Headline

This is boldface Elite
This is underlined Elite
This is underlined boldface Elite
```

Figure 10-4. Sample Apple Imagewriter type styles

```
10 REM ..Set up command characters..
20 REM
30 D$ = CHR$ (4): REM ..ProDOS/DOS command prefix
40 SSC$ = CHR$ (9): REM ..Super Serial Card prefix
50 ESC$ = CHR$ (27): REM .."Escape" character
60 EX$ = ESC$ + "n": REM ..Extended
70 PN$ = ESC$ + "N": REM ..Pica
80 EN$ = ESC$ + "E": REM ..Elite
90 PP$ = ESC$ + "p": REM ..Pica proportional
100 EP$ = ESC$ + "P": REM ..Elite proportional
110 SC$ = ESC$ + "e": REM ..Semicondensed
120 C$ = ESC$ + "q": REM ..Condensed
130 UC$ = ESC$ + "Q": REM ..Ultracondensed
140 HS$ = CHR$ (14): REM ..Headline start
150 HE$ = CHR$ (15): REM ..Headline end
160 BS$ = ESC$ + "!": REM ..Boldface start
170 BE$ = ESC$ + CHR$ (34): REM ..Boldface end
```

Figure 10-5. Sample Type-Style Print program

```
180 US$ = ESC$ + "X": REM ..Underline start
190 UE$ = ESC$ + "Y": REM ..Underline end
200 CF$ = ESC$ + "c": REM ..Cancel all special
    features
1000 PRINT CHR$ (21): REM ..Deactivate 80-col.
    card
1010 PRINT D$;"PR#1": REM ..Switch to printer
1020 PRINT SSC$;"132N": REM ..Line width &
    display off
1030 PRINT HS$;BS$;EX$;" ";US$;"Imagewriter
    Type Samples";CF$
1040 PRINT: PRINT
1050 PRINT EX$;"Extended prints 72 characters
    per eight-inch line."
1060 PRINT PN$;"Pica prints 80 characters
    per eight-inch line."
1070 PRINT EN$;"Elite prints 96 characters per
    eight-inch line."
1080 PRINT PP$;"Pica proportional prints different
    width characters at 1152 dots per eight-
    inch line."
1090 PRINT EP$;"Elite proportional prints
    different width characters at 1280 dots per
    eight-inch line."
1100 PRINT SC$;"Semicondensed prints 107
    characters per eight-inch line."
1110 PRINT C$;"Condensed prints 120 characters per
    eight-inch line."
1120 PRINT UC$;"Ultracondensed prints 136
    characters per eight-inch line."
1130 PRINT: PRINT HS$
1140 PRINT EX$;"Extended Headline"
1150 PRINT PN$;"Pica Headline"
1160 PRINT EN$;"Elite Headline"
1170 PRINT PP$;"Pica Proportional Headline"
1180 PRINT EP$;"Elite Proportional Headline"
1190 PRINT SC$;"Semicondensed Headline"
1200 PRINT C$;"Condensed Headline"
1210 PRINT UC$;"Ultracondensed Headline"
1220 PRINT HE$: PRINT
1230 PRINT BS$;EN$;"This is boldface Elite";BE$
1240 PRINT US$;"This is underlined Elite"
1250 PRINT BS$;"This is underlined boldface
    Elite";BE$;UE$
1260 PRINT SSC$;"R": REM ..Switch back to display
    screen
1270 END
```

Figure 10-5. Sample Type-Style Print program (*continued*)

usually set vertical tabs. The following program shows how:

```
]100 PRINT CHR$ (21): REM ..Deactivate
     80-col. card
]110 PRINT "** PRINTER PAGE LENGTH SETUP **"
]120 PRINT
130 INPUT "Leave how many lines blank? ";MARGIN
]140 PRINT CHR$ (4);"PR#1":
     REM ..Switch to printer
]150 PRINT CHR$ (9);"80N":
     REM ..No screen echo
]160 FOR X = 1 TO 132:A$ = A$ + "@": NEXT X:
     REM ..String of @ characters
]170 PRINT CHR$ (29);"A@"; LEFT$ (A$,2 * (64 -
     MARGIN));"C@";       LEFT$ (A$,2 *
     MARGIN);"A@";  CHR$ (30);
]180 PRINT CHR$ (9);"R": REM ..Switch to display
]190 PRINT
]200 PRINT "Load paper into the Imagewriter"
]210 PRINT INT (MARGIN / 2 + 0.5);" lines below
     the top edge."
]220 PRINT "Text will be vertically centered,
     with"
]230 PRINT 66 - MARGIN;" lines per page."
]240 END
```

The program begins by deactivating the 80-column adapter (if any) and inputting the number of lines to leave blank between pages (lines 100-140). Next the program switches to the printer and turns off output to the display screen (lines 140 and 150). Then the program prints the Imagewriter command characters that set the page length and margin between pages (lines 160 and 170). Finally, the program switches back to the display screen and displays some instructions (lines 180 to 230).

The page length remains in effect until you turn off the Imagewriter or run the program again. PR# commands have no effect, since they affect the serial card, not the printer.

Programming Disk Data Files 11

Did you notice the serious flaw in the mailing-list program that was presented in the last two chapters? In both versions of the program, each new name and address you enter erases all memory of the one entered before it. The program in Chapter 10 solves this problem by printing out each name and address as you enter it, but if you want to print the list again, you must reenter it. You could change the program to store several names and addresses in arrays, but before long you would use up all of the Apple II's memory. In addition, the names and addresses would vanish the minute you turned the power off. A disk drive takes care of this problem. Instead of throwing away information after it is entered, a program can save it on a disk for later use.

Generally, the same BASIC commands can be used for storing and retrieving data on disks whether you use the ProDOS operating system or the DOS 3.3 operating system. Some differences exist, but the two operating systems are more alike than not. Unless stated otherwise, the examples and explanations in this chapter apply to both operating systems.

Data File Structure

The computer stores data on a disk in *files*, much as you might store information in a filing cabinet. Each disk is the equivalent of a filing cabinet, and each disk file is the equivalent of a file folder in the cabinet. A disk can contain one file or many, just as a filing cabinet can contain one folder or many. A disk file can have nothing in it, as can a file folder.

Data files are further divided into *records* and *fields*. You might think of a record as a piece of paper in a file folder, and a field as one line of information on the piece of paper. There can be any number of records in a data file, as long as the disk has room to hold them all. A record can have any assortment of fields, although all records in the same file generally have the same configuration. The number of fields, their sequence, and often their lengths are all the same from one record to the next. For example, one file might contain a mailing list. Each record in the mailing-list file would contain the same kind of information: a name and address. The same five fields would make up every record: name, street, city, state, and ZIP code. Every record has the same fields; only the values of the fields vary.

Therefore, two things define a file's structure: the configuration of fields in a record and the number of records the file contains. Thus, to describe a file's structure, you can usually just list the fields contained in one record and state the number of records in the file. The result is called a *file layout* and is shown in Figure 11-1. The file layout shows the description of each field, its length, and the variable name used to hold the value of each field in a BASIC program.

File Accessing Methods

You can locate a particular record in a disk file in either of two ways. The simplest method is called *sequential access*, because the program starts at the beginning of the file and reads each record in turn until it finds the one it wants. The alternative, *random access*, lets the program access records by number in any order.

Each accessing method has its advantages and disadvantages. Sequential access is somewhat easier to program than random access and tends to use less disk space. In operation, however, sequential access is usually slower than random access, especially if you need a record near the end of a large file. Also, updating existing records is either difficult or impossible in a sequential-access file. In a random-access file, updating records is easy.

Every record in a random-access file must have the same length, so each field in a record gets a fixed amount of space. Your program must abbreviate long values to fit in the space allotted. To minimize the loss of data inherent in abbreviation,

FILE LAYOUT

File Name	Record Size	No. of Records
ADDRESS	76	——

Description: Random-access mailing list.

Variable	Field Description	Max. Size	Comments
NA$	Name	20	
SR$	Street	20	
CI$	City	20	
ST$	State	2	
ZI$	ZIP Code	9	

Figure 11-1. File layout for a sample mailing list file

it's a good idea to make the records long enough for the largest likely field values.

The lengths of records in a sequential-access file can vary. In this case, your program need not adjust field values to fit within a fixed length.

Opening Data Files

To access a particular field in a record, a program must first open the file. Then it can locate the record, transfer it from disk to the Apple II's memory, and finally isolate the desired field as the value of a variable. Writing data to a file is similar, but in this case the program transfers data in the other direction, from the Apple II's memory to the disk file.

The OPEN command opens a disk file. It is allowed only in programmed mode, and it must be in a PRINT statement and be preceded by the usual ProDOS and DOS 3.3 prefix character (ASCII code 4). Here is an example:

```
]150 PRINT CHR$(4);"OPEN SAMPLE"
```

This opens the disk file named SAMPLE on the currently active disk drive. The CHR$(4) function generates the character that tells the Apple II to execute the operating system command that follows, and not to display or print it as text. If the file does not exist, the operating system creates a new file entry in the disk directory. You can use the CAT or CATALOG command to verify that the file has been created.

With ProDOS, you can specify slot and drive numbers. With DOS 3.3, you can also specify a volume number. The following example illustrates:

```
]150 PRINT CHR$(4);"OPEN SAMPLE,S6,D2"
```

ProDOS looks for a simple file name (no directory path specified) in the volume directory. If the program has used the PREFIX command to set up a pathname prefix, however, ProDOS combines the file name you specify in the OPEN command with the prefix to form a complete pathname. You can also specify a full or partial pathname as part of an OPEN command. The following example illustrates:

```
]1000 SF$ = "/STUDIO/PRODUCER/STUNT/WOMEN"
]1010 PRINT CHR$(4);"OPEN ";SF$
```

Warning: Once you open a ProDOS file, you must refer to it by exactly the same name throughout the rest of your program, even if you later change the prefix with the PREFIX command. For example, suppose the prefix is STUDIO/PRODUCER/STUNT and your program opens a file named WOMEN. The program must continue to use the name WOMEN for that file, even if the program later changes the prefix to STUDIO/PRODUCER/DIRECTORS. However, the next time you open the file, you can change the way you refer to it.

File Buffers

ProDOS and DOS 3.3 reduce the number of times they access the disk by transferring data to and from the disk in blocks, rather than one field or record at a time. Both operating systems set aside part of memory for transfer areas, called *file buffers.* When a program opens a file, the operating system assigns the file its own buffer.

Normally, ProDOS can allocate space in memory for as many as eight file buffers, which means there can be as many as eight files open simultaneously. DOS 3.3 normally allocates memory space for three file buffers, although you can raise this limit to as high as 16 with the MAXFILES command, as described later in this chapter.

Closing Data Files

Generally, ProDOS and DOS 3.3 manage the file buffers automatically, and you do not have to be concerned with them. But when a program finishes writing to a file, there will probably be some data left in the file buffer that the operating system has not written to the disk. The program must somehow force the operating system to write out the final buffer contents. Closing a file does that. At the same time it updates the disk directory with changes to the file extents and other statistics kept there. Therefore, when a program finishes with a file, it must close the file or risk losing part of the file's contents.

The CLOSE command closes a disk file. In programmed mode, it must be in a PRINT statement and be preceded by the usual prefix character (ASCII code 4). Here is an example:

```
]290 PRINT CHR$(4);"CLOSE SAMPLE"
```

This closes the disk file named SAMPLE on the currently active disk drive. The CHR$(4) function generates the character that tells the Apple II to execute the operating system command that follows it and not to display or print it as text. If the file does not exist, the operating system ignores the command.

A single CLOSE command can close all open files. To do that, use just the command word with no mention of a file name. The following example illustrates:

```
]290 PRINT CHR$(4);"CLOSE"
```

Slot and drive numbers are not allowed with either form of the CLOSE command. DOS 3.3 also does not allow volume numbers. The operating system knows where the file is, since the file is already open.

SEQUENTIAL-ACCESS FILES

BASIC programs can easily do three things with a sequential-access data file: save data starting at the beginning of a new file, save data starting at the end of an existing file, or read data from an existing file. It is also possible to rewrite a record in the same place in the same file, but this is a risky procedure with sequential access.

Writing to Sequential Files

Information is sent to the disk drives in the same way it is sent to the screen or printer: via the PRINT statement. Anything you can print can be put in a disk file. In fact, you might visualize a sequential file as a display screen, or more accurately, as paper in a printer.

When you print something in a file, the operating system updates an internal pointer that points to the next location on the disk surface where data will be stored, just as a printer advances paper to the next line. Since a sequential file pointer can only be moved forward, you need to reissue the OPEN command to move the pointer back to the beginning of the file.

Before you can output data to a disk file, you must first use a WRITE command to tell ProDOS or DOS 3.3 that subsequent PRINT statements are to write to the file instead of the display screen. For sequential files, the WRITE command looks like this:

```
]200 PRINT CHR$(4);"WRITE SAMPLE"
```

After you issue the WRITE command, subsequent output is directed to the named file. DOS 3.3 outputs even the prompt messages of INPUT statements and the text of error messages to an open disk file. If an error occurs, the program stops, the WRITE command is canceled, and you see the cursor and the BASIC prompt character on the screen.

In contrast to DOS 3.3, ProDOS does not output INPUT statement prompts or error messages to a disk file. However, the occurrence of an error does stop the program. Any time the program stops before closing ProDOS files it opened (except when you press (CONTROL-RESET), the message **FILE(S) STILL OPEN** is displayed. You should type a simple CLOSE command in immediate mode to close all open files.

The WRITE command must be in a PRINT statement and preceded by the usual prefix character (ASCII code 4). If you issue the WRITE command in immediate mode, you will see the error message **NOT DIRECT COMMAND**.

The following program opens a file (or creates it if it does not already exist), stores data on the file, and closes the file. Notice that the operating system command prefix character (ASCII code 4) only prefixes operating system commands, not the data to be stored.

```
]100 D$ = CHR$ (4): REM ..ProDOS/DOS
     command prefix
]150 PRINT D$;"OPEN SAMPLE"
]200 PRINT D$;"WRITE SAMPLE"
]210 PRINT "This text will be stored in the file"
]290 PRINT D$;"CLOSE SAMPLE"
]500 END
```

You may insert as many PRINT statements as you like between lines 200 and 290. They may output text, numbers, or the values of variables in any combination. All data will be written to the file. With DOS 3.3 you must be careful not to output to a file while a FLASH or INVERSE statement is in effect, as DOS 3.3 does not handle flashing or inverse characters correctly. However, ProDOS converts inverse and flashing characters to normal characters.

Each time you run this program, whatever is in the PRINT

statements will overwrite and erase data already stored in the file. If you output fewer characters than are already in the file, the tail end of the previous data will remain, following the new data.

One way to circumvent the problem of leftover data is to erase the old file before you store new data in it. The DELETE command (in the usual PRINT statement context) may be incorporated into the program just prior to the OPEN command. Every time the program is run, the file is deleted and then recreated by the OPEN command.

An error occurs if you try to run the program when the file named in the DELETE command is not on the disk. You can prevent this by adding another OPEN command and a matching CLOSE command just before the DELETE command. This is what happens:

- The first OPEN command creates a file if one does not already exist, and the matching CLOSE command closes it.
- The DELETE command erases the file, no matter when it was created.
- The second OPEN command creates a new, empty file.

Try changing the last example as just described. The modified program looks like this:

```
]100 D$ = CHR$ (4): REM ..ProDOS/DOS
     command prefix
]110 PRINT D$;"OPEN SAMPLE": REM ..Create the
     file if necessary
]120 PRINT D$;"CLOSE SAMPLE"
]130 PRINT D$;"DELETE SAMPLE": REM ..Delete
     the file
]150 PRINT D$;"OPEN SAMPLE"
]200 PRINT D$;"WRITE SAMPLE"
]210 PRINT "This text will be stored in the file"
]290 PRINT D$;"CLOSE SAMPLE"
]500 END
```

This new program would be more useful if it let you input the text to be stored, instead of having to add PRINT statements between lines 200 and 290. Here is one approach:

```
]100 D$ = CHR$ (4): REM ..ProDOS/DOS command
     prefix
]110 PRINT D$;"OPEN SAMPLE": REM ..Create the
     file if necessary
```

```
]120 PRINT D$;"CLOSE SAMPLE"
]130 PRINT D$;"DELETE SAMPLE": REM ..Delete
     the file
]150 PRINT D$;"OPEN SAMPLE"
]160 PRINT "Enter some text to save: ";:
     REM ..Entry prompt
]170 INPUT "";T$: REM ..Supress question mark
]180 IF T$ = "END" THEN 290
]200 PRINT D$;"WRITE SAMPLE"
]210 PRINT T$
]230 GOTO 160
]290 PRINT D$;"CLOSE SAMPLE"
]500 END
```

This program accepts a string value to be saved on disk (lines 160 and 170). The program ends if the word END (which must be capitalized) is input (line 180). Otherwise, it writes the entry to the file (lines 200 and 210) and branches back to get another string for output.

A serious error occurs the second time line 160 is executed. Remember that the WRITE command directs all output to the disk file. This includes the prompt **Enter some text to save:** output by the PRINT statement on line 160. You must cancel the WRITE command before displaying or printing anything not intended for the disk. Any operating system command will cancel the WRITE command, but the safest one to use is the *null command*, which is the usual operating system prefix character (ASCII code 4) by itself. Add the following line to the program:

```
]225 PRINT D$
```

With this change complete, you now have a program that allows you to store any amount of text up to the maximum amount the disk will hold.

Reading Sequential Files

Just as output can be directed to the disk, input can be accepted from a disk file. The READ command identifies a disk file as the source for data input. For sequential files the READ command looks like this:

```
]360 PRINT D$;"READ SAMPLE"
```

The READ command must be in a PRINT statement, preceded by the usual prefix character (ASCII code 4). If you issue the

READ command in immediate mode, you will see the error message **NOT DIRECT COMMAND**.

After the READ command has been executed, subsequent INPUT statements receive data from the specified file until another operating system command, or an error, cancels the READ command.

The following program will display everything the last example saved on the disk file named SAMPLE:

```
]100 D$ = CHR$ (4): REM ..ProDOS/DOS
     command prefix
]350 PRINT D$;"OPEN SAMPLE"
]360 PRINT D$;"READ SAMPLE"
]400 INPUT T$
]410 PRINT T$
]420 GOTO 400
]500 END
```

The example contains a small loop that reads a string from the disk with an INPUT statement and uses the familiar PRINT statement to display it on the screen (lines 400-420). This PRINT statement does not output to the disk file because there is no WRITE command in effect. The program would loop indefinitely if the supply of data were endless, but eventually the INPUT statement has nothing left to input. The message **END OF DATA** appears; the program stops with the message **BREAK IN 400**, and with ProDOS, **FILE(S) STILL OPEN**.

Recognizing the End of a File

A program should not display error messages and stop under circumstances as predictable as reaching the end of data in a file. Instead, the program should recognize the end of data and branch to a CLOSE command.

Applesoft has a special statement that allows you to intercept an error before Applesoft displays an error message and halts program execution. The ONERR GOTO statement stipulates a line number to which Applesoft will branch upon detecting an error. Here is an example:

```
]90 ONERR GOTO 8000
```

Most programmers place a statement like this one in the first part of a program and put a special routine at the specified line number to handle the errors that occur. The type of error can be determined with function PEEK(222), which produces an error code number. For example, the error number for an end-of-data error is 5. Appendix B includes a list of all error code numbers.

The error-handling routine can take different action depending on the error number. But sometimes an error number alone is not enough. For example, a program that uses more than one data file may encounter an end-of-data error on any file, and it may need to handle each error differently. The program can determine by using PEEK(219)*256+PEEK(218), the line on which an error occurred. By knowing the line number, the program can differentiate between errors that have the same code number.

The error-handling routine can end with a regular GOTO statement, an ON GOTO statement, an END statement, or a RESUME statement. The RESUME statement causes a branch back to the statement where the error occurred.

Use the statement POKE 216,0 to deactivate the ONERR GOTO statement so that Applesoft will halt the program and print an error message when an error occurs.

The following program shows how to use error interception to detect the end of a file:

```
]90 ONERR GOTO 8000
]100 D$ = CHR$ (4): REM ..ProDOS command prefix
]350 PRINT D$;"OPEN SAMPLE"
]360 PRINT D$;"READ SAMPLE"
]400 INPUT T$
]410 PRINT T$
]420 GOTO 400
]500 END
]8000 REM ...Error Handling Routine...
]8010 EN = PEEK (222): REM ..Get error number
]8020 EL = PEEK (219) * 256 + PEEK (218):
      REM ..Error line
]8030 IF EN = 5 AND EL = 400 THEN 8200:
      REM ..End of file SAMPLE?
]8090 REM ..No--unexpected error occurred
]8100 POKE 216,0: REM ..Turn off error trapping
]8110 RESUME: REM ..Re-execute error
]8200 PRINT D$;"CLOSE SAMPLE": REM ..End of
      file found
]8210 GOTO 500
```

This program adds an ONERR GOTO statement and error-handling routine to the previous example. When an error occurs, it is intercepted (line 90), and execution branches to line 8000. There the program determines the error code number and the line number at which the error occurred (lines 8010 and 8020). If an end-of-data error occurs on line 400, the program closes the file and ends (lines 8030, 8200, and 8210). Otherwise, the program disables error interception and reexecutes the statement that caused the error (lines 8100 and 8110). This causes the error to occur again without being intercepted, and a standard error message appears.

For Integer BASIC programmers, there is a way to recognize the end of a file without an ONERR GOTO statement. Here is how it works. Any program that writes to a file must save a special trailer record just before closing the file, giving the trailer record a value that is not likely to occur or impossible as real data. A program that reads the file later can check each value it reads for the special trailer record value. When that value comes up, the program knows the end of the file has been reached. This method also works in Applesoft programs.

Error Interception Problems

Except on an Enhanced Apple IIe, there are some irregularities in the performance of the ONERR GOTO and RESUME statements. When the TRACE command is active, or in a program with a PRINT statement, the 43rd error interception stops the program and passes control of the Apple II to the Machine Language Monitor. This does not happen, however, if the errors are intercepted in INPUT statements and resolved with RESUME statements. But if the INPUT errors are resolved with GOTO instead of RESUME statements, the program stops and passes control of the Apple II to the Machine Language Monitor after the 86th INPUT error. From the Machine Language Monitor, you must type CONTROL-C and press RETURN to get back to BASIC.

Also, a program that uses the RESUME statement after intercepting errors in GET statements will lock up the Apple II if two consecutive GET errors occur without an intervening successful GET. To regain keyboard control, type CONTROL-RESET. On some standard Apple II machines you then must type CONTROL-C and press the RETURN key in order to get back to BASIC.

You can get around some of these irregularities by calling a short machine language subroutine after intercepting each error, as part of your error-handling routine. The machine language subroutine is not built into the Apple II, but your BASIC program can put it in memory with POKE statements. It can usually reside between memory locations 768 and 777. The following program lines will put it there:

```
]50 REM ..Set up the fix for ONERR GOTO
]60 DATA 104,168,104,166,223,154,72,152,72,96
]70 FOR ML = 768 TO 777: READ MC: POKE ML,MC:
    NEXT ML
```

The DATA statement (line 60) contains the necessary machine language instructions to fix some of the error-interception irregularities. The FOR-NEXT loop reads the machine language instructions from the DATA statement and puts them in memory locations 768 to 777 with a POKE statement (line 70). After executing the lines above, a program must call the machine language subroutine with a CALL 768 statement each time it intercepts an error.

Separating Fields

In order for INPUT statements to read values from a disk file correctly, the values must be separated from each other on the disk file. If they are not separated, an INPUT statement will run neighboring values together. Consider what happens in the following Applesoft example:

```
]10 D$ = CHR$ (4): REM ..ProDOS prefix character
]100 PRINT D$;"OPEN TEST1"
]110 PRINT D$;"WRITE TEST1"
]120 PRINT "CARBON";6;12.011
]130 PRINT D$;"CLOSE TEST1"
]140 PRINT D$;"OPEN TEST1"
]150 PRINT D$;"READ TEST1"
]160 INPUT ELEMENT$
]170 PRINT ELEMENT$
]200 PRINT D$;"CLOSE TEST1"
]210 END
```

Line 120 looks as if it would write three values out to disk file TEST1, and line 160 looks as if it would read back the first value,

CARBON, and display it on the screen. In fact, this is what happens:

```
]RUN
CARBON612.011
]▒
```

The PRINT statement (line 120) writes three values, but the semicolons that separate them cause them to run together in the file. When the INPUT statement tries to read the first one back (line 160), all the values come back combined into one value.

In Applesoft, fields are separated on disk by a comma or carriage return character. Carriage return characters also separate fields in Integer BASIC, but commas can separate only numbers, not text fields. There are many ways to make sure a carriage return character occurs between values. One easy way is to use a separate PRINT statement for every field value, like this:

```
]120 PRINT "CARBON"
]122 PRINT 6
]124 PRINT 12.011
```

Remember that a PRINT statement always generates a carriage return character as its last action, unless it ends with a semicolon.

Appending Sequential Files

To add data to the end of a file, you must first find the end of the file. You could read each item in the file until you reach the last one, but that can be very time-consuming with large files. The APPEND command does the work for you.

The APPEND command places the file pointer at the first unused character beyond the end of the file. If you read after the APPEND command has been issued, you'll get an **END OF DATA** error. If you write after an APPEND, the new data will be added to the end of the data already in the file.

The APPEND command takes the place of an OPEN command; however, there are some important differences between APPEND and OPEN:

- APPEND places the pointer at the end of the file. OPEN places the pointer at the beginning of the file.
- With ProDOS, APPEND automatically issues a WRITE command, so the next output goes directly to the file. To can-

cel the WRITE command, use the null ProDOS command, PRINT CHR$(4), or its equivalent.

- With DOS 3.3, APPEND requires that the file already exist. If it does not, the error message **FILE NOT FOUND** appears. Unlike OPEN, APPEND will not create a new file.

The format for the APPEND command is the same as for the OPEN command. Here is an example:

```
]110 PRINT CHR$(4);"APPEND SAMPLE"
```

Drive and slot numbers are optional in ProDOS and DOS 3.3, as is a volume number in DOS 3.3.

Skipping Past Fields

Another useful command is the POSITION command. The POSITION command moves the pointer *forward* (never backward) by the specified number of fields relative to the current position of the file pointer. With ProDOS, the POSITION command looks like this:

```
]160 PRINT CHR$ (4);"POSITION SAMPLE,F30"
```

The letter F indicates relative field; the number after the letter F is the number of fields to skip. Every field ends with a carriage return character, so the POSITION command above counts 30 carriage return characters beyond the current position and moves the file pointer there. If you specify only F, the pointer is not moved.

With DOS 3.3, the POSITION command works the same as with ProDOS, but you specify the relative field number with the letter R instead of the letter F. (The letter R happens to work with ProDOS, too.) Here is an example:

```
]160 PRINT CHR$(4);"POSITION SAMPLE,R30"
```

POSITION examines the file character by character, starting from the current pointer position. If there are not enough carriage return characters, the **END OF DATA** error message is displayed immediately. The error occurs whether or not an INPUT statement is executed.

A file must be open before it can be referenced by a POSITION command. Opening a file with the OPEN command sets the pointer to the beginning of the file.

Remember, just like any other ProDOS or DOS 3.3 command, POSITION cancels both the READ and WRITE commands. Be sure to execute POSITION before issuing a READ or WRITE command, not after doing so.

Since a POSITION command is usually followed by a READ or WRITE command, the program would be much simpler if you could specify the field number as part of the READ or WRITE command. In fact, ProDOS allows this shortcut. The following example illustrates:

```
]360 PRINT CHR$ (4);"READ SAMPLE,F";RECRD%
```

This READ command skips ahead the number of fields determined by the value of variable RECRD%. The next INPUT statement will read the field at that point.

Be careful if you use the POSITION command before a WRITE command, or the F option with a ProDOS WRITE command, in a sequential file. You can use either technique to position to an existing field and then write a new value over the old one, but you risk disrupting the file in the process. The new value you write must be exactly the same length as the old value it replaces. If the new value is shorter, you'll end up with an extra carriage return character (and hence an extra field) in the file. If it is longer, you'll write over part of the following field.

USING SEQUENTIAL-ACCESS FILES

Sequential access is adequate for files whose contents do not change, or for files that have new records added to them only from time to time. A few changes made to the Mailing-List Entry program presented in Chapter 9 (Figure 9-10) will turn it into a useful sequential-access program, one that creates a mailing-list file on a ProDOS disk. Then a separate program can read the mailing-list file and print the names and addresses on plain paper, labels, or envelopes.

Mailing-List Creation Program

Figure 11-2 shows the changes (shaded in gray) required to make the Mailing-List Entry program in Figure 9-10 create a

```
900 ONERR GOTO 8000: REM ..Enable error trapping
1000 GOSUB 10000: REM ..Initialize variables
1010 PRINT: PRINT D$;"PR#3": REM ..Activate
     enhanced video
1020 PRINT W4$;: REM ..Set display width to 40
1025 GOSUB 16000: REM ..Display welcome and
     set up disk
1030 GOSUB 11000: REM ..DisplayEntryWindow
1040 FOR X1 = 1 TO LF%
1050 FIELD% = X1: GOSUB 23500: REM ..Display
     field description
1060 NEXT X1
1063 CHANGED = 0: REM ..Reset changes-made flag
1070 FOR X1 = 1 TO 5: REM ..Enter all fields
1080 FIELD% = X1
1090 GOSUB 23000: GOSUB 12000: GOSUB 23500:
     REM ..SelectField:EnterField:DeselectField
1100 NEXT X1
1110 FIELD% = 6: GOSUB 23000: REM ..SelectField
1120 GOSUB 22000: REM ..GetFieldNumber
1130 IF FIELD% = 6 THEN GOSUB 17000:FR% = 4:
     LR% = 8: GOSUB 30100: GOSUB 23500: GOTO 1040:
     REM ..If field=6, WriteRecord, blank last
     entries, deselect and get another
1140 IF FIELD% < LF% THEN GOSUB 12000: GOTO 1120:
     REM ..EnterField
1150 REM ...Quit?...
1160 T% = 12:L% = 4:B% = 17:R% = 37: GOSUB 30200:
     REM ..DisplayBox
1170 VTAB 14: HTAB 5: PRINT BEEP$;"Are you sure
     you want to quit?";
1180 VTAB 16: HTAB 8:C$ = "Y": GOSUB 21000:
     REM ..GetYesNo
1190 IF NTRY$ = "NO" THEN FR% = 12:LR% = 17:
     GOSUB 30100: GOSUB 23000: GOTO 1120:
     REM ..If no, erase box, restore field, and
     get another field
1200 GOSUB 17000: REM ..WriteRecord
1210 PRINT: PRINT D$;"CLOSE"
1220 HOME: VTAB 12: HTAB 8: PRINT "End of
     Mailing-List Entry"
1230 VTAB 23: HTAB 1: END
7989 REM
7990 REM ...ErrorHandler...
7991 REM
8000 EN = PEEK (222): REM ..Error number
8010 EL = PEEK (219) * 256 + PEEK (218):
     REM ..Error line
```

Figure 11-2. Sequential-access Mailing-List Creation program

```
8040 PRINT BEEP$;BEEP$;
8050 FR% = 9:LR% = 14: GOSUB 30100:
     REM ..ClearDisplayLines
8060 T% = 9:L% = 4:B% = 14:R% = 37: GOSUB 30200:
     REM ..DisplayBox
8070 VTAB 11: REM ..Position for error message
8080 ON EN GOTO 8100, 8100, 8500, 8200, 8100,
     8400, 8400, 8500, 8600, 8700
8100 HTAB 5: PRINT "Unexpected error
     (code ";EN;")."
8110 PRINT
8120 HTAB 5: PRINT "Press RETURN to quit. ";
8130 GOSUB 30000: REM ..GetChar
8140 IF C$ < > CHR$ (13) THEN 8130: REM ..Wait
     for RETURN
8150 GOTO 1210: REM ..Quit
8200 HTAB 5: PRINT "Disk is write-protected."
8210 HTAB 5: PRINT "Remove tab or use
     another disk"
8220 GOTO 8120
8400 HTAB 5: PRINT "Volume not found."
8410 HTAB 5: PRINT "Check prefix and drive."
8420 GOTO 8120
8500 HTAB 5: PRINT "Disk or drive error."
8510 HTAB 5: PRINT "Check disk, drive,
     and prefix."
8520 GOTO 8120
8600 HTAB 5: PRINT "Disk full."
8610 HTAB 5: PRINT "Last few records may
     be missing."
8620 GOTO 8120
8700 HTAB 5: PRINT "File ";FILE$;" locked."
8710 PRINT: GOTO 8120
9989 REM
9990 REM ...InitializeVariables...
9991 REM
10000 D$ = CHR$ (4): REM ..ProDOS/DOS 3.3 prefix
10010 W4$ = CHR$ (17): REM ..Display width 40
10020 BEEP$ = CHR$ (07): REM ..Beep char.
10030 FOR X1 = 1 TO 40
10040 EF$ = EF$ + ".": REM ..Entry field chars.
10050 TL$ = TL$ + "_": REM ..Top line chars.
10060 BL$ = BL$ + "‾": REM ..Bottom line chars.
10070 NEXT X1
10080 SL$ = "|": REM ..Side line chars.
10090 LF% = 7: REM ..Last field number
10100 DIM FR%(2,LF%),FC%(2,LF%),FD$(2,LF%)
```

Figure 11-2. Sequential-access Mailing-List Creation program (*continued*)

```
10110 FOR X1 = 1 TO LF%: REM ..Read field
      locations and descriptions
10120 READ FR%(1,X1),FC%(1,X1),FD$(1,X1)
10130 READ FR%(2,X1),FC%(2,X1),FD$(2,X1)
10140 NEXT X1
10170 FILE$ = "MAILING.LIST"
10200 RETURN
10489 REM
10490 REM ...Field Descriptions and Locations...
10491 REM
10500 DATA 4,3," 1. <NAME:>   "
10510 DATA 4,3," 1.  Name:    "
10520 DATA 5,3," 2. <STREET:>"
10530 DATA 5,3," 2.  Street: "
10540 DATA 6,3," 3. <CITY:>   "
10550 DATA 6,3," 3.  City:    "
10560 DATA 7,3," 4. <STATE:> "
10570 DATA 7,3," 4.  State:  "
10580 DATA 8,3," 5. <ZIP:>    "
10590 DATA 8,3," 5.  Zip:     "
10600 DATA 11,3," 6. <ANOTHER RECORD>"
10610 DATA 11,3," 6.  Another Record "
10620 DATA 12,3," 7. <QUIT>"
10630 DATA 12,3," 7.  Quit "
10989 REM
10990 REM ...DisplayEntryWindow...
10991 REM
11000 HOME
11010 T% = 1:L% = 1:B% = 22:R% = 39: GOSUB 30200:
      REM ..DisplayBox
11020 TITLE$ = "Mailing-List Entry"
11030 INVERSE: VTAB 1: HTAB (40 - LEN (TITLE$))
      / 2: PRINT TITLE$;: NORMAL: REM ..Display
      title
11040 RETURN
11989 REM
11990 REM ...EnterField...
11991 REM
12000 VTAB 20: HTAB 3: PRINT "Enter the selected
      field."
12010 HTAB 3: PRINT "Then press RETURN to confirm
      entry.";
12020 ON FIELD% GOSUB 13100,13200,
      13300,13400,13500
12030 FR% = 19:LR% = 21: GOSUB 30100:
      REM ..ClearDisplayLines
12040 IF NTRY$ < > "" THEN CHANGED = 1:
```

Figure 11-2. Sequential-access Mailing-List Creation program (*continued*)

```
      REM ..Set changes-made flag
12050 RETURN
13089 REM
13090 REM ...EnterName...
13100 ML% = 20: VTAB 4: HTAB 17: GOSUB 20000
13110 NAME$ = NTRY$: RETURN
13189 REM
13190 REM ...EnterStreet...
13200 ML% = 20: VTAB 5: HTAB 17: GOSUB 20000
13210 STREET$ = NTRY$: RETURN
13289 REM
13290 REM ...EnterCity...
13300 ML% = 20: VTAB 6: HTAB 17: GOSUB 20000
13310 CITY$ = NTRY$: RETURN
13389 REM
13390 REM ...EnterState...
13400 ML% = 2: VTAB 7: HTAB 17: GOSUB 20000
13410 SE$ = NTRY$: RETURN
13489 REM
13490 REM ...EnterZip...
13500 ML% = 9: VTAB 8: HTAB 17: GOSUB 20000
13510 ZIP$ = NTRY$: RETURN
15989 REM
15990 REM ...Display welcome and set up disk...
15991 REM
16000 HOME
16010 VTAB 3: HTAB 5: PRINT LEFT$ (TL$,31):
      REM ..Draw top line
16020 VTAB 5: HTAB 6: PRINT "Welcome to
      Mailing-List Entry"
16030 VTAB 10: HTAB 12: PRINT "Just a minute..."
16040 VTAB 16: HTAB 9: PRINT "A Forrest Lake
      Program"
16050 HTAB 5: PRINT LEFT$ (BL$,31):
      REM ..Draw bottom line
16060 PRINT D$;"APPEND ";FILE$
16070 PRINT D$: REM ..Cancel automatic WRITE
      command
16080 RETURN
16989 REM
16990 REM ...WriteRecord...
16991 REM
17000 IF NOT CHANGED THEN RETURN: REM ..Don't
      write unless changes made
17010 VTAB 21: HTAB 3: PRINT "Saving to disk...";
17020 PRINT: PRINT D$;"WRITE ";FILE$
17030 PRINT NAME$
17040 PRINT STREET$
```

Figure 11-2. Sequential-access Mailing-List Creation program (*continued*)

```
17050 PRINT CITY$
17060 PRINT SE$
17070 PRINT ZIP$
17080 PRINT D$: REM ..Deactivate disk output
17090 FR% = 21:LR% = 21: GOSUB 30100:
      REM ..ClearDisplayLines
17100 RETURN
19989 REM
19990 REM ...GetEntry...
19991 REM
20000 HT% = PEEK (36) + 1: REM  ..Cursor column
20010 NTRY$ = "": REM ..Empty entry
20020 CL% = LEN (NTRY$): REM ..Current
      entry length
20030 HTAB HT%: PRINT NTRY$;
20040 IF ML% > CL% THEN PRINT LEFT$ (EF$,ML% -
      CL%);: REM ..Fill unused entry field
20050 HTAB HT% + CL%: GOSUB 30000: REM ..Get one
      character
20060 IF C$ = CHR$ (127) AND CL% < = 1 THEN 20010:
      REM ..Delete key with empty entry?
20070 IF C$ = CHR$ (127) THEN NTRY$ =
      LEFT$ (NTRY$,CL% - 1): GOTO 20020:
      REM ..Delete key?
20080 IF C$ = CHR$ (24) THEN 20010:
      REM ..Control-X means cancel
20090 IF C$ = CHR$ (13) THEN PRINT SPC( ML% -
      CL%);: RETURN: REM ..Return means done
20100 IF C$ > = " " AND C$ < = "~" AND CL% < ML%
      THEN NTRY$ = NTRY$ + C$: REM ..Add valid
      characters if room
20110 GOTO 20020: REM ..Get another keystroke
20989 REM
20990 REM ...GetYesNo...
20991 REM
21000 HT% = PEEK (36) + 1:VT% = PEEK (37) + 1:
      REM ..Cursor position
21010 IF C$ = "Y" OR C$ = "y" OR (C$ = CHR$ (8)
      AND NTRY$ = "NO") THEN VTAB VT%: HTAB HT%:
      PRINT "<YES>  No ";:NTRY$ = "YES"
21020 IF C$ = "N" OR C$ = "n" OR (C$ = CHR$ (21)
      AND NTRY$ = "YES") THEN VTAB VT%: HTAB HT%:
      PRINT " Yes  <NO>";:NTRY$ = "NO"
21030 VTAB 19: HTAB 3: PRINT "Type Y for Yes or N
      for No,"
21040 HTAB 3: PRINT "or press <-- or --> to
      change."
21050 HTAB 3: PRINT "Then press RETURN.  ";
```

Figure 11-2. Sequential-access Mailing-List Creation program (*continued*)

```
21060 GOSUB 30000: REM ..GetChar
21070 IF C$ = " " THEN C$ = CHR$ (21):
      REM ..Accommodate 80-col. card "feature"
21080 IF C$ < > CHR$ (13) THEN 21010: REM ..Only
      RETURN confirms
21090 FR% = 19:LR% = 21: GOSUB 30100:
      REM ..ClearDisplayLines
21100 RETURN
21989 REM
21990 REM ...GetFieldNumber...
21991 REM
22000 VTAB 19: HTAB 3: PRINT "To select a field,
      type a number or "
22010 HTAB 3: PRINT "press UP-ARROW or
      DOWN-ARROW."
22020 HTAB 3: PRINT "Then press RETURN.  ";
22030 GOSUB 30000: REM ..GetChar
22040 IF C$ = CHR$ (10) AND FIELD% < LF% THEN
      GOSUB 23500:FIELD% = FIELD% + 1:
      GOSUB 23000: REM ..Down-arrow key
22050 IF C$ = CHR$ (11) AND FIELD% > 1 THEN
      GOSUB 23500: FIELD% = FIELD% - 1:
      GOSUB 23000: REM ..Up-arrow key
22060 IF C$ > = "1" AND C$ < = STR$ (LF%) THEN
      GOSUB 23500:FIELD% = VAL (C$): GOSUB 23000:
      REM ..Digit key
22070 IF C$ < > CHR$ (13) THEN 22030: REM ..Only
      RETURN confirms
22080 FR% = 19:LR% = 21: GOSUB 30100:
      REM ..ClearDisplayLines
22090 RETURN
22989 REM
22990 REM ...SelectField...
22991 REM
23000 VT% = PEEK (37) + 1:HT% = PEEK (36) + 1:
      REM ..Cursor location
23010 VTAB FR%(1,FIELD%): HTAB FC%(1,FIELD%):
      PRINT FD$(1,FIELD%);: REM ..Display selected
      description
23020 VTAB VT%: HTAB HT%: REM ..Reset cursor
23030 RETURN
23489 REM
23490 REM ...DeselectField...
23491 REM
23500 VT% = PEEK (37) + 1:HT% = PEEK (36) + 1:
      REM ..Cursor location
23510 VTAB FR%(2,FIELD%): HTAB FC%(2,FIELD%):
```

Figure 11-2. Sequential-access Mailing-List Creation program (*continued*)

```
       PRINT FD$(2,FIELD%);: REM ..Display
       deselected description
23520 VTAB VT%: HTAB HT%: REM ..Reset cursor
23530 RETURN
29989 REM
29990 REM ...GetCharacter...
29991 REM
30000 GET C$: REM ..Wait for keystroke
30010 RETURN
30089 REM
30090 REM ...ClearDisplayLines...
30091 REM
30100 FOR ROW = FR% TO LR%
30110 VTAB ROW: HTAB 2: PRINT SPC( 37);
30120 NEXT ROW
30130 RETURN
30189 REM
30190 REM ...DisplayBox...
30191 REM
30200 VTAB T%: HTAB L% + 1
30210 PRINT LEFT$ (TL$,R% - L% - 1);:
      REM ..Top line
30220 FOR ROW = T% + 1 TO B%: REM ..Side lines
30230 VTAB ROW: HTAB L%: PRINT SL$;
30240 HTAB R%: PRINT SL$
30250 NEXT ROW
30260 VTAB B%: HTAB L% + 1: PRINT
      LEFT$ (BL$,R% - L% - 1);: REM ..Bottom line
30270 RETURN
```

Figure 11-2. Sequential-access Mailing-List Creation program (*continued*)

ProDOS sequential-access file of names and addresses. The program can handle some of the disk errors that that may arise without halting altogether, because it intercepts errors (line 900) and uses an error-handling routine (lines 8000-8710).

The new version of the program calls a subroutine that displays a welcome message for you to read while it opens the mailing-list file (lines 1025 and 16000-16080). The subroutine uses the APPEND command to open the file, assuming you want to add more names to an existing list. To start a new file, you must delete or rename the mailing-list file before starting the entry program. Note that the program uses a variable for the file name (lines 8700, 10170, 16060, and 17020), so you can change the file name by changing the variable assignment on line 10170.

Aside from lines 1025 and 1063, the program does not differ from Figure 9-10 in the way it displays an entry form, inputs a name and address, and allows changes to the entries (lines 1000-1120). After changes are made, however, the program writes the entries onto the end of the sequential disk file (lines 1130 and 1200). Because ProDOS accumulates data headed for the disk in a file buffer, the disk drive will come to life only when the buffer fills up. The program closes the file after the last entry, forcing ProDOS to write the final, partially filled file buffer onto the disk (line 1210).

When the user chooses field 6 (Another Record), the program calls a subroutine to write out the most recent entries (line 1130). The subroutine (lines 17000-17100) writes a record only if variable CHANGED has a nonzero value, which is equivalent to a logical value of True (lines 1063, 12040, and 17000). This allows the user to quit without having to enter a new record. By pressing RETURN at fields 1-5 and then choosing field 7, the user gives the variable CHANGED a zero value, which is the same as a logical value of False, at quitting time.

As the program ends, it calls the record-writing subroutine (line 1200). Then it closes all files, clears the screen, and displays a parting message in the middle of the screen (lines 1210 and 1220).

The ErrorHandler subroutine starts by determining the error code (line 8000) and line number (line 8010). Next it beeps the console speaker, clears a space on the screen, and draws a box in which to display an error message (lines 8040-8070). The subroutine then uses the error code number to branch to the lines that will display an appropriate message (line 8080).

For error codes 3 (no device), 4 (write-protected), 6 and 7 (path not found), 8 (can't read or write to the disk—I/O error), 9 (disk full), and 10 (file locked), the program displays a specific message (lines 8200-8710). For all other codes, it displays a general message that includes the code number (line 8100). After displaying a message, the program waits for the user to press RETURN before quitting (lines 8120-8150).

By expanding ErrorHandler, you could have the program let the user fix certain problems and continue instead of quitting. For example, if the disk were write-protected, the program could wait while the user removed the tape that covers the notch, and then resume when the user pressed RETURN. If the file were locked, the program could offer the option of unlocking and resuming, or of not unlocking and quitting. If you decide to make improvements like these, be sure to leave the user a way out that is free of consequences. For example, don't force the user to remove the write-protect tab in order to quit.

The sequential-access Mailing-List Creation program will not always work properly with DOS 3.3. Error diagnosis will be inaccurate because DOS 3.3 errors do not exactly match those of ProDOS. Also, the APPEND command will not create a DOS 3.3 file if none exists. These differences can be accommodated by rewriting the ErrorHandler subroutine as follows:

```
]7989 REM
]7990 REM ...ErrorHandler...
]7991 REM
]8000 EN = PEEK (222): REM ..Error number
]8010 EL = PEEK (219) * 256 + PEEK (218):
      REM ..Error line
]8040 PRINT BEEP$;BEEP$;
]8050 FR% = 9:LR% = 14: GOSUB 30100:
      REM ..ClearDisplayLines
]8060 T% = 9:L% = 4:B% = 14:R% = 37: GOSUB 30200:
      REM ..DisplayBox
]8070 VTAB 11: REM ..Position for error message
]8080 ON EN GOTO 8100, 8100, 8100, 8200, 8100,
      8400, 8400, 8500, 8600, 8700
]8100 HTAB 5: PRINT "Unexpected error
      (code ";EN;")."
]8110 PRINT
]8120 HTAB 5: PRINT "Press RETURN to quit. ";
]8130 GOSUB 30000: REM ..GetChar
]8140 IF C$ < > CHR$ (13) THEN 8130:
      REM ..Wait for RETURN
]8150 GOTO 1210: REM ..Quit
]8200 HTAB 5: PRINT "Disk is write-protected."
]8210 HTAB 5: PRINT "Remove tab or use another
      disk"
]8220 GOTO 8120
]8400 HTAB 5: PRINT "File ";FILE$;" missing."
]8410 HTAB 5: PRINT "Create a new one?"
]8420 HTAB 8:C$ = "Y": GOSUB 21000: REM ..GetYesNo
]8430 IF NTRY$ = "NO" THEN GOTO 1210: REM ..If no,
      then quit
]8440 PRINT: PRINT D$;"OPEN ";FILE$
]8450 GOTO 1030
]8500 HTAB 5: PRINT "Disk or drive error."
]8510 HTAB 5: PRINT "Check disk, drive,
      and cable."
```

```
]8520 GOTO 8120
]8600 HTAB 5: PRINT "Disk full."
]8610 HTAB 5: PRINT "Last few records may be
      missing."
]8620 GOTO 8120
]8700 HTAB 5: PRINT "File ";FILE$;" locked."
]8710 PRINT: GOTO 8120
```

This DOS 3.3 version of ErrorHandler handles error code 3 (Range Error) as an unexpected error (line 8080). Also, the message for error code 8 (I/O Error) is slightly different (line 8510). The major change is in the handling of a nonexistent file (lines 8400-8450). The program now offers the user a choice: create a new file or quit.

Mailing-List Print Program

By combining parts of the sequential-access Mailing-List Creation program (Figure 11-2) and the Mailing-List Print Program (Figure 10-3), you can construct a new program to print the sequential-access mailing-list file. The new program will display the form shown in Figure 11-3; you input the first and last record numbers to be printed.

This program uses subroutines from Figure 10-3 to print a list of names and addresses, one entry per line. This program also uses variations on the subroutines in Figure 11-2 that display a welcome message, open the file, and handle errors. The only completely new subroutine reads records. Figure 11-4 lists the new Mailing-List Print program; the areas shaded in gray are different from Figure 11-2. The new program also eliminates lines 1063, 8700-8710, 10580-10630, 12050, 13289-13510, 16080, and 16989-17100 from Figure 11-2.

Believe it or not, the main part of the print program in Figure 11-4 is almost identical to the main part of the entry program in Figure 11-2. However, the print program has only two input fields: which record will be the first to print and which will be the second. Another difference is that when the user finishes the entries, the program calls a subroutine to print the requested range of records (lines 1130 and 3000-3110). When the printing finishes, the program branches back to get another range of record numbers (line 1130). And as usual, the user ends the program by choosing the displayed Quit option (lines 1150-1220).

```
                MAILILNG-LIST PRINT

      1.  <FIRST RECORD TO PRINT:> ...
      2.  Last Record to Print:

      3.  Print
      4.  Quit




      Enter the selected field.
      Then press RETURN to confirm entry
```

Figure 11-3. Mailing-List Print program entries

```
900 ONERR GOTO 8000: REM ..Enable error trapping
1000 GOSUB 10000: REM ..Initialize variables
1010 PRINT CHR$ (21): REM ..Deactivate
     80-col. card
1020 REM ..Display width is 40
1025 GOSUB 16000: REM ..Display welcome and set up
     disk
1030 GOSUB 11000: REM ..DisplayEntryWindow
1040 FOR X1 = 1 TO LF%
1050 FIELD% = X1: GOSUB 23500: REM ..Display field
     description
1060 NEXT X1
1070 FOR X1 = 1 TO 2: REM ..Enter all fields
1080 FIELD% = X1
1090 GOSUB 23000: GOSUB 12000: GOSUB 23500:
     REM ..SelectField:EnterField:DeselectField
```

Figure 11-4. Sequential-access Mailing-List Print program

```
1100 NEXT X1
1110 FIELD% = 3: GOSUB 23000: REM ..SelectField
1120 GOSUB 22000: REM ..GetFieldNumber
1130 IF FIELD% = 3 THEN GOSUB 3000:FR% = 4:
     LR% = 5: GOSUB 30100: GOSUB 23500: GOTO 1040:
     REM ..If field=3, print requested records,
     blank last entries, deselect and get another
    range
1140 IF FIELD% < LF% THEN GOSUB 12000: GOTO 1120:
     REM ..EnterField
1150 REM ...Quit?...
1160 T% = 12:L% = 4:B% = 17:R% = 37: GOSUB 30200:
     REM ..DisplayBox
1170 VTAB 14: HTAB 5: PRINT BEEP$;"Are you sure
     you want to quit?";
1180 VTAB 16: HTAB 8:C$ = "Y": GOSUB 21000:
     REM ..GetYesNo
1190 IF NTRY$ = "NO" THEN FR% = 12:LR% = 17:
     GOSUB 30100: GOSUB 23000: GOTO 1120:
     REM ..If no, erase box, restore field, and
     get another field
1200 PRINT: PRINT D$;"CLOSE"
1210 HOME: VTAB 12: HTAB 8: PRINT "End of
     Mailing-List Print"
1220 VTAB 23: HTAB 1: END
2989 REM
2990 REM ...Print the selected range of records...
2991 REM
3000 VTAB 21: HTAB 3: PRINT "Finding
     first record..."
3010 PRINT D$;"OPEN ";FILE$
3020 PRINT: IF EN < > 5 THEN PRINT D$;
     "POSITION ";FILE$;",F";5 * (SR% - 1)

3030 FR% = 21:LR% = 21: GOSUB 30100:
     REM ..ClearDisplayLines
3040 FOR RECRD = SR% TO ER%
3050 GOSUB 18000: REM ..ReadRecord
3060 IF EN = 5 THEN RECRD = ER%: GOTO 3080:
     REM ..handle end-of-file
3070 GOSUB 14000: REM ..PrintRecord
3080 NEXT RECRD
3090 EN = 0: REM ..Clear error flag
3100 PRINT: PRINT D$;"CLOSE ";FILE$
3110 RETURN
7989 REM
7990 REM ...ErrorHandler...
7991 REM
```

Figure 11-4. Sequential-access Mailing-List Print program (*continued*)

```
8000 EN = PEEK (222): REM ..Error number
8010 EL = PEEK (219) * 256 + PEEK (218):
     REM ..Error line
8020 IF EN = 5 THEN RESUME: REM ..End of file
8030 PRINT BEEP$;BEEP$;
8040 FR% = 9:LR% = 14: GOSUB 30100:
     REM ..ClearDisplayLines
8050 T% = 9:L% = 4:B% = 14:R% = 37: GOSUB 30200:
     REM ..DisplayBox
8060 VTAB 11: REM ..Position for error messg.
8390 IF EN < > 6 AND EN < > 7 THEN 8490
8400 HTAB 5: PRINT "File ";FILE$;" not found."
8410 HTAB 5: PRINT "Check prefix and drive."
8420 GOTO 8620: REM ..Quit
8490 IF EN < > 8 THEN 8600
8500 HTAB 5: PRINT "Disk or drive error."
8510 HTAB 5: PRINT "Check disk, drive,
     and prefix."
8520 GOTO 8620: REM ..Quit
8600 HTAB 5: PRINT "Unexpected error
     (code ";EN;")."
8610 PRINT
8620 HTAB 5: PRINT "Press RETURN to quit. ";
8630 GOSUB 30000: REM ..GetChar
8640 IF C$ < > CHR$ (13) THEN 8630:
     REM ..Wait for RETURN
8650 GOTO 1200: REM ..Quit
9989 REM
9990 REM ...InitializeVariables...
9991 REM
10000 D$ = CHR$ (4): REM ..ProDOS/DOS 3.3 prefix
10010 W4$ = CHR$ (17): REM ..Display width 40
10020 BEEP$ = CHR$ (07): REM ..Beep char.
10030 FOR X1 = 1 TO 40
10040 EF$ = EF$ + ".": REM ..Entry field chars.
10050 TL$ = TL$ + "_": REM ..Top line chars.
10060 BL$ = BL$ + "‾": REM ..Bottom line chars.
10070 NEXT X1
10080 SL$ = "|": REM ..Side line chars.
10090 LF% = 4: REM ..Last field number
10100 DIM FR%(2,LF%),FC%(2,LF%),FD$(2,LF%)
10110 FOR X1 = 1 TO LF%: REM ..Read
      field locations and descriptions
10120 READ FR%(1,X1),FC%(1,X1),FD$(1,X1)
10130 READ FR%(2,X1),FC%(2,X1),FD$(2,X1)
10140 NEXT X1
10170 FILE$ = "MAILING.LIST"
10190 PL% = 65: REM ..Force headings on 1st
```

Figure 11-4. Sequential-access Mailing-List Print program (*continued*)

```
      printed page
10200 RETURN
10489 REM
10490  REM ...Field Descriptions and Locations...
10491 REM
10500 DATA 4,3," 1. <FIRST RECORD TO PRINT:>"
10510 DATA 4,3," 1.  First Record to Print: "
10520 DATA 5,3," 2. <LAST RECORD TO PRINT:> "
10530 DATA 5,3," 2.  Last Record to Print:  "
10540 DATA 8,3," 3. <PRINT>  "
10550 DATA 8,3," 3.  Print   "
10560 DATA 9,3," 4. <QUIT>  "
10570 DATA 9,3," 4.  Quit   "
10989 REM
10990  REM ...DisplayEntryWindow...
10991 REM
11000 HOME
11010 T% = 1:L% = 1:B% = 22:R% = 39: GOSUB 30200:
      REM ..DisplayBox
11020 TITLE$ = "MAILING-LIST PRINT"
11030 INVERSE: VTAB 1: HTAB (40 - LEN (TITLE$))
      / 2: PRINT TITLE$;: NORMAL: REM ..Display
      title
11040 RETURN
11989 REM
11990  REM ...EnterField...
11991 REM
12000 VTAB 20: HTAB 3: PRINT "Enter the selected
      field."
12010 HTAB 3: PRINT "Then press RETURN to confirm
      entry.";
12020 ON FIELD% GOSUB 13100,13200
12030 FR% = 19:LR% = 21: GOSUB 30100:
      REM ..ClearDisplayLines
12040 RETURN
13089 REM
13090  REM ...EnterFirstRecordNumber...
13100 ML% = 3: VTAB 4: HTAB 32: GOSUB 20000
13110 SR% = VAL (NTRY$): IF SR% < 1 THEN 13100
13120 RETURN
13189 REM
13190  REM ...EnterLastRecordNumber...
13200 ML% = 3: VTAB 5: HTAB 32: GOSUB 20000
13210 ER% = VAL (NTRY$): IF ER% < 1 THEN 13200
13220 RETURN
13989 REM
13990 REM ...PrintRecord...
```

Figure 11-4. Sequential-access Mailing-List Print program (*continued*)

```
13991 REM
14000 VTAB 21: HTAB 3: PRINT "Printing...";
14010 PRINT: PRINT D$;"PR#1": REM ..Switch
      to printer
14020 PRINT CHR$ (9);"80N";: REM ..Line width 80
14030 PL% = PL% + 1: GOSUB 15000: REM ..TopPage
14040 PRINT NAME$;
14050 HTAB 22: PRINT STREET$;
14060 POKE 36,42: PRINT CITY$;", ";SE$;" ";ZIP$
14070 IF PL% / 5 = INT (PL% / 5) THEN PRINT:
      PL% = PL% + 1: REM ..Print a blank line
      every 5th address
14080 PRINT CHR$ (9);"R": REM ..Switch to screen
14090 VTAB 21: HTAB 2: PRINT SPC( 37);:
      REM ..Clear bottom line
14100 RETURN
14989 REM
14990 REM ...TopPage...
14991 REM
15000 IF PL% < 55 THEN RETURN: REM ..Page
      full yet?
15010 FOR X1 = 1 TO (66 - PL%): REM ..Space to
      bottom of page
15020 PRINT: NEXT X1
15030 PRINT TAB( 28);"MAILING LIST"
15040 PRINT
15050 PRINT "NAME"; SPC( 18);"STREET";
      SPC( 16);"CITY, STATE,ZIP"
15060 PRINT "____________________";
15070 PRINT "____________________";
15080 PRINT "_________________________________"
15090 PRINT
15100 PL% = 6: RETURN: REM ..Reset printed
      line counter
15989 REM
15990 REM ...Display welcome and set up disk...
15991 REM
16000 HOME
16010 VTAB 2: HTAB 5: PRINT LEFT$ (TL$,31):
      REM ..Draw top line
16020 VTAB 5: HTAB 6: PRINT "Welcome to
      Mailing-List Print"
16030 VTAB 10: HTAB 12: PRINT "Just a minute..."
16040 VTAB 16: HTAB 9: PRINT "A Forrest
      Lake Program"
16050 HTAB 5: PRINT LEFT$ (BL$,31): REM ..Draw
      bottom line
```

Figure 11-4. Sequential-access Mailing-List Print program (*continued*)

```
16060 PRINT D$;"RENAME ";FILE$;",";FILE$:
      REM ..See if file exists
16070 RETURN
17989 REM
17990 REM ...ReadRecord...
17991 REM
18000 PRINT: PRINT D$;"READ ";FILE$
18010 VTAB 23: HTAB 39: REM ..Accomodate
      INPUT "feature"
18020 IF EN < > 5 THEN
      INPUT "";NAME$,STREET$,CITY$,SE$,ZIP$
18030 PRINT D$: REM ..Deactivate READ command
18040 RETURN
19989 REM
19990 REM ...GetEntry...
19991 REM
20000 HT% = PEEK (36) + 1: REM  ..Cursor column
20010 NTRY$ = "": REM ..Empty entry
20020 CL% = LEN (NTRY$): REM ..Current entry
      length
20030 HTAB HT%: PRINT NTRY$;
20040 IF ML% > CL% THEN PRINT LEFT$
      (EF$,ML% - CL%);: REM ..Fill unused entry
      field
20050 HTAB HT% + CL%: GOSUB 30000: REM ..Get
      one character
20060 IF C$ = CHR$ (127) AND CL% < = 1 THEN 20010:
      REM ..Delete key with empty entry?
20070 IF C$ = CHR$ (127) THEN NTRY$ =
      LEFT$ (NTRY$,CL% - 1): GOTO 20020:
      REM ..Delete key?
20080 IF C$ = CHR$ (24) THEN 20010:
      REM ..Control-X means cancel
20090 IF C$ = CHR$ (13) THEN PRINT
      SPC( ML% - CL%);: RETURN: REM ..Return
      means done
20100 IF C$ > = " " AND C$ < = "~" AND CL% <
      ML% THEN NTRY$ = NTRY$ + C$: REM ..Add valid
      characters if room
20110 GOTO 20020: REM ..Get another keystroke
20989 REM
20990 REM ...GetYesNo...
20991 REM
21000 HT% = PEEK (36) + 1:VT% = PEEK (37) + 1:
      REM ..Cursor position
21010 IF C$ = "Y" OR C$ = "y" OR (C$ = CHR$ (8)
      AND NTRY$ = "NO") THEN VTAB VT%: HTAB HT%:
```

Figure 11-4. Sequential-access Mailing-List Print program (*continued*)

```
      PRINT "<YES>  No ";:NTRY$ = "YES"
21020 IF C$ = "N" OR C$ = "n" OR (C$ = CHR$ (21)
      AND NTRY$ = "YES") THEN VTAB VT%: HTAB HT%:
      PRINT " Yes  <NO>";:NTRY$ = "NO"
21030 VTAB 19: HTAB 3: PRINT "Type Y for Yes or
      N for No,"
21040 HTAB 3: PRINT "or press <-- or --> to
      change."
21050 HTAB 3: PRINT "Then press RETURN.  ";
21060 GOSUB 30000: REM ..GetChar
21070 IF C$ = " " THEN C$ = CHR$ (21):
      REM ..Accommodate 80-col. card "feature"
21080 IF C$ < > CHR$ (13) THEN 21010: REM ..Only
      RETURN confirms
21090 FR% = 19:LR% = 21: GOSUB 30100:
      REM ..ClearDisplayLines
21100 RETURN
21989 REM
21990 REM ...GetFieldNumber...
21991 REM
22000 VTAB 19: HTAB 3: PRINT "To select a field,
      type a number or "
22010 HTAB 3: PRINT "press UP-ARROW or
      DOWN-ARROW."
22020 HTAB 3: PRINT "Then press RETURN.  ";
22030 GOSUB 30000: REM ..GetChar
22040 IF C$ = CHR$ (10) AND FIELD% < LF% THEN
      GOSUB 23500:FIELD% = FIELD% + 1: GOSUB
      23000: REM ..Down-arrow key
22050 IF C$ = CHR$ (11) AND FIELD% > 1 THEN
      GOSUB 23500:FIELD% = FIELD% - 1:
      GOSUB 23000: REM ..Up-arrow key
22060 IF C$ > = "1" AND C$ < = STR$ (LF%) THEN
      GOSUB 23500:FIELD% = VAL (C$): GOSUB 23000:
      REM ..Digit key
22070 IF C$ < > CHR$ (13) THEN 22030: REM ..Only
      RETURN confirms
22080 FR% = 19:LR% = 21: GOSUB 30100:
      REM ..ClearDisplayLines
22090 RETURN
22989 REM
22990 REM ...SelectField...
22991 REM
23000 VT% = PEEK (37) + 1:HT% = PEEK (36) + 1:
      REM ..Cursor location
23010 VTAB FR%(1,FIELD%): HTAB FC%(1,FIELD%):
      PRINT FD$(1,FIELD%);: REM ..Display selected
      description
```

Figure 11-4. Sequential-access Mailing-List Print program (*continued*)

```
23020 VTAB VT%: HTAB HT%: REM ..Reset cursor
23030 RETURN
23489 REM
23490 REM ...DeselectField...
23491 REM
23500 VT% = PEEK (37) + 1:HT% = PEEK (36) + 1:
      REM ..Cursor location
23510 VTAB FR%(2,FIELD%): HTAB FC%(2,FIELD%):
      PRINT FD$(2,FIELD%);: REM ..Display
      deselected description
23520 VTAB VT%: HTAB HT%: REM ..Reset cursor
23530 RETURN
29989 REM
29990 REM ...GetCharacter...
29991 REM
30000 GET C$: REM ..Wait for keystroke
30010 RETURN
30089 REM
30090 REM ...ClearDisplayLines...
30091 REM
30100 FOR ROW = FR% TO LR%
30110 VTAB ROW: HTAB 2: PRINT SPC( 37);
30120 NEXT ROW
30130 RETURN
30189 REM
30190 REM ...DisplayBox...
30191 REM
30200 VTAB T%: HTAB L% + 1
30210 PRINT LEFT$ (TL$,R% - L% - 1);:
      REM ..Top line
30220 FOR ROW = T% + 1 TO B%: REM ..Side lines
30230 VTAB ROW: HTAB L%: PRINT SL$;
30240 HTAB R%: PRINT SL$
30250 NEXT ROW
30260 VTAB B%: HTAB L% + 1: PRINT
      LEFT$ (BL$,R% - L% - 1);: REM ..Bottom line
30270 RETURN
```

Figure 11-4. Sequential-access Mailing-List Print program (*continued*)

The field descriptions are new (lines 10500-10570), and so is the title (line 11020). A new version of the EnterField subroutine inputs the first and last record numbers to be printed (lines 12000-13220). The subroutine that displays a welcome message (lines 16000-16070) does not open the mailing-list file; it only checks to see if the file exists by attempting to rename the file with its existing name (line 16060).

The new subroutine that prints a report (lines 3000-3110) starts by displaying an advisory in case it takes a while to find the first record (line 3000). It then opens the mailing-list file and positions to the first record in the file (lines 3010 and 3020). Next it erases the advisory message (line 3030) and starts a loop that reads and prints records sequentially (lines 3040-3080). If the end-of-data condition turns up before the loop ends, the program forces an end to the report (line 3060). When the report is finished, the subroutine resets the error code in case it was set to 5 by an end-of-data condition (line 3090). Finally, it closes the file and returns to the main program.

Another new subroutine, ReadRecord, reads the next record from the mailing-list file (lines 18000-18040). The subroutine does a couple of weird things to counter certain irregularities in Applesoft and ProDOS. Under some mysterious circumstances, using an INPUT statement to read from a disk file may erase the display screen from the current cursor position to the end of the current display line. Therefore, the subroutine moves the cursor to a spot on the screen where this "feature" cannot disrupt the display (line 18010). What's more, an INPUT statement that reads from the disk may display a question mark on the screen unless it contains a null prompt string (line 18020). Notice that the INPUT statement is not executed if an end-of-data condition has occurred; this is because trying to read past the end of the file simply causes another end-of-data error.

The program checks specifically for three errors: end-of-data errors, file-not-found errors, and disk-drive errors (lines 8000-8650). If and end-of-data error (code 5) occurs, the program simply reexecutes the statement that caused the error. This would normally result in an endless program loop, but the POSITION and INPUT statements, which cause the end-of-data error, are executed only if the error number is not 5 (lines 3020 and 18020). There are specific messages for a file-not-found error (lines 8390-8420) and a disk-drive error (lines 8490-8520).

All other errors use the same general message (lines 8600 and 8610). After displaying an error message, the program waits for the user to press RETURN before ending automatically (lines 8620-8650).

The Byte Number

You can specify a byte (character) number with the READ and WRITE commands to move the file pointer ahead a specified number of characters. With ProDOS, you can also specify a byte number with the POSITION command. To the file name (or pathname in ProDOS) you add a comma, the letter B, and the number of characters you want to move the pointer. Here is an example:

```
]160 PRINT CHR$(4);"READ SAMPLE,B64"
```

With ProDOS, both a field and a byte number can be listed in the same command. In that case, ProDOS first advances the file pointer by the number of fields specified (by the READ, WRITE, or POSTION command), and then advances the pointer again by the number of bytes specified by the same command.

THE EXEC COMMAND

With the EXEC command you can turn control of the Apple II over to a sequential file. Text from the file you name is used instead of being typed from the keyboard. Here is an example:

```
]EXEC FILENAME,R3,D2,S5
```

As usual, the slot and drive numbers are optional.

When EXEC is issued, the file specified is opened, then implicit READ and INPUT statements follow. The whole file is retrieved, starting with the first line if no R parameter is present. If R is present, the line specified by R is retrieved (R0 for the first line, R1 for the second, and so on). With ProDOS, you may specify the line to use first with the letter F instead of the letter R.

The retrieved line is treated as if it were typed on the keyboard in immediate mode. If the line is meaningless, you will see the message **?SYNTAX ERROR** or *****SYNTAX ERR**. If it is a program line, such as

```
100 PRINT "THIS IS A TEST"
```

it will be stored in the Apple II's memory as if you had just typed it. If it is a direct command like LIST or RUN, it will be executed.

After the action caused by the first line is completed, the next line is read and acted upon. This continues until the end of the file has been reached, at which time control of the Apple II returns to the keyboard.

Merging Programs

One application of the EXEC command is program merging. For example, you could use this method to copy subroutines from the original Mailing-List Entry program (Figure 9-10) to the sequential-access Mailing-List Creation program (Figure 11-2).

Start by loading the program from which you want to copy lines. Next, enter a few program lines at the beginning of the program, as follows:

```
]1 D$ = CHR$ (4): REM ..ProDOS command prefix
]2 F$ = "FIG.11.2A": REM ..Name of sequential file
]3 POKE 33,33: REM ..Inhibit LIST formatting
]4 PRINT D$;"OPEN ";F$
]5 PRINT D$;"WRITE ";F$
]6 LIST 9989 - 13510
]7 LIST 19989 - 30270
]8 PRINT D$;"CLOSE ";F$
]9 POKE 33,40: END: REM ..Enable LIST formatting
```

The Apple II now has the source program plus these lines in its memory. When executed, these lines open a sequential file named FIG.11.2A, list lines 9989-13510 and 19989-30270 from memory into FIG.11.2A, close the file, and end. The source program itself never executes, thanks to the END statement on line 9. Because of the WRITE command on line 5, the listed program lines go into the sequential file named FIG.11.2A, not onto the screen. If you want to copy other line numbers, change lines 6 and 7. You can also use a different name for the sequential file by changing line 2.

After creating the sequential file containing the program lines you want to copy, load the second program that you want to merge. If it doesn't exist, clear the existing program with a NEW command and type in the new program. Finally, use an EXEC command to "type" the lines from the sequential file into Apple II memory, where they will merge with the existing lines. The following statement works with the sequential file created by the previous example:

```
]EXEC FIG.11.2A
```

The commands, program lines, and data taken from the sequential file are stored in memory but not displayed on the screen. You see nothing on the screen but a series of Applesoft prompt characters (]). During the process of merging two files, if any two lines have the same number, the last line loaded will be preserved.

RANDOM-ACCESS FILES

Random access solves the two major problems of sequential access: it makes access time to all records identical and allows easy record updating. The only constraint is that all records in a random-access file must be the same length. The record length fixes the amount of information that can be stored in one record at a number of bytes (characters) that you specify.

A record is identified by a number indicating its position in the file. The first record in every file is record number 0, the next is number 1, followed by record 2, and so on.

The smallest random-access file has one record. Files expand as new records are added, but they do not shrink. To remove unwanted records from a random-access file and shrink the size of the file, you must copy the records to be preserved into a new random-access file.

Programs must specify which record of a random-access file is selected. They may also specify what part of the record is to be accessed.

Opening Random-Access Files

To define a file as a random-access file, you must include an additional parameter when the file is opened: the *length parameter*, L. The length parameter specifies the length of each record.

```
]200 PRINT D$;"OPEN SAMPLE,L40"
```

The length parameter must have a value ranging from 1 to 65535 (32767 with DOS 3.3). You can also list drive and slot numbers (and a volume number with DOS 3.3) in addition to the record length. The record length does not have to be the first item in the list, but it must be present if the file is to be random-access. Other parameters, including the slot, drive, and record numbers, may also be present in any order.

To compute the length of a record, start by writing down a list of the fields it contains, noting the maximum number of bytes (characters) each will occupy (Figure 11-5). Next, add up the field

FILE LAYOUT

File Name	Record Size	No. of Records
MAILING LIST	n/a (sequential)	———

Description

Variable	Field Description	Max. Size	Comments
NA$	Name	20	
SR$	Street	20	
CI$	City	20	
ST$	State	2	
ZI$	ZIP Code	9	

Figure 11-5. File layout for a sample random-access mailing-list file

lengths. To that sum add one extra byte per field, thereby taking into account the carriage return characters that separate the fields. The result is the record length.

Programs should never write records that are longer—including carriage return characters—than the number of bytes specified by the length parameter in the OPEN command. If too many characters are stored in a record, the succeeding record may be overwritten or combined with the first one.

Closing Random-Access Files

The CLOSE command is identical for both sequential- and random-access files.

Random-Access Read and Write

The READ and WRITE commands require a *record parameter,* R, for random-access files. The record parameter moves the file pointer to the beginning of a record. The following example uses the record parameter:

```
]250 PRINT D$;"WRITE SAMPLE,R";RN
]350 PRINT D$;"READ SAMPLE,R";RN
```

Both statements in this example access the record specified by the value of variable RN. If the record parameter is not present, the pointer is not moved.

With ProDOS random-access files, the READ and WRITE commands can include a field number, a byte (character) number, or both. Starting at the beginning of the current record, the field number moves the file pointer ahead the specified number of fields, and from there the byte number moves the pointer a specified number of bytes.

With DOS 3.3 random-access files, the READ and WRITE commands can include a byte (character) number, but not a field number. Starting at the beginning of the current record, the byte number moves the pointer ahead a specified number of bytes.

The field and byte numbers can be used only to advance within the current record of the random-access file. If either attempts to move out of the record, an end-of-data error occurs.

After a random-access READ or WRITE command, you can use a POSITION command to move the file pointer forward in the current record. However, the POSITION command also cancels the last READ or WRITE command. To read or write at the new position in the record, you must use another READ or WRITE command, this time *without* a record number.

End of File

At any given time, the nominal end of a random-access file falls right after the highest record number written. ProDOS and DOS 3.3 behave differently if a program tries to read a record with a higher number than that of the last record. With DOS 3.3, an end-of-data error (error code 5) occurs, but with ProDOS, a range error (code 2) occurs.

With DOS 3.3, an end-of-data error (error code 5) also occurs if a program tries to read a record that has never been written. For example, suppose only records 1, 3, and 500 have been written. The end-of-data error will occur if a program tries to read any other record, including (but not limited to) records 2, 100, and 501. Also, when an end-of-data error occurs, DOS 3.3 resets the random-access record length to 1.

If a program tries to read a ProDOS record that has never been written, an end-of-data error (code 5) may occur, or there may be no error at all. For example, suppose only records 1, 3, and 500 have been written. The end-of-data error may occur if a program tries to read any other record, including (but not limited to) records 2, 100, and 501. If no error occurs, the first field read will be empty.

USING RANDOM-ACCESS FILES

While a sequential-access mailing-list file is better than no file at all, it is not as convenient as a random-access file. A few changes made to the sequential-access Mailing-List Creation program (Figure 11-2) will convert it to use a random-access file, allowing you to change existing records. A few similar changes to the sequential-access Mailing-List Print program will convert it to use the same new random-access file.

Random-Access Mailing-List Program

Like the sequential-access Mailing-List Creation program, a random-access version must be able to create new records. Unlike the sequential-access program, the random-access program must also be able to read an existing record, display it, and allow changes to it. Where formerly there was just one operation, record creation, now there are three: record creation, record review, and record changes.

Both record review and record changes begin by reading an existing record and displaying its values. But those values must be input from the keyboard to create the record. How does the program know where to go for record input? It can ask the program user to indicate this, or it can make the decision itself. Suppose the program tries to read a nonexistent record from a file. One of three things happens:

- An end-of-data error (code 5) occurs
- A range error (code 2) occurs
- No error occurs, but the first field is empty.

The program can intercept the errors with an ONERR GOTO statement and an error-handling routine. In addition, it can test the variable containing the first field value to see if it is empty. If any of the three conditions occurs, the program assumes the record is new and asks the user to enter all five fields in sequence before it allows field-by-field changes.

The complete listing for the random-access Mailing-List Entry/Review program appears in Figure 11-6, with changes to the original sequential-access version from Figure 11-2 shaded. In addition to the shaded changes, line 16070 from Figure 11-2 must be deleted.

```
900 ONERR GOTO 8000: REM ..Enable error trapping
1000 GOSUB 10000: REM ..Initialize variables
1010 PRINT: PRINT D$;"PR#3": REM ..Activate
     80-col. card
1020 PRINT W4$;: REM ..Set display width to 40
1025 GOSUB 16000: REM ..Display welcome and set
     up disk
1030 GOSUB 11000: REM ..DisplayEntryWindow
1033 EN = 0: REM ..Clear end-of-data condition
1036 VTAB 3: HTAB 8: PRINT "Record:  ";RECRD;
     SPC( 5)
```

Figure 11-6. Random-access Mailing-List Entry/Review program

```
1040 FOR X1 = 1 TO LF%
1050 FIELD% = X1: GOSUB 23500: REM ..Display field
     description
1060 NEXT X1
1063 GOSUB 18000: REM ..ReadRecord
1066 IF EN < > 5 THEN GOSUB 19000: GOTO 1110:
     REM ..If not end-of-data, DisplayRecord
1070 FOR X1 = 1 TO 5: REM ..Enter all fields
1080 FIELD% = X1
1090 GOSUB 23000: GOSUB 12000: GOSUB 23500:
     REM ..SelectField:EnterField:DeselectField
1100 NEXT X1
1110 FIELD% = 6: GOSUB 23000: REM ..SelectField
1120 GOSUB 22000: REM ..GetFieldNumber
1130 IF FIELD% = 6 THEN GOSUB 17000: GOSUB 23500:
     GOSUB 13600:FR% = 3:LR% = 8: GOSUB 30100:
     GOTO 1033: REM ..WriteRecord, DeselectField,
     GetRecordNumber, ClearDisplayLines, then go
     get another
1140 IF FIELD% < LF% THEN GOSUB 12000: GOTO 1120:
     REM ..EnterField
1150  REM ...Quit?...
1160 T% = 12:L% = 4:B% = 17:R% = 37: GOSUB 30200:
     REM ..DisplayBox
1170 VTAB 14: HTAB 5: PRINT BEEP$;"Are you sure
     you want to quit?";
1180 VTAB 16: HTAB 8:C$ = "Y": GOSUB 21000:
     REM ..GetYesNo
1190 IF NTRY$ = "NO" THEN FR% = 12:LR% = 17:
     GOSUB 30100: GOSUB 23000: GOTO 1120:
     REM ..If no, erase box, restore field, and
     get another field
1200 GOSUB 17000: REM ..WriteRecord
1210 PRINT: PRINT D$;"CLOSE"
1220 HOME: VTAB 12: HTAB 5: PRINT "End of
     Mailing-List Entry/Review"
1230 VTAB 23: HTAB 1: END
7989 REM
7990 REM ...ErrorHandler...
7991 REM
8000 EN = PEEK (222): REM ..Error number
8010 EL = PEEK (219) * 256 + PEEK (218):
     REM ..Error line
8020 IF EN = 2 THEN EN = 5: REM ..Attempted read
     past last record
8030 IF EN = 5 THEN RESUME: REM ..End of data
     encountered
8040 PRINT BEEP$;BEEP$;
```

Figure 11-6. Random-access Mailing-List Entry/Review program (*continued*)

```
8050 FR% = 9:LR% = 14: GOSUB 30100:
     REM ..ClearDisplayLines
8060 T% = 9:L% = 4:B% = 14:R% = 37: GOSUB 30200:
     REM ..DisplayBox
8070 VTAB 11: REM ..Position for error message
8080 ON EN GOTO 8100, 8100, 8500, 8200, 8100,
     8400, 8400, 8500, 8600, 8700
8100 HTAB 5: PRINT "Unexpected error
     (code ";EN;")."
8110 PRINT
8120 HTAB 5: PRINT "Press RETURN to quit. ";
8130 GOSUB 30000: REM ..GetChar
8140 IF C$ < > CHR$ (13) THEN 8130: REM ..Wait for
     RETURN
8150 GOTO 1210: REM ..Quit
8200 HTAB 5: PRINT "Disk is write-protected."
8210 HTAB 5: PRINT "Remove tab or use
     another disk"
8220 GOTO 8120
8400 HTAB 5: PRINT "Volume not found."
8410 HTAB 5: PRINT "Check prefix and drive."
8420 GOTO 8120
8500 HTAB 5: PRINT "Disk or drive error."
8510 HTAB 5: PRINT "Check disk, drive,
     and prefix."
8520 GOTO 8120
8600 HTAB 5: PRINT "Disk full."
8610 HTAB 5: PRINT "Last few records may
     be missing."
8620 GOTO 8120
8700 HTAB 5: PRINT "File ";FILE$;" locked."
8710 PRINT: GOTO 8120
9989 REM
9990 REM ...InitializeVariables...
9991 REM
10000 D$ = CHR$ (4): REM ..ProDOS/DOS 3.3 prefix
10010 W4$ = CHR$ (17): REM ..Display width 40
10020 BEEP$ = CHR$ (07): REM ..Beep char.
10030 FOR X1 = 1 TO 40
10040 EF$ = EF$ + ".": REM ..Entry field chars.
10050 TL$ = TL$ + "_": REM ..Top line chars.
10060 BL$ = BL$ + "‾": REM ..Bottom line chars.
10070 NEXT X1
10080 SL$ = "|": REM ..Side line chars.
10090 LF% = 7: REM ..Last field number
10100 DIM FR%(2,LF%),FC%(2,LF%),FD$(2,LF%)
10110 FOR X1 = 1 TO LF%: REM ..Read field
```

Figure 11-6. Random-access Mailing-List Entry/Review program (*continued*)

```
      locations and descriptions
10120 READ FR%(1,X1),FC%(1,X1),FD$(1,X1)
10130 READ FR%(2,X1),FC%(2,X1),FD$(2,X1)
10140 NEXT X1
10170 FILE$ = "ADDRESS"
10180 RECRD = 1: REM ..Start with record 1
10200 RETURN
10489 REM
10490 REM ...Field Descriptions and Locations...
10491 REM
10500 DATA 4,3," 1. <NAME:>   "
10510 DATA 4,3," 1.  Name:    "
10520 DATA 5,3," 2. <STREET:>"
10530 DATA 5,3," 2.  Street: "
10540 DATA 6,3," 3. <CITY:>   "
10550 DATA 6,3," 3.  City:    "
10560 DATA 7,3," 4. <STATE:> "
10570 DATA 7,3," 4.  State:  "
10580 DATA 8,3," 5. <ZIP:>    "
10590 DATA 8,3," 5.  Zip:     "
10600 DATA 11,3," 6. <ANOTHER RECORD>"
10610 DATA 11,3," 6.  Another Record "
10620 DATA 12,3," 7. <QUIT>"
10630 DATA 12,3," 7.  Quit "
10989 REM
10990 REM ...DisplayEntryWindow...
10991 REM
11000 HOME
11010 T% = 1:L% = 1:B% = 22:R% = 39: GOSUB 30200:
      REM ..DisplayBox
11020 TITLE$ = "Mailing-List Entry/Review"
11030 INVERSE: VTAB 1: HTAB (40 - LEN (TITLE$))
      / 2: PRINT TITLE$;: NORMAL: REM ..Display
      title
11040 RETURN
11989 REM
11990 REM ...EnterField...
11991 REM
12000 VTAB 20: HTAB 3: PRINT "Enter the
      selected field."
12010 HTAB 3: PRINT "Then press RETURN to
      confirm entry.";
12020 ON FIELD% GOSUB 13100,13200,
      13300,13400,13500
12030 FR% = 19:LR% = 21: GOSUB 30100:
      REM ..ClearDisplayLines
12040 CHANGED = 1: REM ..Set changes-made flag
12050 RETURN
```

Figure 11-6. Random-access Mailing-List Entry/Review program (*continued*)

```
13089 REM
13090  REM ...EnterName...
13100 ML% = 20: VTAB 4: HTAB 17: GOSUB 20000
13110 NAME$ = NTRY$: RETURN
13189 REM
13190  REM ...EnterStreet...
13200 ML% = 20: VTAB 5: HTAB 17: GOSUB 20000
13210 STREET$ = NTRY$: RETURN
13289 REM
13290  REM ...EnterCity...
13300 ML% = 20: VTAB 6: HTAB 17: GOSUB 20000
13310 CITY$ = NTRY$: RETURN
13389 REM
13390  REM ...EnterState...
13400 ML% = 2: VTAB 7: HTAB 17: GOSUB 20000
13410 SE$ = NTRY$: RETURN
13489 REM
13490  REM ...EnterZip...
13500 ML% = 9: VTAB 8: HTAB 17: GOSUB 20000
13510 ZIP$ = NTRY$: RETURN
13589 REM
13590  REM ...GetRecordNumber...
13600 VTAB 19: HTAB 3: PRINT "Type the number of
      a record"
13610 HTAB 3: PRINT "to enter, review, or change."
13620 HTAB 3: PRINT "Then press RETURN."
13630 VTAB 3: HTAB 7: PRINT "<RECORD:>"; SPC( 10)
13640 ML% = 3: VTAB 3: HTAB 17: GOSUB 20000:
      REM ..GetEntry
13650 RECRD = VAL (NTRY$): IF RECRD < 0 THEN
      PRINT BEEP$;: GOTO 13640
13660 FR% = 19:LR% = 21: GOSUB 30100:
      REM ..ClearDisplayLines
13670 RETURN
15989 REM
15990 REM ...Display welcome and set up disk...
15991 REM
16000 HOME
16010 VTAB 3: PRINT LEFT$ (TL$,39): REM ..Draw
      top line
16020 VTAB 5: HTAB 2: PRINT "Welcome to
      Mailing-List Entry/Review"
16030 VTAB 10: HTAB 12: PRINT "Just a minute..."
16040 VTAB 16: HTAB 9: PRINT "A Forrest
      Lake Program"
16050 PRINT LEFT$ (BL$,39): REM ..Draw bottom line
16060 PRINT D$;"OPEN ";FILE$;",L76"
16080 RETURN
```

Figure 11-6. Random-access Mailing-List Entry/Review program (*continued*)

```
16989 REM
16990 REM ...WriteRecord...
16991 REM
17000 IF NOT CHANGED THEN RETURN: REM ..Don't
      write unless changes made
17010 VTAB 21: HTAB 3: PRINT "Saving to disk...";
17020 PRINT:  PRINT D$;"WRITE ";FILE$;",R";RECRD
17030 PRINT NAME$
17040 PRINT STREET$
17050 PRINT CITY$
17060 PRINT SE$
17070 PRINT ZIP$
17080 PRINT D$: REM ..Deactivate disk output
17090 FR% = 21:LR% = 21: GOSUB 30100:
      REM ..ClearDisplayLines
17100 RETURN
17989 REM
17990 REM ...ReadRecord...
17991 REM
18000 VTAB 21: HTAB 3: PRINT "Reading
      record ";RECRD;" from disk..."; SPC( 5)
18010 PRINT: IF EN < > 5 THEN PRINT D$;
      "READ ";FILE$;",R";RECRD
18020 VTAB 23: HTAB 39: REM ..Accomodate
      INPUT "feature"
18030 IF EN < > 5 THEN INPUT
      "";NAME$,STREET$,CITY$,SE$,ZIP$
18040 PRINT D$: REM ..Deactivate READ command
18050 IF NAME$ = "" THEN EN = 5: REM ..Handle
      nonexistent records
18060 FR% = 21:LR% = 21: GOSUB 30100:
      REM ..ClearDisplayLines
18070 IF EN = 5 THEN VTAB 19: HTAB 3: PRINT "New
      Record."
18080 CHANGED = 0: REM ..Reset changes-made flag
18090 RETURN
18989 REM
18990 REM ...DisplayRecord...
18991 REM
19000 VTAB 4: HTAB 17: PRINT NAME$
19010 VTAB 5: HTAB 17: PRINT STREET$
19020 VTAB 6: HTAB 17: PRINT CITY$
19030 VTAB 7: HTAB 17: PRINT SE$
19040 VTAB 8: HTAB 17: PRINT ZIP$
19050 RETURN
19989 REM
19990 REM ...GetEntry...
19991 REM
```

Figure 11-6. Random-access Mailing-List Entry/Review program (*continued*)

```
20000 HT% = PEEK (36) + 1: REM  ..Cursor column
20010 NTRY$ = "": REM ..Empty entry
20020 CL% = LEN (NTRY$): REM ..Current
      entry length
20030 HTAB HT%: PRINT NTRY$;
20040 IF ML% > CL% THEN PRINT LEFT$
      (EF$,ML% - CL%);: REM ..Fill unused entry
      field
20050 HTAB HT% + CL%: GOSUB 30000: REM ..Get one
      character
20060 IF C$ = CHR$ (127) AND CL% < = 1 THEN 20010:
      REM ..Delete key with empty entry?
20070 IF C$ = CHR$ (127) THEN NTRY$ =
      LEFT$ (NTRY$,CL% - 1): GOTO 20020:
      REM ..Delete key?
20080 IF C$ = CHR$ (24) THEN 20010: REM ..Control-
      X means cancel
20090 IF C$ = CHR$ (13) THEN PRINT
      SPC( ML% - CL%);: RETURN: REM ..Return means
      done
20100 IF C$ > = " " AND C$ < = "~" AND CL% < ML%
      THEN NTRY$ = NTRY$ + C$: REM ..Add valid
      characters if room
20110 GOTO 20020: REM ..Get another keystroke
20989 REM
20990 REM ...GetYesNo...
20991 REM
21000 HT% = PEEK (36) + 1:VT% = PEEK (37) + 1:
      REM ..Cursor position
21010 IF C$ = "Y" OR C$ = "y" OR (C$ = CHR$ (8)
      AND NTRY$ = "NO") THEN VTAB VT%: HTAB HT%:
      PRINT "<YES>  No ";:NTRY$ = "YES"
21020 IF C$ = "N" OR C$ = "n" OR (C$ = CHR$ (21)
      AND NTRY$ = "YES") THEN VTAB VT%: HTAB HT%:
      PRINT " Yes  <NO>";:NTRY$ = "NO"
21030 VTAB 19: HTAB 3: PRINT "Type Y for Yes or N
      for No,"
21040 HTAB 3: PRINT "or press <-- or --> to
      change."
21050 HTAB 3: PRINT "Then press RETURN.  ";
21060 GOSUB 30000: REM ..GetChar
21070 IF C$ = " " THEN C$ = CHR$ (21):
      REM ..Accommodate 80-col. card "feature"
21080 IF C$ < > CHR$ (13) THEN 21010: REM ..Only
      RETURN confirms
21090 FR% = 19:LR% = 21: GOSUB 30100:
      REM ..ClearDisplayLines
```

Figure 11-6. Random-access Mailing-List Entry/Review program (*continued*)

```
21100 RETURN
21989 REM
21990 REM ...GetFieldNumber...
21991 REM
22000 VTAB 19: HTAB 3: PRINT "To select a field,
      type a number or "
22010 HTAB 3: PRINT "press UP-ARROW or
      DOWN-ARROW."
22020 HTAB 3: PRINT "Then press RETURN.  ";
22030 GOSUB 30000: REM ..GetChar
22040 IF C$ = CHR$ (10) AND FIELD% < LF% THEN
      GOSUB 23500:FIELD% = FIELD% + 1:
      GOSUB 23000: REM ..Down-arrow key
22050 IF C$ = CHR$ (11) AND FIELD% > 1 THEN GOSUB
      23500:FIELD% = FIELD% - 1: GOSUB 23000:
      REM ..Up-arrow key
22060 IF C$ > = "1" AND C$ < = STR$ (LF%) THEN
      GOSUB 23500:FIELD% = VAL (C$): GOSUB 23000:
      REM ..Digit key
22070 IF C$ < > CHR$ (13) THEN 22030: REM ..Only
      RETURN confirms
22080 FR% = 19:LR% = 21: GOSUB 30100:
      REM ..ClearDisplayLines
22090 RETURN
22989 REM
22990 REM ...SelectField...
22991 REM
23000 VT% = PEEK (37) + 1:HT% = PEEK (36) + 1:
      REM ..Cursor location
23010 VTAB FR%(1,FIELD%): HTAB FC%(1,FIELD%):
      PRINT FD$(1,FIELD%);: REM ..Display selected
      description
23020 VTAB VT%: HTAB HT%: REM ..Reset cursor
23030 RETURN
23489 REM
23490 REM ...DeselectField...
23491 REM
23500 VT% = PEEK (37) + 1:HT% = PEEK (36) + 1:
      REM ..Cursor location
23510 VTAB FR%(2,FIELD%): HTAB FC%(2,FIELD%):
      PRINT FD$(2,FIELD%);: REM ..Display
      deselected description
23520 VTAB VT%: HTAB HT%: REM ..Reset cursor
23530 RETURN
29989 REM
29990 REM ...GetCharacter...
29991 REM
30000 GET C$: REM ..Wait for keystroke
```

Figure 11-6. Random-access Mailing-List Entry/Review program (*continued*)

```
30010 RETURN
30089 REM
30090 REM ...ClearDisplayLines...
30091 REM
30100 FOR ROW = FR% TO LR%
30110 VTAB ROW: HTAB 2: PRINT SPC( 37);
30120 NEXT ROW
30130 RETURN
30189 REM
30190 REM ...DisplayBox...
30191 REM
30200 VTAB T%: HTAB L% + 1
30210 PRINT LEFT$ (TL$,R% - L% - 1);: REM ..Top
      line
30220 FOR ROW = T% + 1 TO B%: REM ..Side lines
30230 VTAB ROW: HTAB L%: PRINT SL$;
30240 HTAB R%: PRINT SL$
30250 NEXT ROW
30260 VTAB B%: HTAB L% + 1: PRINT LEFT$
      (BL$,R% - L% - 1);: REM ..Bottom line
30270 RETURN
```

Figure 11-6. Random-access Mailing-List Entry/Review program (*continued*)

The random-access program begins in the usual manner, by enabling error interception, initializing variables, activating the 80-column adapter, setting the display width, displaying a welcome message, opening the mailing-list file, and displaying the entry window (lines 900-1030). The variable initialization subroutine sets the file name to ADDRESS and the initial record number to 1 (lines 10170 and 10180). Next, the program clears variable EN, which contains the code number of the most recent error intercepted, if any (line 1033). After that, it displays the current record number and field descriptions (lines 1036-1060). It then tries to read the record (line 1063). If successful, the program displays the record values (line 1066). If unsuccessful, it has the user input the values at the keyboard (lines 1070-1100).

After displaying the values of an existing record or inputting values for a new record, the program selects field 6 (Another Entry) and waits for the user to confirm that selection or make another (lines 1110 and 1120). If the user chooses field 6, the program writes the current record to disk, asks for another record number, clears the old record from the screen, and branches back to display or input the requested record (line 1130). If the user chooses a field between 1 and 5 instead, the program requests a new value for it (line 1140). If the user chooses field 7, the program quits (lines 1150-1230). Quitting involves getting the user's approval (lines 1160-1190), writing the last record (line 1200), closing all files (line 1210), and displaying a parting message in the middle of an empty screen (lines 1220 and 1230).

The error-handling routine is almost identical to the one in the sequential-access entry program. It displays specific messages for a few error codes and a general message for the rest (lines 8040-8710). It also checks for error codes 2 and 5, which indicate an attempt to read a nonexistent record (lines 8020 and 8030). In either case, variable EN is set to 5 and the statement that caused the error is reexecuted. The rest of the program uses variable EN to determine whether it is dealing with a nonexistent record.

The DisplayEntryWindow subroutine (lines 11000-11060) is identical to the subroutine in Figure 11-2 except for the title on the entry window display.

The EnterField subroutine (lines 12000-13510) is also identical with one exception: just before returning, the subroutine always sets variable CHANGED to 1, which is the same as the logical value of True. Later, the variable CHANGED tells the Write-Record subroutine to write the record, since it may have been changed.

The GetRecordNumber subroutine is new (lines 13600-13640). It replaces the current record number with a message that prompts the user to enter another record number (line 13630); it then inputs the record number (line 13640). If the number is less than 0, the console speaker beeps and the subroutine asks the user to enter another number. Before returning, the subroutine erases the instructions it displayed at the bottom of the screen (line 13660).

The subroutine used to display a welcome message and set up the disk in the sequential-access entry program can be used here (lines 16000-16070). The display is slightly changed (lines 16010-16020 and 16050). Also, the file is opened by indicating a record length, thus identifying it as a random-access file (line 16060).

With a few changes, the same subroutines that read and write records sequentially in Figure 11-2 will work for a random-access file (lines 17000-17100 and 18000-18090). The READ and WRITE commands now specify a record number (lines 17020 and 18010). The ReadRecord subroutine checks for an empty value in the first field. If the value is empty, the subroutine sets variable EN to indicate that an attempt was made to read a non-existent record (line 18050). If the record is empty or if an end-of-data error or a range error occurred while it tried to read the record, the subroutine displays the message **New Record** (line 18070).

A new subroutine, DisplayRecord, displays the current record alongside the field descriptions on the screen (lines 19000-19050).

The random-access Mailing-List Entry/Review program works with DOS 3.3 with just one change. Since DOS 3.3 resets the record length to 1 when an end-of-data error occurs, the program must reset the record length to its proper value at that time. Adding an OPEN command to the ErrorHandler subroutine does the job:

```
]8030 IF EN = 5 THEN PRINT: PRINT D$;
      "OPEN ";FILE$;",L76": RESUME: REM.. End of
      data; reset length
```

The FLUSH Command

You may recall that ProDOS uses disk buffers to cut down on the number of times it must physically record information on the disk. Both the sequential-access and random-access entry programs demonstrate this feature clearly. In the previous program, the message **Saving to disk . . .** flashes by quickly as the record is written into the disk buffer in the Apple II's memory. Only after the buffer is full and the information is recorded on the disk does the message linger. If the power is interrupted before the buffer is written to the disk, the new records and changed records still in the buffer will never be written on the disk.

The FLUSH command prevents this loss of data by forcing ProDOS to write the disk buffer onto the disk. Here is an example:

```
]17075 PRINT D$;"FLUSH ";FILE$
```

If you add this program line to either of the entry programs (Figure 11-2 or Figure 11-6), the disk buffer will immediately be written to the disk every time a record is saved. The program will slow down noticeably, but you may consider the sacrifice worth the security.

A file name or pathname is optional in the FLUSH command. If it is absent, the buffers for all open files are written to disk.

Random-Access Print Program

It takes very few changes to convert the sequential-access Mailing-List Print program (Figure 11-4) to a random-access printing program as shown in Figure 11-7. The changes from Figure 11-4 are shaded; you must also delete line 3020.

First, you need to change the file name to the name of the random-access file (line 10170). Next, replace the sequential-access ReadRecord subroutine (lines 18000-18040) with the random-access subroutine from the random-access Mailing-List program (Figure 11-6, lines 18000-18090). You should eliminate line 18070 since there is no need to display a **New Record** message in the print program. The print program will not print nonexistent records.

The error-handling routine must check for a range error (code 2), which will occur if the user specifies a nonexistent record number beyond the highest record number (line 8015).

The subroutine that prints the report (lines 3000-3110) must open the file with a proper record length (line 3010). It no longer needs a POSITION command since the READ command in the ReadRecord subroutine specifies the record by number, so line 3020 must be deleted. Finally, the subroutine must skip each nonexistent record it encounters in the middle of the file and each record that causes an end-of-data error. Variable EN will have a value of 5 in those instances (line 3060).

```
900 ONERR GOTO 8000: REM ..Enable error trapping
1000 GOSUB 10000: REM ..Initialize variables
1010 PRINT CHR$ (21): REM ..Deactivate
     80-col. card
1020 REM ..Display width is 40
1025 GOSUB 16000: REM ..Display welcome and
     set up disk
1030 GOSUB 11000: REM ..DisplayEntryWindow
1040 FOR X1 = 1 TO LF%
```

Figure 11-7. Random-access Mailing-List Print program

```
1050 FIELD% = X1: GOSUB 23500: REM ..Display field
     description
1060 NEXT X1
1070 FOR X1 = 1 TO 2: REM ..Enter all fields
1080 FIELD% = X1
1090 GOSUB 23000: GOSUB 12000: GOSUB 23500:
     REM ..SelectField:EnterField:DeselectField
1100 NEXT X1
1110 FIELD% = 3: GOSUB 23000: REM ..SelectField
1120 GOSUB 22000: REM ..GetFieldNumber
1130 IF FIELD% = 3 THEN GOSUB 3000:FR% = 4:
     LR% = 5: GOSUB 30100: GOSUB 23500: GOTO 1040:
     REM ..If field=3, print requested records,
     blank last entries, deselect and get another
     range
1140 IF FIELD% < LF% THEN GOSUB 12000: GOTO 1120:
     REM ..EnterField
1150 REM ...Quit?...
1160 T% = 12:L% = 4:B% = 17:R% = 37: GOSUB 30200:
     REM ..DisplayBox
1170 VTAB 14: HTAB 5: PRINT BEEP$;"Are you sure
     you want to quit?";
1180 VTAB 16: HTAB 8:C$ = "Y": GOSUB 21000:
     REM ..GetYesNo
1190 IF NTRY$ = "NO" THEN FR% = 12:LR% = 17:
     GOSUB 30100: GOSUB 23000: GOTO 1120: REM ..If
     no, erase box, restore field, and get another
     field
1200 PRINT: PRINT D$;"CLOSE"
1210 HOME: VTAB 12: HTAB 8: PRINT "End of
     Mailing-List Print"
1220 VTAB 23: HTAB 1: END
2989 REM
2990 REM ...Print the selected range of records...
2991 REM
3000 VTAB 21: HTAB 3: PRINT "Finding
     first record..."
3010 PRINT D$;"OPEN ";FILE$;",L76"
3030 FR% = 21:LR% = 21: GOSUB 30100:
     REM ..ClearDisplayLines
3040 FOR RECRD = SR% TO ER%
3050 GOSUB 18000: REM ..ReadRecord
3060 IF EN = 5 THEN EN = 0: GOTO 3080:
     REM ..Skip nonexistent records
3070 GOSUB 14000: REM ..PrintRecord
3080 NEXT RECRD
3090 EN = 0: REM ..Clear error flag
3100 PRINT: PRINT D$;"CLOSE ";FILE$
```

Figure 11-7. Random-access Mailing-List Print program (*continued*)

```
3110 RETURN
7989 REM
7990 REM ...ErrorHandler...
7991 REM
8000 EN = PEEK (222): REM ..Error number
8010 EL = PEEK (219) * 256 + PEEK (218):
     REM ..Error line
8015 IF EN = 2 THEN EN = 5: REM ..Past end of file
8020 IF EN = 5 THEN RESUME: REM ..End of file
8030 PRINT BEEP$;BEEP$;
8040 FR% = 9:LR% = 14: GOSUB 30100:
     REM ..ClearDisplayLines
8050 T% = 9:L% = 4:B% = 14:R% = 37: GOSUB 30200:
     REM ..DisplayBox
8060 VTAB 11: REM ..Position for error messg.
8390 IF EN < > 6 AND EN < > 7 THEN 8490
8400 HTAB 5: PRINT "File ";FILE$;" not found."
8410 HTAB 5: PRINT "Check prefix and drive."
8420 GOTO 8620: REM ..Quit
8490 IF EN < > 8 THEN 8600
8500 HTAB 5: PRINT "Disk or drive error."
8510 HTAB 5: PRINT "Check disk, drive,
     and prefix."
8520 GOTO 8620: REM ..Quit
8600 HTAB 5: PRINT "Unexpected error
     (code ";EN;")."
8610 PRINT
8620 HTAB 5: PRINT "Press RETURN to quit. ";
8630 GOSUB 30000: REM ..GetChar
8640 IF C$ < > CHR$ (13) THEN 8630: REM ..Wait
     for RETURN
8650 GOTO 1200: REM ..Quit
9989 REM
9990 REM ...InitializeVariables...
9991 REM
10000 D$ = CHR$ (4): REM ..ProDOS/DOS 3.3 prefix
10010 W4$ = CHR$ (17): REM ..Display width 40
10020 BEEP$ = CHR$ (07): REM ..Beep char.
10030 FOR X1 = 1 TO 40
10040 EF$ = EF$ + ".": REM ..Entry field chars.
10050 TL$ = TL$ + "_": REM ..Top line chars.
10060 BL$ = BL$ + "‾": REM ..Bottom line chars.
10070 NEXT X1
10080 SL$ = "|": REM ..Side line chars.
10090 LF% = 4: REM ..Last field number
10100 DIM FR%(2,LF%),FC%(2,LF%),FD$(2,LF%)
10110 FOR X1 = 1 TO LF%: REM ..Read field
      locations and descriptions
```

Figure 11-7. Random-access Mailing-List Print program (*continued*)

```
10120 READ FR%(1,X1),FC%(1,X1),FD$(1,X1)
10130 READ FR%(2,X1),FC%(2,X1),FD$(2,X1)
10140 NEXT X1
10170 FILE$ = "ADDRESS"
10190 PL% = 65: REM ..Force headings on 1st
      printed page
10200 RETURN
10489 REM
10490 REM ...Field Descriptions and Locations...
10491 REM
10500 DATA 4,3," 1. <FIRST RECORD TO PRINT:>"
10510 DATA 4,3," 1.  First Record to Print: "
10520 DATA 5,3," 2. <LAST RECORD TO PRINT:> "
10530 DATA 5,3," 2.  Last Record to Print:  "
10540 DATA 8,3," 3. <PRINT>   "
10550 DATA 8,3," 3.  Print    "
10560 DATA 9,3," 4. <QUIT>   "
10570 DATA 9,3," 4.  Quit    "
10989 REM
10990 REM ...DisplayEntryWindow...
10991 REM
11000 HOME
11010 T% = 1:L% = 1:B% = 22:R% = 39: GOSUB 30200:
      REM ..DisplayBox
11020 TITLE$ = "MAILING-LIST PRINT"
11030 INVERSE: VTAB 1: HTAB (40 - LEN (TITLE$)) /
      2: PRINT TITLE$;: NORMAL: REM ..Display
      title
11040 RETURN
11989 REM
11990 REM ...EnterField...
11991 REM
12000 VTAB 20: HTAB 3: PRINT "Enter the selected
      field."
12010 HTAB 3: PRINT "Then press RETURN to confirm
      entry.";
12020 ON FIELD% GOSUB 13100,13200
12030 FR% = 19:LR% = 21: GOSUB 30100:
      REM ..ClearDisplayLines
12040 RETURN
13089 REM
13090 REM ...EnterFirstRecordNumber...
13100 ML% = 3: VTAB 4: HTAB 32: GOSUB 20000
13110 SR% = VAL (NTRY$): IF SR% < 1 THEN 13100
13120 RETURN
13189 REM
13190 REM ...EnterLastRecordNumber...
```

Figure 11-7. Random-access Mailing-List Print program (*continued*)

```
13200 ML% = 3: VTAB 5: HTAB 32: GOSUB 20000
13210 ER% = VAL (NTRY$): IF ER% < 1 THEN 13200
13220 RETURN
13989 REM
13990 REM ...PrintRecord...
13991 REM
14000 VTAB 21: HTAB 3: PRINT "Printing...";
14010 PRINT: PRINT D$;"PR#1": REM ..Switch
      to printer
14020 PRINT CHR$ (9);"80N";: REM ..Line width 80
14030 PL% = PL% + 1: GOSUB 15000: REM ..TopPage
14040 PRINT NAME$;
14050 HTAB 22: PRINT STREET$;
14060 POKE 36,42: PRINT CITY$;", ";SE$;" ";ZIP$
14070 IF PL% / 5 = INT (PL% / 5) THEN PRINT:
      PL% = PL% + 1: REM ..Print a blank line
      every 5th address
14080 PRINT CHR$ (9);"R": REM ..Switch to screen
14090 VTAB 21: HTAB 2: PRINT SPC( 37);:
      REM ..Clear bottom line
14100 RETURN
14989 REM
14990 REM ...TopPage...
14991 REM
15000 IF PL% < 55 THEN RETURN: REM ..Page
      full yet?
15010 FOR X1 = 1 TO (66 - PL%): REM ..Space to
      bottom of page
15020 PRINT: NEXT X1
15030 PRINT TAB( 28);"MAILING LIST"
15040 PRINT
15050 PRINT "NAME"; SPC( 18);"STREET";
      SPC( 16);"CITY, STATE,ZIP"
15060 PRINT "____________________ ";
15070 PRINT "____________________ ";
15080 PRINT "__________________________________"
15090 PRINT
15100 PL% = 6: RETURN: REM ..Reset printed
      line counter
15989 REM
15990 REM ...Display welcome and set up disk...
15991 REM
16000 HOME
16010 VTAB 2: HTAB 5: PRINT LEFT$ (TL$,31):
      REM ..Draw top line
16020 VTAB 5: HTAB 6: PRINT "Welcome to
      Mailing-List Print"
16030 VTAB 10: HTAB 12: PRINT "Just a minute..."
```

Figure 11-7. Random-access Mailing-List Print program (*continued*)

```
16040 VTAB 16: HTAB 9: PRINT "A Forrest
      Lake Program"
16050 HTAB 5: PRINT LEFT$ (BL$,31): REM ..Draw
      bottom line
16060 PRINT D$;"RENAME ";FILE$;",";FILE$:
      REM ..See if file exists
16070 RETURN
17989 REM
17990 REM ...ReadRecord...
17991 REM
18000 VTAB 21: HTAB 3: PRINT "Reading
      record ";RECRD;" from disk..."; SPC( 5)
18010 PRINT: IF EN < > 5 THEN PRINT D$;"READ
      ";FILE$;",R";RECRD
18020 VTAB 23: HTAB 39: REM ..Accomodate INPUT
      "feature"
18030 IF EN < > 5 THEN INPUT
      "";NAME$,STREET$,CITY$,SE$,ZIP$
18040 PRINT D$: REM ..Deactivate READ command
18050 IF NAME$ = "" THEN EN = 5: REM ..Handle
      nonexistent records
18060 FR% = 21:LR% = 21: GOSUB 30100:
      REM ..ClearDisplayLines
18080 CHANGED = 0: REM ..Reset changes-made flag
18090 RETURN
19989 REM
19990 REM ...GetEntry...
19991 REM
20000 HT% = PEEK (36) + 1: REM  ..Cursor column
20010 NTRY$ = "": REM ..Empty entry
20020 CL% = LEN (NTRY$): REM ..Current entry
      length
20030 HTAB HT%: PRINT NTRY$;
20040 IF ML% > CL% THEN PRINT LEFT$
      (EF$,ML% - CL%);: REM ..Fill unused entry
      field
20050 HTAB HT% + CL%: GOSUB 30000: REM ..Get one
      character
20060 IF C$ = CHR$ (127) AND CL% < = 1 THEN 20010:
      REM ..Delete key with empty entry?
20070 IF C$ = CHR$ (127) THEN NTRY$ = LEFT$
      (NTRY$,CL% - 1): GOTO 20020: REM ..Delete
      key?
20080 IF C$ = CHR$ (24) THEN 20010: REM ..Control-
      X means cancel
20090 IF C$ = CHR$ (13) THEN PRINT
      SPC( ML% - CL%);: RETURN: REM ..Return
      means done
```

Figure 11-7. Random-access Mailing-List Print program (*continued*)

```
20100 IF C$ > = " " AND C$ < = "~" AND CL% < ML%
      THEN NTRY$ = NTRY$ + C$: REM ..Add valid
      characters if room
20110 GOTO 20020: REM ..Get another keystroke
20989 REM
20990 REM ...GetYesNo...
20991 REM
21000 HT% = PEEK (36) + 1:VT% = PEEK (37) + 1:
      REM ..Cursor position
21010 IF C$ = "Y" OR C$ = "y" OR (C$ = CHR$ (8)
      AND NTRY$ = "NO") THEN VTAB VT%: HTAB HT%:
      PRINT "<YES>  No ";:NTRY$ = "YES"
21020 IF C$ = "N" OR C$ = "n" OR (C$ = CHR$ (21)
      AND NTRY$ = "YES") THEN VTAB VT%: HTAB HT%:
      PRINT " Yes  <NO>";:NTRY$ = "NO"
21030 VTAB 19: HTAB 3: PRINT "Type Y for Yes or
      N for No,"
21040 HTAB 3: PRINT "or press <-- or -->
      to change."
21050 HTAB 3: PRINT "Then press RETURN.  ";
21060 GOSUB 30000: REM ..GetChar
21070 IF C$ = " " THEN C$ = CHR$ (21):
      REM ..Accommodate 80-col. card "feature"
21080 IF C$ < > CHR$ (13) THEN 21010: REM ..Only
      RETURN confirms
21090 FR% = 19:LR% = 21: GOSUB 30100:
      REM ..ClearDisplayLines
21100 RETURN
21989 REM
21990 REM ...GetFieldNumber...
21991 REM
22000 VTAB 19: HTAB 3: PRINT "To select a field,
      type a number or "
22010 HTAB 3: PRINT "press UP-ARROW or
      DOWN-ARROW."
22020 HTAB 3: PRINT "Then press RETURN.  ";
22030 GOSUB 30000: REM ..GetChar
22040 IF C$ = CHR$ (10) AND FIELD% < LF% THEN
      GOSUB 23500:FIELD% = FIELD% + 1: GOSUB
      23000: REM ..Down-arrow key
22050 IF C$ = CHR$ (11) AND FIELD% > 1 THEN
      GOSUB 23500:FIELD% = FIELD% - 1:
      GOSUB 23000: REM ..Up-arrow key
22060 IF C$ > = "1" AND C$ < = STR$ (LF%) THEN
      GOSUB 23500:FIELD% = VAL (C$): GOSUB 23000:
      REM ..Digit key
22070 IF C$ < > CHR$ (13) THEN 22030: REM ..Only
      RETURN confirms
```

Figure 11-7. Random-Access Mailing-List Print program (*continued*)

```
22080 FR% = 19:LR% = 21: GOSUB 30100:
      REM ..ClearDisplayLines
22090 RETURN
22989 REM
22990 REM ...SelectField...
22991 REM
23000 VT% = PEEK (37) + 1:HT% = PEEK (36) + 1:
      REM ..Cursor location
23010 VTAB FR%(1,FIELD%): HTAB FC%(1,FIELD%):
      PRINT FD$(1,FIELD%);: REM ..Display selected
      description
23020 VTAB VT%: HTAB HT%: REM ..Reset cursor
23030 RETURN
23489 REM
23490 REM ...DeselectField...
23491 REM
23500 VT% = PEEK (37) + 1:HT% = PEEK (36) + 1:
      REM ..Cursor location
23510 VTAB FR%(2,FIELD%): HTAB FC%(2,FIELD%):
      PRINT FD$(2,FIELD%);: REM ..Display
      deselected description
23520 VTAB VT%: HTAB HT%: REM ..Reset cursor
23530 RETURN
29989 REM
29990 REM ...GetCharacter...
29991 REM
30000 GET C$: REM ..Wait for keystroke
30010 RETURN
30089 REM
30090 REM ...ClearDisplayLines...
30091 REM
30100 FOR ROW = FR% TO LR%
30110 VTAB ROW: HTAB 2: PRINT SPC( 37);
30120 NEXT ROW
30130 RETURN
30189 REM
30190 REM ...DisplayBox...
30191 REM
30200 VTAB T%: HTAB L% + 1
30210 PRINT LEFT$ (TL$,R% - L% - 1);:
      REM ..Top line
30220 FOR ROW = T% + 1 TO B%: REM ..Side lines
30230 VTAB ROW: HTAB L%: PRINT SL$;
30240 HTAB R%: PRINT SL$
30250 NEXT ROW
30260 VTAB B%: HTAB L% + 1: PRINT
      LEFT$ (BL$,R% - L% - 1);: REM ..Bottom line
30270 RETURN
```

Figure 11-7. Random-access Mailing-List Print program (*continued*)

MACHINE LANGUAGE (BINARY IMAGE) DISK FILES

ProDOS supports machine language and binary image (graphics) files. These files are shown with a BIN file type code next to the file in a ProDOS disk directory, or the letter B in a DOS 3.3 catalog. Both low- and high-resolution graphics images can be stored on disk for later recall and display. Machine language programs can be loaded and executed directly, or they can be called by BASIC programs using the CALL statement or USR function.

ProDOS and DOS 3.3 have three commands that are specifically designed for binary files. They are BSAVE, BLOAD, and BRUN. The function of each command corresponds to its nonbinary equivalent—SAVE, LOAD, and RUN. With ProDOS, the BLOAD and BSAVE commands can be used to load and save files of any type.

The BSAVE Command

BSAVE, as the name implies, saves a binary image on disk. Here is an example:

```
]BSAVE FILENAME,A378,L21,S6,D2
```

Note that there are two parameters not found in other ProDOS commands. These parameters are *not* optional; they must be specified. The drive and slot numbers are optional, as usual.

The first parameter, A, is the *address* parameter; it refers to the starting memory address of the binary image to be saved. The address may be either a decimal or hexadecimal constant. Hexadecimal values must be preceded by a dollar sign. Decimal values must be in the range 0-65535. Negative values are prohibited.

The L parameter specifies the *length* of the binary image to be saved. The length is the number of bytes in the image. It may be specified as a decimal or hexadecimal number, with hexadecimal values preceded by a dollar sign. The length must be in the range 0 through 65535 with ProDOS (1 through 32767 with DOS 3.3), or an error message will be displayed.

With ProDOS, instead of specifying the length with the L

parameter, you could specify the ending address in memory with the E parameter. The following example is equivalent to the last one:

```
]BSAVE FILENAME,A378,E399,S6,D2
```

Normally, the BSAVE command starts saving at the beginning of the file. ProDOS lets you specify an offset by including the B parameter. The following example skips over the first 30 bytes of the file before it starts saving:

```
]BSAVE FILENAME,A378,E399,B30
```

Another ProDOS option lets you specify the type of file you want saved. All you do is add a comma, the letter T, and the file type code. Table 11-1 lists ProDOS file type codes. Any file type listed in the table is allowed, not just BIN. However, it is your responsibility to make sure the contents of the file are consistent with the file type you specify. For example, there would be no point in specifying type BAS (for "BASIC program") with graphics data written in binary.

The BLOAD Command

BLOAD retrieves the contents of binary files and loads them into memory. The BLOAD command looks like this:

```
]BLOAD FILENAME,A378,B30,L21
```

Table 11-1. ProDOS File Type Codes

File Code	Meaning
DIR	Directory
TXT	Human-readable letters, digits, and symbols
BAS	Applesoft BASIC program
VAR	Applesoft BASIC variables
BIN	Machine code or data
REI	Machine code that can be loaded anywhere in memory
$F*n*	User- (programmer-) defined type number *n*
SYS	System program or data

With ProDOS, all the parameters available with the BSAVE command can be used with the BLOAD command: A for starting address, L for length or E for ending address, T for type, D for drive number, and S for slot number. With BLOAD, however, all of these parameters are optional. DOS 3.3 also allows a volume number parameter, V, but does not allow the L, E, and T parameters.

BLOAD requires only a file name. If the starting address is absent, the image will be loaded starting at the address that was specified when the image was saved. Machine language programs may not function properly if they are loaded into the wrong memory addresses.

Unlike the LOAD command, BLOAD will not erase programs and data values that reside in the memory locations where the image will be stored. Only those locations within the BLOAD range are affected; no other memory values are changed.

No error will occur if you specify read-only memory (ROM) locations as part of the BLOAD range. The ROM locations will be unchanged, of course.

The BRUN Command

BRUN is identical to BLOAD except that after the file has been loaded, BRUN executes a machine language JMP (jump) instruction to the starting address. If no address is specified, the jump is to the address from which the image was saved. The following is an example of BRUN:

```
]BRUN FILENAME,A378
```

The BRUN command allows several optional parameters: A for starting address, D for drive number, and S for slot number. With ProDOS, you can also specify L for length or E for ending address, and T for type. If the starting address is missing, the file is loaded and run starting at the address from which it was saved. If the L and E parameters are absent, the whole file is loaded.

Use BRUN only with files that contain machine language programs. If you use it with a BASIC program file, an error message appears. The results are unpredictable if you use it with graphics or other data and may cause the Apple II to lock up, forcing you to restart with CONTROL-OPEN APPLE-RESET.

THE PRODOS SMART RUN COMMAND

If you're not sure which type of program resides in memory, use the ProDOS - command. That's right, the command is a dash (the HYPHEN key). It is a smart run command that can determine whether the file is a BASIC program, a machine language program, or an EXEC command file. Here is an example:

```
]-FILENAME
```

The - command has only two options: drive and slot numbers. None of the options available with RUN, EXEC, or BRUN are available with the - command.

THE DOS 3.3 MAXFILES COMMAND

The DOS 3.3 MAXFILES command allows you to specify the maximum number of files that may be open at any one time. Each open file reserves 595 bytes of memory for use as a file buffer. There are two 256-byte sections in each buffer, one for reading and the other for writing. The remaining 83 bytes are used for housekeeping information. The following example specifies a maximum of eight files:

```
]MAXFILES 8
```

The number of files must be an integer from 1 to 16. Initially, three buffers are allocated. MAXFILES may be set higher if you intend to use more than three files simultaneously. MAXFILES may be set lower if you need those extra bytes of memory for your BASIC program.

All DOS 3.3 commands except PR#, IN#, and MAXFILES require a file buffer to execute. Thus, if you have opened disk files up to the limit and then use a RENAME command, the error **NO BUFFERS AVAILABLE** occurs. No buffer is required for commands used outside of the disk context, however (cassette LOAD, for example).

When a MAXFILES command is executed in immediate mode, Integer BASIC programs are erased and Applesoft strings become garbled. You should therefore execute MAXFILES before loading or running a program. MAXFILES also disables the RENUMBER program.

MAXFILES may be executed within Applesoft programs if preceded by the usual prefix character (ASCII code 4) in a PRINT statement. MAXFILES will cause GOTO, GOSUB, and other instructions to malfunction unless it is the first statement in the program. In order to avoid destroying string values, use MAXFILES as follows:

```
]1 REM First use MAXFILES command
]2 PRINT CHR$(4);"MAXFILES 9"
]3 REM Then begin regular program
```

You can use MAXFILES in Integer BASIC only in immediate mode. ProDOS manages file buffers automatically, so it has no MAXFILES command.

THE DOS 3.3 MON AND NOMON COMMANDS

The MON command allows you to monitor the information going to and coming from the disk. MON uses three parameters, as shown in the following example:

```
]MON C I O
```

MON parameters specify the type of information to be displayed. The letter C causes commands to the disk to be displayed. The letter I causes input from the disk to be displayed. The letter O causes output to the disk to be displayed.

The NOMON command cancels the effect of the MON command. NOMON uses the same three parameters MON uses, but the NOMON parameters specify which data is not to be monitored. For example, assuming you have issued MON C I O, the command NOMON O will cancel monitoring of output to the disk, but input from the disk and DOS 3.3 commands will continue to be displayed.

The MON and NOMON parameters may appear in any order and in any combination. Blank spaces and commas between the parameters are optional. At least one parameter must be present or the command will be ignored. MON remains in effect until a NOMON, INT, or FP command is executed, or until DOS 3.3 is restarted.

Graphics 12

The Apple II's color graphics can add another dimension to the programs you use, as well as to those you might write yourself. Graphics are not difficult to master, especially in a high-level language like BASIC. This chapter explains how graphics displays are produced and shows some practical and recreational applications.

DISPLAY MODES

The Apple II display screen has four modes of operation. PRINT statements always display in *text mode* using letters, digits, and symbols from the Apple II character set (see Appendix E). The other three modes display points and lines that you can combine to create graphics. The chief difference between the three graphics modes is the size and number of points each can fit on the display screen. *Low-resolution graphics* uses larger points than do *high-resolution graphics* and *double high-resolution graphics*, and consequently has room on the screen for fewer points. Another difference is the number of colors available on the screen simultaneously; low-resolution and double high-resolution graphics both permit up to 16, and high-resolution allows six. In all graphics modes the bottom of the screen can be reserved for a four-line text window, where you can immediately see mode commands or display characters.

LOW-RESOLUTION GRAPHICS

Low-resolution graphics mode divides the screen into 40 columns and 48 rows (see Figure 12-1). Each coordinate (intersection of a row and column) appears as a small rectangle on the display screen. There are 1920 coordinates in all (40 columns times 48 rows), and you can assign any one of 16 colors to each coordinate. Table 12-1 shows the available hues. You don't have to know the inner workings of the Apple II in order to use low-resolution graphics; a working knowledge of programming in BASIC is sufficient to get you started.

Selecting Low-Resolution Mode

When using BASIC, you switch to low-resolution graphics mode from text mode by using the following statement:

```
]GR
```

Once this statement executes, the display screen goes black except for four lines of text at the bottom. This lower area of the screen is called the *text window*. With the text window at the bottom of the screen, the space available for low-resolution graphics

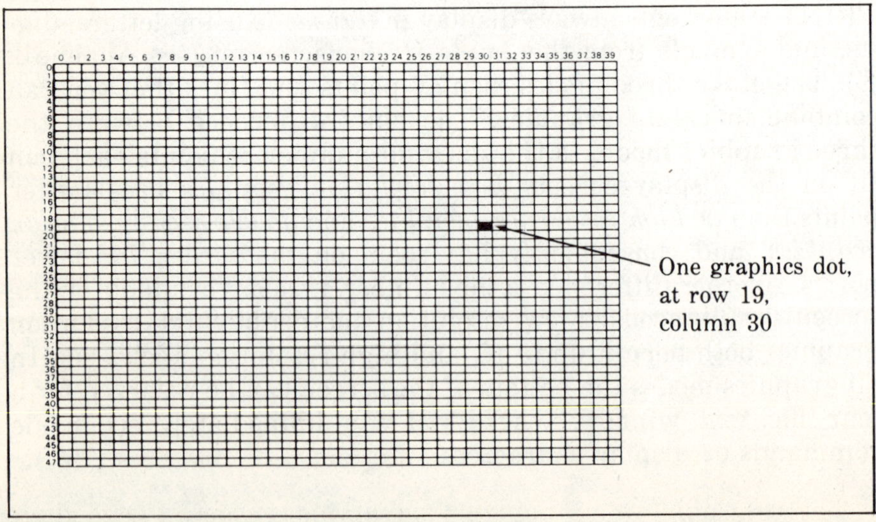

Figure 12-1. Low-resolution graphics screen

Table 12-1. Low-Resolution Graphics Colors

Color	Number	Color	Number
Black	0	Brown	8
Magenta	1	Orange	9
Dark Blue	2	Grey #2	10
Purple	3	Pink	11
Dark Green	4	Light Green	12
Grey #1	5	Yellow	13
Medium Blue	6	Aqua	14
Light Blue	7	White	15

shrinks from 48 to 40 rows. You can use the GR statement more than once in a program, even in low-resolution graphics mode, as a means of clearing the screen.

You can activate the 80-column adapter if you wish; doing so has no effect on the graphics area. The text window at the bottom of the screen can be 40 or 80 characters wide. However, the small characters used when the width is 80 are almost impossible to read on most television sets.

Full-Screen Graphics

After executing the GR statement, you can eliminate the text window in order to display graphics in the last eight lines. You do this by entering

```
]POKE -16302,0
```

The text window disappears and is replaced by graphics. Anything you type in immediate mode will still appear in the text window, but because the Apple II is now using that area of the screen for graphics, the characters will appear as graphics points, not characters. Commands will still work properly as long as you type them correctly.

To clear all 48 rows of the graphics screen, including the four-line text window, use the following command:

```
]CALL -1998
```

This command works best in programmed mode. In immediate mode the Apple II automatically displays the graphics equivalents of the Applesoft prompt character (a yellow square), the cursor (a blue or flashing white square), and a row of blank spaces (a gray line).

Restoring the Text Window

If the Apple II is in full-screen graphics mode, you can restore the text window in two ways. To clear the graphics screen and restore the text window at the same time, use the GR statement. If you want to restore the text window without altering the first 40 rows of graphics, enter the following statement:

```
]POKE -16301,0
```

Once executed, this statement reopens the text window at the bottom of the graphics screen. You may see some strange characters on the text window where graphics dots used to be. The characters are caused by the Apple II interpreting the graphics dots as ASCII character codes. You can clear the text window without affecting the graphics area with a HOME or CALL −936 statement.

Returning to Full-Screen Text

To leave low-resolution graphics mode and return to full-screen text mode, use the command TEXT. It resets the display from graphics to characters. The screen will probably be full of odd characters caused by Apple II interpreting graphics dots as text. Clear the text sceen with the HOME or CALL −936 statement.

Color Selection

In Table 12-1, each color listed has a corresponding number from 0 to 15. It is this number that you use in a COLOR statement to set the current low-resolution hue. For example, the following statement sets the drawing color to yellow:

```
]COLOR = 13
```

If you neglect to select a color, the Apple II chooses black, equivalent to COLOR=0, as the default color. Executing a GR command always resets the color number to 0.

Point Plotting

The PLOT statement places a single graphics dot—actually a small rectangle—on the Apple II display screen at the coordinates you specify.

The statement

```
]PLOT 23,18
```

illuminates the graphics point at the 24th column and 19th row in the hue selected by the last COLOR statement executed. The row number ranges from 0 to 47, and the column value from 0 to 39. If you exceed these limits in a PLOT statement, you will see an error message and your program will stop. As with any low-resolution graphics statement (except GR), you can replace constants with variables or expressions:

```
]PLOT Y/2 + 12, X-4
```

Diagonal Lines

The following Applesoft program uses all of the low-resolution graphics statements discussed so far in this chapter. It plots a diagonal line from the upper-left corner to the lower-right corner of the screen.

```
]10 REM ..Draw a diagonal line across the
    low-res screen
]20 GR
]30 HOME
]40 COLOR= RND (16) * 16 + 1
]50 FOR Y = 0 TO 39
]60 PLOT Y,Y
]70 NEXT Y
]80 GOTO 40
```

The display screen will look like Figure 12-2, except that the diagonal line will change colors randomly. Since the program runs continuously, you must press CONTROL-C to interrupt it.

To use this program in Integer BASIC, change line 40 as follows:

```
>40 COLOR = RND(16) + 1
```

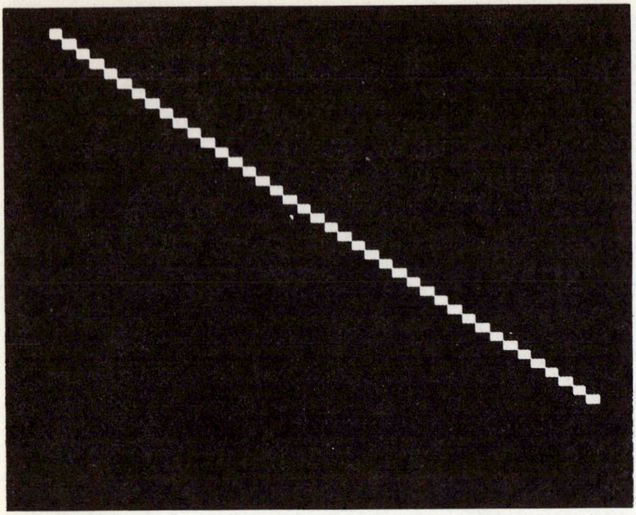

Figure 12-2. A low-resolution diagonal line

Horizontal Lines

The HLIN statement allows you to draw lines of varying lengths from left to right on the low-resolution graphics screen. The following statement draws a horizontal line at the extreme top of the screen, from the left margin to the right margin:

```
]HLIN 0,39 AT 0
```

HLIN stands for horizontal line. The first two numbers specify the columns between which the line is drawn. The last number specifies at which row the line is drawn.

Neither of the column numbers can be negative, and both must be less than 39. The row number cannot be negative or larger than 47. Numbers outside the limits in an Applesoft program cause an error message to appear. In Integer BASIC, the results are unpredictable.

Vertical Lines

The VLIN (or vertical line) statement draws a line in a selected color from one row to another at a specified column. For example, the following VLIN command will draw a line starting in row 12 down and ending in row 30, at column 33.

```
]VLIN 12,30 AT 33
```

In a VLIN command, row numbers must be between 0 and 39, and column numbers must be between 0 and 47. If any value is outside of this range, an error message is displayed.

Background Color

By repeatedly using the VLIN statement, you can fill the entire screen with one color, effectively changing the background color on which subsequent statements will draw lines and plot points. The following program illustrates this:

```
]10 REM ..Low-res background color demo
]20 GR
]30 INPUT "BACKGROUND COLOR? ";C
]40 COLOR= C
]50 GOSUB 1040
]60 GOTO 30
]1000 REM ..Subroutine to fill lo-res
]1010 REM   screen with one color.
]1020 REM   Assumes color has already
]1030 REM   been set.
]1040 FOR J = 0 TO 39
]1050 VLIN 0,39 AT J
]1060 NEXT J
]1070 RETURN
```

In this program, the subroutine beginning at line 1040 fills in the screen. It assumes the background color was set with a COLOR statement before it was called. As written, the VLIN statement at line 1050 does not draw into the text window.

Random Colors Program

This program shows how you can create a simple animated pattern of randomly changing colors with just one HLIN statement and one VLIN statement. It employs a full-screen version of the subroutine just introduced to set a background color. To halt the program, press CONTROL-C.

```
]10 REM ..Low-res HLIN and VLIN demo
]20 GR
]30 POKE -16302,0: REM ..Full screen
```

```
]40 COLOR= 14: GOSUB 1040: REM ..Background color
]50 REM ..Use random colors and locations
]60 COLOR= RND (1) * 16 + 1
]70 HLIN 0,39 AT RND (1) * 48
]80 COLOR= RND (16)
]90 VLIN 0,47 AT RND (1) * 40
]100 GOTO 60
]1000 REM ..Subroutine to fill lo-res
]1010 REM   screen with one color.
]1020 REM   Assumes color has already
]1030 REM   been set.
]1040 FOR J = 0 TO 39
]1050 VLIN 0,47 AT J
]1060 NEXT J
]1070 RETURN
```

Determining Point Color

The SCRN function is a bit more subtle than the low-resolution graphics statements presented so far. Suppose you want the computer to figure out what color is displayed at a certain point on the screen. SCRN does this. The statement

```
]X = SCRN(12,24)
```

assigns the color number of the point at column 12, row 24 to the variable X. The color passed back to the variable is numbered from 0 to 15; the number corresponds to one of the low-resolution colors listed in Table 12-1. For example, if you enter the following immediate mode statements

```
]GR
]COLOR=14
]PLOT 12,12
]PRINT SCRN(12,12)
```

the Apple II responds with

```
14

]▒
```

Future Projections Program

Many programs that display a list of values could display a graph instead. Graphing is one practical application for low-resolution graphics. For example, a program that makes future projections based on past amounts could display the exact amount of each projection, or it could draw a graph that illustrates the general trend. In this case, a graph is clearly superior because the projections are only estimates, and the trend is more important than the exact numbers.

There are several statistical methods used to calculate future projections, and there are different circumstances that dictate using one rather than another. One popular method uses a technique called *exponential regression*, which projects the increase or decrease of anything with an exponential growth factor. A typical application is a birth or reproduction rate, and that can be extended to include such related items as sales, income, and patronage.

Figure 12-3 displays three output alternatives for a future projections program: (*a*) a list of numbers, (*b*) a scatter graph, and (*c*) a bar graph. Figure 12-4 lists a program that uses exponential regression to make projections. To use this program, you must know several actual amounts that were measured at equally spaced points in time, like once a month, once a week, or once an hour. The program will calculate a growth factor based on those

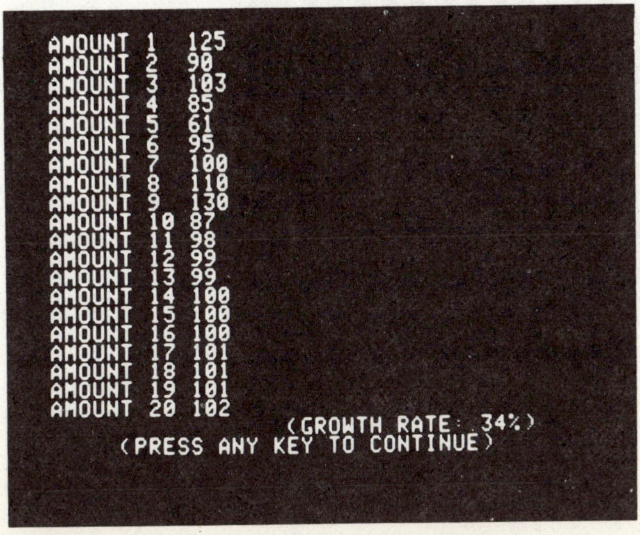

Figure 12-3*a*. Program output alternatives—list of numbers

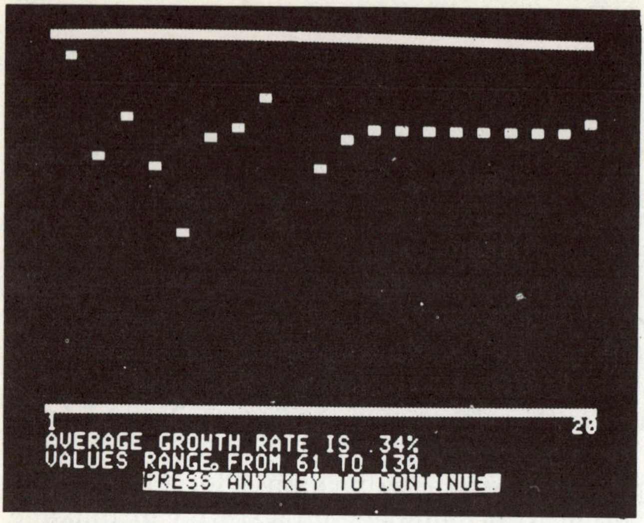

Figure 12-3*b*. Program output alternatives—scatter graph

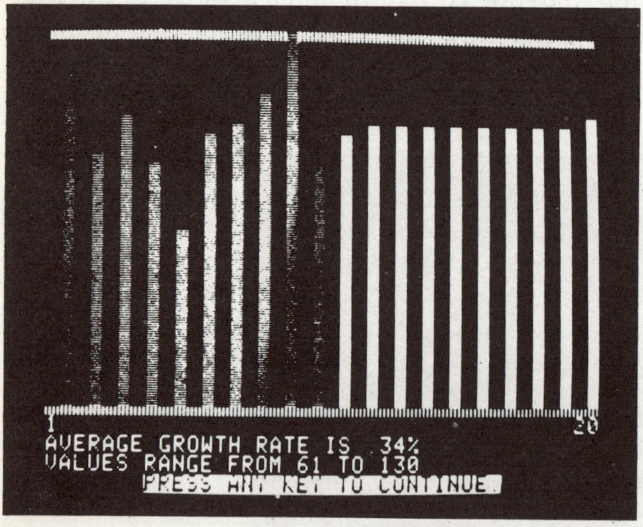

Figure 12-3*c*. Program output alternatives—bar graph

past amounts and will project future amounts by using the same time scale.

The program has been kept simple by using simple keyboard

entry techniques that are not up to the standards discussed in Chapter 9. The program user must divide up the analysis period into past and future (lines 1200-1220) and then must enter each past amount (lines 1230-1340). During the entry phase, the program calculates some cumulative amounts that it will use later to compute the growth factor (lines 1300-1330).

Following the input phase, the program calculates the growth factor and rounds it to the nearest hundredth (lines 1400-1420). Then it uses that factor to compute projections (lines 1500-1520).

For its first display of results, the program prints the exact past and future amounts (lines 1600-1650). It waits for the user to press a key before proceeding to the next display (line 1670).

Before the program can display a graph, it must compute a scaling factor. It will use the scaling factor to make sure the highest point fits on the screen. First it finds the largest value among the past and future amounts (lines 2000-2060). Then it computes a scaling factor by dividing the number of rows available for graphing, 37, by the largest value (line 2080).

The program prepares for graphing by setting low-resolution graphics mode and drawing a purple border above and below the

```
50 DIM AM(21)
60 P1 = 0:P2 = 0:P3 = 0:P4 = 0:P5 = 0
1010 HOME
1100 PRINT
1110 PRINT "  THIS PROGRAM USES AN EXPONENTIAL"
1120 PRINT "REGRESSION TECHNIQUE TO ANALYZE PAST"
1130 PRINT "AMOUNTS AND MAKE FUTURE PROJECTIONS."
1140 PRINT "YOU SPECIFY PAST AMOUNTS AND
     THE NUMBER"
1150 PRINT "OF PAST AND FUTURE AMOUNTS. THE TOTAL"
1160 PRINT "NUMBER OF AMOUNTS CANNOT EXCEED 20."
1170 PRINT
1200 INPUT "HOW MANY PAST AMOUNTS? ";PT%
1210 INPUT "HOW MANY AMOUNTS TO PROJECT? ";FT%
1220 IF PT% + FT% > 20 THEN PRINT: PRINT "ONLY 20
     AMOUNTS, PLEASE!": GOTO 1170
1230 PRINT
1240 PRINT "NOW ENTER PAST AMOUNTS:"
```

Figure 12-4. Average Growth Rate program

```
1250 PRINT
1260 FOR NB = 1 TO PT%
1270 PRINT "AMOUNT ";NB;
1280  INPUT ":";AM(NB)
1285 REM
1290 REM ..Accumulate intermediate exponectial
     regression values
1295 REM
1300 X = NB - 1:Y = LOG (AM(NB))
1310 P1 = P1 + X:P2 = P2 + Y
1320 P3 = P3 + X ^ 2:P4 = P4 + Y ^ 2
1330 P5 = P5 + X * Y
1340 NEXT NB
1345 REM
1390 REM ..Calculate coefficients of
     exponential equations
1395 REM
1400 B = (PT% * P5 - P2 * P1) / (PT% *
     P3 - P1 ^ 2)
1410 A = (P2 - B * P1) / PT%
1420 RT = INT (( EXP (B) - 1) * 10000) / 100
1485 REM
1490 REM ..Project future amounts
1495 REM
1500 FOR NB = PT% + 1 TO PT% + FT%
1510 AM(NB) = INT ( EXP (A) * EXP (B * (NB - 1))
     + 0.5)
1520 NEXT NB
1585 REM
1590 REM ..Display exact amounts
1595 REM
1600 HOME
1610 FOR NB = 1 TO PT% + FT%
1640 PRINT "AMOUNT ";NB; TAB( 11);AM(NB)
1650 NEXT NB
1660  PRINT TAB( 18);"(GROWTH RATE:";RT;"%)"
1670 PRINT TAB( 6);"(PRESS ANY KEY TO CONTINUE)":
     GET A$
1985 REM
1990 REM ..Compute vertical scaling factor
1995 REM
2000 MN = AMT(1)
2010 MX = AMT(1)
2020 REM ..Find max. and min. amounts
2030 FOR NB = 1 TO PT% + FT%
```

Figure 12-4. Average Growth Rate program (*continued*)

```
2040 IF AM(NB) > MX THEN MX = AM(NB)
2050 IF AM(NB) < MN THEN MN = AM(NB)
2060 NEXT NB
2070 REM ..Scale so both max. and min. amounts fit
2080 SC = 37 / MX
2085 REM
2090 REM ..Display scatter graph
2095 REM
2100 GR: COLOR= 3: REM ..Purple border
2110 HLIN 0,39 AT 0: HLIN 0,39 AT 39
2150 FOR NB = 1 TO PT% + FT%
2160 COLOR= 10: IF NB > PT% THEN COLOR= 11:
     REM ..Make projections different color
     than past
2170 PLOT NB * 2 - 1,38 - AM(NB) * SC
2180 NEXT NB
2190 GOSUB 2490
2295 REM
2300 REM ..Display bar graph
2305 REM
2310 GR: COLOR= 3: REM ..Purple border
2320 HLIN 0,39 AT 0: HLIN 0,39 AT 39
2330 FOR NB = 1 TO PT% + FT%
2340 COLOR= 10: IF NB > PT% THEN COLOR= 11:
     REM ..Make projections different color
     than past
2350 VLIN (38 - AM(NB) * SC),38 AT NB * 2 - 1
2360 NEXT NB
2370 GOSUB 2490
2390 TEXT: HOME
2400 END
2485 REM
2490 REM ..Subroutine to print data in text window
2495 REM
2500 HOME: REM ..Clear text window
2510 PRINT "1"; TAB( (PT% + FT%) * 2 - 1);
2520 IF PT% + FT% < 10 THEN PRINT " ";PT% + FT%:
     GOTO 2540
2530 PRINT PT% + FT%
2540 VTAB 22: PRINT "AVERAGE GROWTH
     RATE IS ";RT;"%"
2550 PRINT "VALUES RANGE FROM ";MN;" TO ";MX
2560 HTAB 8: INVERSE: PRINT "PRESS ANY KEY TO
     CONTINUE.";: NORMAL: GET A$
2570 RETURN
```

Figure 12-4. Average Growth Rate program (*continued*)

graph area (lines 2100 and 2110). Next, it uses a loop to plot all of the points (lines 2150-2180). It plots past amounts in gray and future amounts in pink (line 2160). The magnitude of the amount determines on which row the point will appear (line 2170). In the text window at the bottom of the screen, a subroutine displays the amount of the growth factor and the range of values (lines 2500-2570). Once again, the program waits for the user to press a key before proceeding to the next display (line 2560).

Program logic for the bar graph is exactly the same as for the scatter graph (lines 2300-2370), except that the program uses a VLIN statement to draw each bar (line 2350). In this case, the magnitude of each amount determines how tall the bar will be.

HIGH-RESOLUTION GRAPHICS

The Apple II's high-resolution graphics mode trades some color flexibility for sharper drawing detail. Resolution in this mode is 280 horizontal positions by 192 vertical positions, an increase of 7 times on the horizontal axis and 4 times on the vertical axis over low-resolution. Each position on the screen in high-resolution mode is no larger than a dot and is referred to as a *pixel*. Although only six colors are available in high-resolution graphics mode, you can plot much finer lines than you can in low-resolution mode.

Applesoft has three built-in high-resolution graphics commands, HGR, HCOLOR, and HPLOT. In addition, it has several dedicated memory locations and built-in machine language subroutines that you can use with POKE and CALL statements to display high-resolution graphics. Some of the memory locations and built-in subroutines duplicate the Applesoft commands HGR, HCOLOR, and HPLOT, but there are some features that can only be controlled by POKE and CALL statements. Integer BASIC has no special high-resolution graphics commands, only the POKE and CALL statements.

Selecting High-Resolution Mode

To switch the display screen to high-resolution graphics mode, use the Applesoft command HGR. The screen will go black except for the four-line text window at the bottom of the screen.

The presence of the text window shrinks the vertical dimension of the high-resolution area from 192 to 160 positions; the horizontal dimension still contains 280 positions. Executing HGR while in high-resolution mode clears the screen above the text window.

You can eliminate the text window with a POKE −16302,0 command and restore it with a POKE −16301,0 command. Use the TEXT command to switch back to text mode or the GR command to switch to low-resolution graphics mode.

When you switch to high-resolution mode, the cursor may not appear in the text window. Don't worry, the cursor hasn't vanished. The high-resolution screen acts as a curtain over the text screen, and the cursor is not advanced to the text window. This isn't a problem if the cursor is at the bottom of the screen when the switch occurs. To be safe, it is a good idea to include a VTAB statement that moves the cursor to the text window after the program switches to high-resolution mode. If you're working in immediate mode, you can advance the cursor to the text window by pressing RETURN until you see the command prompt.

Color Selection

High-resolution mode has eight color code numbers, but only four different colors plus black and white. Table 12-2 lists the available colors and their corresponding code numbers.

The Applesoft HCOLOR statement specifies one of the eight color codes used in high-resolution mode. As in low-resolution graphics, the default for HCOLOR is 0, which is black. HCOLOR does not change the color of any graphics already on the high-resolution screen, nor does it have any effect on low-resolution graphics.

Table 12-2. High-Resolution Graphics Colors

Color	Number	Color	Number
Black	0	Black	4
Green	1	Orange	5
Purple	2	Blue	6
White	3	White	7

Points and Lines

One great advantage of Applesoft high-resolution graphics is its ability to plot lines at any angle as well as individual points and horizontal or vertical lines. The HPLOT statement can be used in three ways. Here is one way:

```
]HPLOT 12,12
```

This statement plots a single point on the currently selected high-resolution page at the intersection of the thirteenth column and thirteenth row in the currently selected high-resolution plotting color.

The second use of HPLOT is shown here:

```
]HPLOT 0,0 TO 279,191
```

This statement draws a diagonal line from the upper-left corner to the lower-right corner of the screen. Using HPLOT with two sets of coordinates, as shown in the example, you can plot from one point to another on the screen.

The third use of HPLOT is more sophisticated:

```
]HPLOT 0,0 TO 279,0 TO 279,159 TO 0,159 TO 0,0
```

This example draws a rectangle around the perimeter of the high-resolution screen. Each additional coordinate is used as the endpoint of another line segment. All segments are drawn in the same color, but you see different colors due to phenomena explained in the next section.

Color Phenomena

Because of the way televisions generate colors, the Apple II can only plot certain colors in odd-numbered columns and other colors in even-numbered columns. Even-numbered columns can display black, purple, or blue (color number 0, 2, 4, or 6). Odd-numbered columns can display black, green, or orange (color number 0, 1, 4, or 5). If you try to plot a green or orange point in an even-numbered column, it will be black instead. Attempting to plot purple or blue in an odd-numbered column will also yield black.

However, if neither of two adjacent dots in the same row is black, both appear white. Therefore, plotting a green point next to a purple point turns both points white, and the same thing happens with orange and blue. Plotting white (color number 3 or 7) next to green, purple, orange, or blue also makes both points white. In fact, you can display white only by plotting two adjacent nonblack points. If you set the color to white (color number 3 or 7) and plot in an even-numbered column with black on both sides, the point will appear purple or blue. Likewise, plotting a white point in an odd-numbered column with black on both sides actually produces a green or orange point.

The Apple II can display six colors in high-resolution graphics mode, but it divides them into two palettes. One palette has black, green, purple, and white (color numbers 0-3) and the other has black, orange, blue, and white (colors 4-7). The Apple II also subdivides each high-resolution row into 40 zones of 7 columns each. A single zone can only display colors from one of the two palettes. Both palettes have white and black, so those colors are always available. But a single zone—columns 0 through 6, for instance—cannot contain both green and orange or both purple and blue. If green and purple points are displayed in a zone and you later display either an orange or a blue point in the same zone, all of the green points immediately turn orange and the purple points turn blue. The reverse is also true: plotting green or purple changes any orange or blue points in the same zone to green or purple. Table 12-2 identifies the two palettes and their colors.

Background Colors

Filling the entire screen with a single color is easier in high-resolution graphics mode than in low-resolution mode, although it does involve using a CALL statement. To clear the screen to black, use this command:

```
]CALL -3086
```

In order to fill the screen with a color other than black, you must set the color you want with an HCOLOR statement, plot a point anywhere, and then use a CALL −3082 statement. The following example fills the high-resolution screen with blue:

```
]10 HGR
]20 HCOLOR = 6: REM ..Blue
]30 HPLOT 1,1: CALL -3082: REM ..Fill screen
```

Circles

Applesoft has no command that draws circles, but you can easily write a circle-drawing subroutine with HPLOT. The following program draws five concentric circles, each in a different color (Figure 12-5*a*):

```
]10 REM ..Circle drawing demo
]20 HOME: HGR
]30 X = 140:Y = 90: REM ..Center point
]40 FOR J = 1 TO 5
]50 READ R,HC
]60 HCOLOR= HC: GOSUB 9200
]70 NEXT J
]80 END
]100 DATA 80,1,70,2,60,3,50,5,40,6
]9189 REM
]9190 REM ..Subroutine to draw circles
]9191 REM   Parameters are:
]9192 REM    X,Y - center coordinates
]9193 REM    R - radius
]9194 REM   Routine assumes that all
]9195 REM   these parameters are set
]9196 REM   by the calling program.
]9197 REM   This routine also uses the
]9198 REM   variables CX,CY,CT
]9199 REM
]9200 HPLOT X + R,Y: REM ..Plot 1ST point
]9210 REM ..Now plot all 360 points
]9220 FOR CT = 0 TO 6.28318531 STEP .0174532925
]9230 CX = R * COS (CT):CY = 6 / 7 * R * SIN (CT)
]9240 HPLOT TO (X + CX),(Y - CY)
]9250 NEXT CT
]9260 RETURN
```

The subroutine beginning on line 9200 assumes that the screen is already in high-resolution graphics mode and that the desired color has been set. Variable X must be assigned the column number and variable Y the row number for the center of the circle. The value of variable R determines the radius of the circle; one unit of radius equals the width of one column.

The subroutine constructs a circle by plotting 360 individual points along the circumference of the circle and by connecting the points with short line segments. It uses SIN and COS functions to compute the column and row coordinates of each point, and compensates for the difference in size between the columns and rows by multiplying the row coordinate by a factor of 6/7.

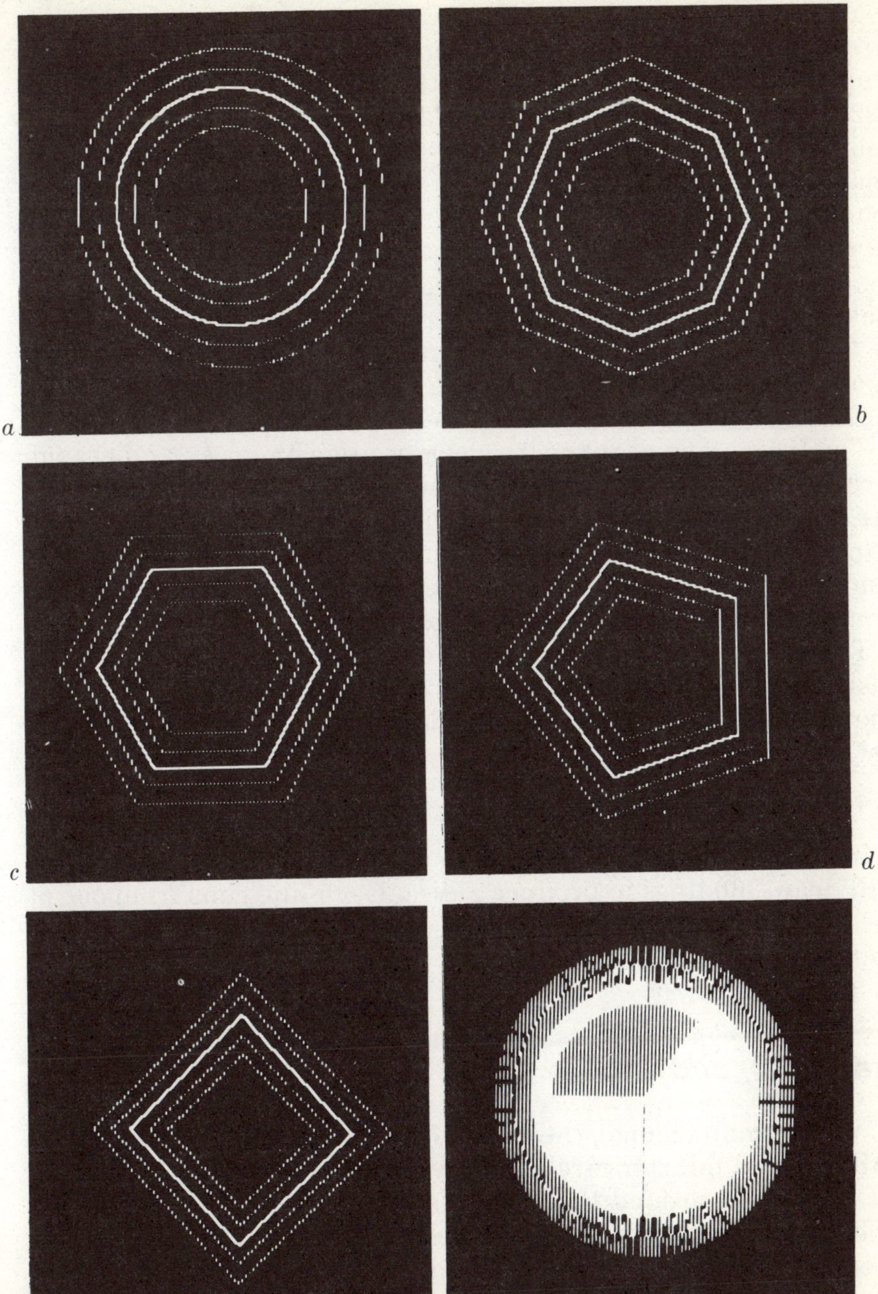

Figure 12-5. High-resolution circles (*a*), octagons (*b*), hexagons (*c*), pentagons (*d*), squares (*e*), and discs (*f*)

You may notice that it takes about 25 seconds to draw each circle, which is rather a long time. The drawing time is controlled by the STEP value in the FOR-NEXT loop on line 9220: larger STEP values mean faster but coarser plotting, and smaller values mean finer but slower plotting. For example, changing the STEP value to 0.125 draws a fair circle in less than four seconds. As the STEP value increases, the number of points plotted decreases, making the circle less and less round. When the STEP value exceeds about 0.448, the subroutine's drawings look less like circles and more like polygons. For example, a value of 0.7853 draws an octagon (Figure 12-5*b*), 1.047 draws a hexagon (Figure 12-5*c*), 1.256 draws a pentagon (Figure 12-5*d*), and 1.57 draws a square (Figure 12-5*e*).

The large gaps near the 9 o'clock position on green and orange circles, and near the 3 o'clock position on purple and blue circles, are due to the color phenomenon related to odd-even column numbering as described earlier in this chapter. The same phenomenon makes white circles appear green in the 3 o'clock position and purple in the 9 o'clock position.

The circle-drawing subroutine can draw solid-color discs as easily as hollow circles (Figure 12-5*f*). All it takes is a simple change to the HPLOT statement. Substitute this line in the original example:

```
]9240 HPLOT (X+CX),(Y+CY) TO X,Y
```

Instead of plotting 360 points to define a circle, the subroutine will draw 360 lines to produce a disc. Each line runs from one of the 360 points along the circumference of the circle to the center point.

Arcs, Rays, and Ellipses

With a small change, the circle-drawing subroutine can draw a half-circle, a quarter-circle, or any other arc. Instead of plotting all 360 points around the circumference of a circle, the subroutine could plot only those on a designated arc. But how do you specify which arc to draw? The answer relies on the fact that every circle has 360 degrees, just like a compass. There is one small difference, however. A circle starts with 0 degrees at the 3 o'clock position and goes counterclockwise, with 90 degrees at 12 o'clock, 180 degrees at 9 o'clock, 270 degrees at 6 o'clock, and back around to 3 o'clock for 360 degrees.

Mathematics measures circles not in degrees, but in *radians* (Figure 12-6). One degree equals 0.0174532925 radians. In fact, the circle-drawing subroutine plots points in a loop that goes from 0 radians to 6.283183531 radians in steps of 0.0174532925 radians (line 9220). To draw part of a circle, you need only change the starting and ending FOR-NEXT loop values in the circle-drawing subroutine. For example, plotting from 0 radians to 3.141592654 radians draws a half-circle, from 2.35619449 radians to 3.92699082 radians draws a quarter-circle, and from 4.5 radians to 5 radians draws a small arc (Figure 12-7).

There is another feature worth adding to the circle-drawing subroutine: the ability to draw a line from the center of the circle to either arc endpoint. This can be done by having the subroutine draw a ray to an endpoint that is specified by a negative value. Of course, the subroutine will have to ignore the signs of the endpoints when it draws the arc. Also, since the Apple II treats −0 and +0 as the same number, you will have to use −0.001 instead of −0 if you want an arc drawn to the 0-degree endpoint.

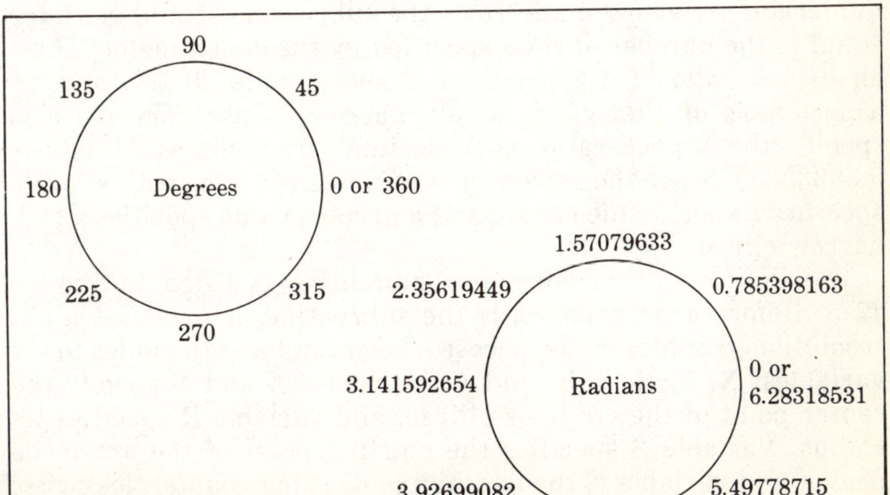

Figure 12-6. Degrees and radians

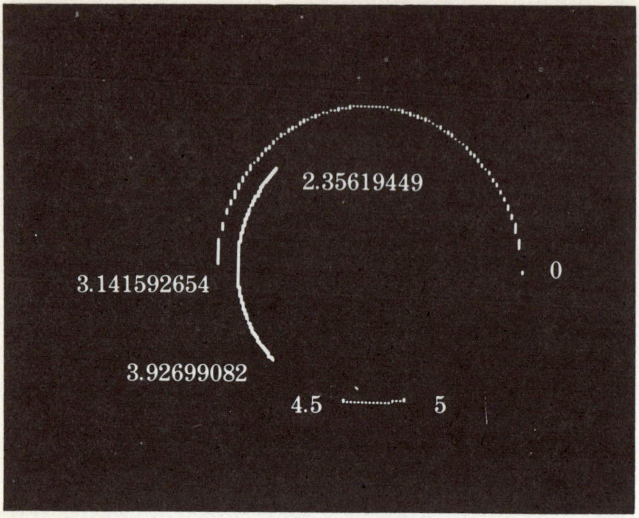

Figure 12-7. Endpoints of sample arcs

One last refinement to the subroutine will allow you to draw ellipses as well as circles. All this requires is specifying the *aspect ratio* of the ellipse, that is, the ratio of height to width. You can think of the aspect ratio as a fraction like 1/2 or 10/3. The numerator tells how many rows the subroutine should consider equal to the number of rows specified by the denominator. Thus, an aspect ratio of 1/2 produces a short, wide ellipse, and an aspect ratio of 10/3 yields a tall, narrow ellipse. You can also specify the aspect ratio as a decimal fraction, as in 0.5 or 3.33333333. Since the aspect ratio of a circle is 1, a smaller value specifies a short, wide ellipse and a greater value specifies a tall, narrow ellipse.

The improved circle-drawing subroutine is listed in Figure 12-8. Before a program calls the subroutine, it must set high-resolution graphics mode, choose a color, and assign values to six variables: X, Y, R, S, E, and A. Variables X and Y specify the center point of the circle or ellipse, and variable R specifies its radius. Variable S specifies the starting point of the arc to be drawn and variable E the ending point, going counterclockwise. Use radians for both S and E. A negative value for S or E yields a ray to that end of the arc. Variable A specifies the aspect ratio: 1 for a circle, less than 1 for a short ellipse, or greater than 1 for a tall ellipse.

```
8980 REM ..Subroutine to draw circles,
8981 REM    ellipses, and arcs.
8982 REM    Parameters are:
8983 REM     X,Y - center coordinates
8984 REM     R - radius
8985 REM     S - start point (radians)
8986 REM     E - end point (radians)
8987 REM     A - aspect ratio
8988 REM    Draws a ray to neg. start or end point.
8989 REM    Set hi-res mode, HCOLOR, and assign
8990 REM    parameter values before calling
8991 REM    This routine also uses
8992 REM    variables  CA, CB, CX, CY, CT
8993 REM
8994 REM ..First apply aspect ratio for ellipses
9000 IF A < = 1 THEN CA = R:CB = CA * A:
     REM ..Short ellipse
9010 IF A > 1 THEN CB = R:CA = CB * A:
     REM ..Tall ellipse
9020 REM ..Draw ray to negative start point
9030 CX = CA * COS ( ABS (S)):CY = CB * 6 / 7 *
     SIN ( ABS (S))
9040 IF S < 0 THEN HPLOT X,Y TO (X + CX),(Y - CY)
9050 REM ..Plot first point
9060 HPLOT (X + CX),(Y - CY)
9070 REM ..Now plot circle
9080 FOR CT = ABS (S) TO ABS (E) STEP .0174532925
9090 CX = CA * COS (CT):CY = CB * 6 / 7 * SIN (CT)
9100 HPLOT TO (X + CX),(Y - CY)
9110 NEXT CT
9120 REM ..Draw ray to negative endpoint
9130 IF E < 0 THEN HPLOT TO X,Y
9140 RETURN
```

Figure 12-8. Circle-drawing subroutine

The subroutine begins by translating the aspect ratio into vertical and horizontal scaling factors (lines 9000 and 9010). Then it calculates the column and row coordinates of the starting point with COS and SIN functions, applies the aspect-ratio scaling factor to each, and adjusts the height to compensate for the rectangular dimensions of the display screen (line 9030). If the starting point value is negative, the subroutine draws a ray to it (line 9040). Next, it plots the starting point (line 9060). After that, it uses a loop to plot each point on the arc, using an ABS function to ignore the sign of the starting and ending points (lines 9080-9110).

If the ending point value is negative, the subroutine draws a line from it to the center of the circle (line 9130).

Pie Chart Program

The classic practical application of circles and rays is the pie chart (Figure 12-9). The circle-drawing subroutine (Figure 12-8) makes it easy to create pie charts. For example, the program listed in Figure 12-10 constructs a pie chart with as many as 25 wedges.

The program begins by dimensioning an array to hold the size of each wedge and by assigning the number of radians in a half-circle to variable PI (lines 10 and 20). It then clears the display screen and inputs the number of wedges (lines 30-50). Next it inputs the amount of each wedge, keeping a running total of the wedge amounts (lines 70-110).

With the input finished, the program sets high-resolution graphics mode and color, clears the text window, and assigns values to parameters for the circle-drawing subroutine (lines 130-180). It starts the first wedge at 0 radians. Only variables S and E, the arc starting and ending points, will change during construction of the pie chart.

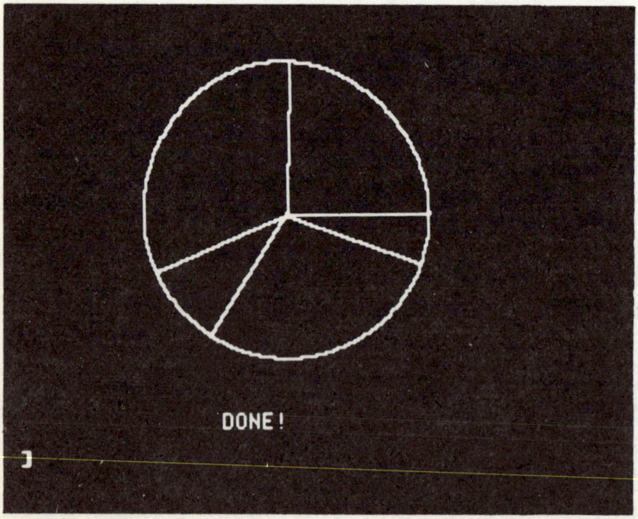

Figure 12-9. Pie chart

```
10 DIM PT(25)
20 PI = 3.141592654
30 TEXT: HOME
40 REM ..Input all amounts
50 INPUT "HOW MANY PARTS? ";N
60 IF N < 0 OR N > 25 THEN PRINT: PRINT "NO MORE
   THAN 25 PARTS, PLEASE!": PRINT: GOTO 50
70 FOR J = 1 TO N
80 PRINT "SIZE OF PART ";J;
90 INPUT "? ";PT(J)
100 TT = TT + PT(J): REM ..Keep running total
110 NEXT J
120 REM ..Prepare to display pie chart
130 HGR: HCOLOR= 3: HOME
140 VTAB 21: HTAB 14
150 PRINT TT;" TOTAL"
160 S = 0: REM ..Start point of first wedge
170 R = 75:X = 140:Y = 80: REM ..radius and
    center coordinates
180 A = 1: REM ..aspect ratio for a circle
190 REM ..Display all wedges
200 FOR J = 1 TO N
210 E = - (2 * PI * PT(J) / TT + S):
    REM ..Compute endpoint
220 VTAB 23: HTAB 1: PRINT "SIZE=";PT(J); SPC( 9);
230 GOSUB 9000: REM ..Draw wedge
240 S = - E: REM ..Next wedge starts where
    last one ended
250 NEXT J
260 VTAB 23: HTAB 0: PRINT "DONE!"
270 END
8980 REM ..Remember to add the circle-drawing
8981 REM   subroutine from Figure 12-8
```

Figure 12-10. Pie Chart program

The program uses a loop to draw the wedges (lines 200-250). First it computes the wedge ending point by using the ratio of the wedge size to the total of all wedges (line 210). It makes the ending point negative so the subroutine will draw a ray to it. Then the program displays the size of the wedge in the text window and calls the subroutine to draw the wedge (lines 220 and 230). The next wedge starts where the current wedge ends (line 240).

Several variations on the Pie Chart program are possible. You could modify the program to fill the screen with a background color before it begins drawing the chart. You could use a polygon instead of a circle for the chart shape. Each wedge could be drawn in a different color or in alternating solid colors. Be sure to keep the background distinct from the pie chart, though. If you plan to construct any wedges in the same color as the background, you should outline all the wedges in a contrasting color.

HIGH-RESOLUTION SHAPES

If you have written any high-resolution graphics programs that plot geometric figures, you have probably wanted to know how you could manipulate those figures on the screen. For instance, you might want to rotate the figure or make it appear larger or smaller on the screen.

Along with coordinate plotting and drawing, the Apple II allows you to define, draw, and manipulate two-dimensional shapes in high-resolution graphics mode. This section describes how to create, design, and use a shape in an Applesoft program. Thorough as it may be, this section only begins to explore the creative possibilities open to you.

There are six steps involved in using shapes:

1. Draw the shape on paper using only straight lines and right angles.
2. Convert the drawing into a sequence of numbers, either using the program presented later in this section or by hand.
3. Assemble one or more coded shapes into a table of shapes.
4. Use POKE statements to store the table of coded shapes in memory.
5. If desired, save the memory image on disk.
6. Use Applesoft commands to draw and manipulate a coded shape from memory.

Defining Shapes

In order to use shapes on the Apple II, you must describe the entire figure before instructing the computer to draw it. You define high-resolution shapes in a *shape table*, so called because it contains the coded characterstics of the figures. The first step in

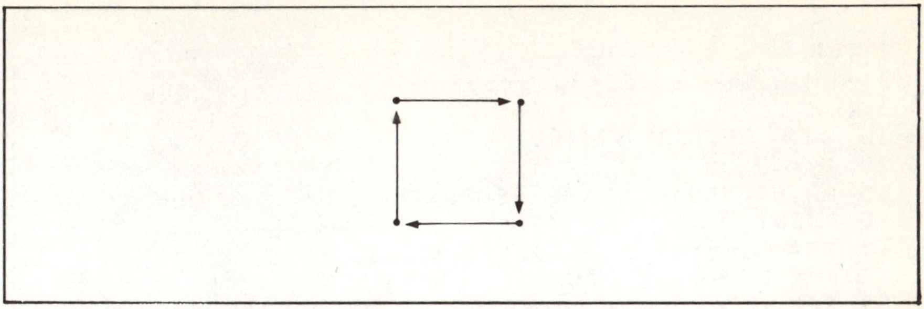

Figure 12-11. Steps in drawing a square

defining a high-resolution shape is to draw the shape on paper. A square, for example, consists of four lines of equal length, each one at a right angle to the previous line drawn (Figure 12-11).

The shape table contains coded instructions for drawing a figure; these instructions are called *plotting vectors.* Each vector describes movement up, down, left, or right (or lack of movement) and shows whether to draw on the screen or not. You can interpret each side of the square in Figure 12-11 as a direction in which to draw: one up, one right, one down, and one left. This is the way Applesoft's shape manipulation commands look at figures.

Figures are more difficult to draw if they contain diagonal lines or curves. A triangle, although it has one side less than a square, involves much more work because it has at least one diagonal line. Since you can only define a shape with vectors that move up, down, or sideways, some shapes, such as circles, may not be worth approximating. In some cases it may be easier to draw complicated shapes with HPLOT than by means of shape tables.

Shape Coding Program

The figure you draw on paper must be converted to coded plotting vectors. This section presents an Applesoft program that does the conversion for you (Figure 12-12). The program asks you to enter each plotting vector and whether or not to plot it. After entering the last vector, press E for "end" and press RETURN. The program asks you to enter the vector, if any, to be changed. If you make any mistakes in entering plotting vectors, you can correct them by entering the number of the plotting vector and then

```
1 REM
2 REM ..Shape Coding program
3 REM
10 DIM S1(100),V1(100)
20 I = 0
30 PRINT "CODE SHAPE VECTORS"
40 PRINT
41 REM ..Enter plot actions
50 V = I: GOSUB 270
59 REM ..Continue entry until M$ equals terminal
   value "E"
60 IF M$ < > "E" THEN S1(I) = M:I = I + 1: GOTO 50
70 PRINT
71 REM ..Allow corrections
80 INPUT "VECTOR TO CHANGE (0=END):";V
90 IF V > 0 THEN V = V - 1: GOSUB 270:S1(V) = M:
   GOTO 80
99 REM ..Pack vectors into V()
100 FOR V = 0 TO I
110 IF B = 2 AND S1(V) > 0 AND S1(V) < 4 THEN 140
120 IF B < 2 AND (S1(V) > 0 OR S1(V) > 4) THEN 140
130 B = 0:Q = Q + 1
140 V1(Q) = V1(Q) + S1(V) * (8 ^ B)
150 B = B + 1
160 IF B > 2 THEN B = 0:Q = Q + 1
170 NEXT V
178 REM
179 REM ..Display the vecotrs as
    hexadecimal numbers
180 PRINT
182 PRINT "MEMORY"; TAB( 10);"POKE"; TAB(
 20);"HEXADECIMAL"
184 PRINT "LOCATION"; TAB( 10);"VALUE";
    TAB( 20);"VALUE"
186 PRINT "--------"; TAB( 10);"-----";
    TAB( 20);"-----"
190 FOR V = 0 TO Q
200 H% = V1(V) / 16
210 L% = V1(V) - H% * 16
220 IF H% > 10 THEN H% = H% + 7
230 IF L% > 10 THEN L% = L% + 7
240 PRINT "+";V; TAB( 10);V1(V); TAB( 20);
    CHR$(H% + 176); CHR$ (L% + 176)
250 NEXT V
260 END
269 REM ..Vector input subroutine
270 PRINT "VECTOR ";V + 1;":";
```

Figure 12-12. Shape Coding program

```
280 INPUT "MOVE: U/D/L/R?";M$
290 M = 0
300 IF M$ = "R" THEN M = 1
310 IF M$ = "D" THEN M = 2
320 IF M$ = "L" THEN M = 3
330 IF M$ = "E" THEN RETURN
340 INPUT "PLOT (Y=YES,N=NO)?";P$
350 IF P$ = "Y" THEN M = M + 4: RETURN
360 IF P$ = "N" THEN RETURN
370 GOTO 340
```

Figure 12-12. Shape Coding Program (*continued*)

reentering the vector and specifying whether or not to plot it. If you have no further corrections to make, enter 0 as the response to **VECTOR TO CHANGE (0=END)**.

The program computes and displays the numeric codes that define the shape for which you entered plotting vectors. Each code number can specify one, two, or three plotting vectors, so don't expect to see one number for each plotting vector. For example, the following dialogue shows how to use the Shape Coding program to code the shape definition for a square:

```
]RUN
CODE SHAPE VECTORS

VECTOR 1:MOVE: U/D/L/R?U
PLOT (Y=YES,N=NO)?Y
VECTOR 2:MOVE: U/D/L/R?R
PLOT (Y=YES,N=NO)?Y
VECTOR 3:MOVE: U/D/L/R?D
PLOT (Y=YES,N=NO)?Y
VECTOR 4:MOVE: U/D/L/R?L
PLOT (Y=YES,N=NO)?Y
VECTOR 5:MOVE: U/D/L/R?E

VECTOR TO CHANGE (0=END):0

MEMORY    POKE        HEXADECIMAL
LOCATION  VALUE       VALUE
--------  -----       -----
+0        44          2C
+1        62          3E
+2        0           00

]▒
```

The program always displays three columns of numbers, which you will use to store the coded shape definition in memory. The left-hand column tells you the memory locations relative to the beginning of the shape definition. The other two columns specify the value to be stored in each memory location. You can use POKE statements to store the coded shape definition values shown in the middle column.

This example shows that the four plotting vectors it takes to define a square require only three memory locations. The last of the three memory locations has a zero value to designate the end of the shape definition.

Coding Shapes by Hand

If you want to understand how the Shape Coding program works, you will have to learn how to code shapes yourself, without the computer. You may take the program on faith and skip this section entirely if you wish. Manual shape coding involves working with binary and hexadecimal numbers, because you must determine bit by bit what the value in each byte, or memory cell, will be.

Plotting vector codes range in value from 0 to 7; each byte of a shape definition can hold as many as three vectors. Table 12-3 shows the possible plotting vector codes. Once a shape is reduced to a set of vectors, the vectors can be placed in memory, where

Table 12-3. Plotting Vectors and Their Binary Codes

Symbol	Action	Binary Code	Decimal Code
↑	Move up without plotting	000	0
→	Move right without plotting	001	1
↓	Move down without plotting	010	2
←	Move left without plotting	011	3
↑	Move up with plotting	100	4
→	Move right with plotting	101	5
↓	Move down with plotting	110	6
←	Move left with plotting	111	7

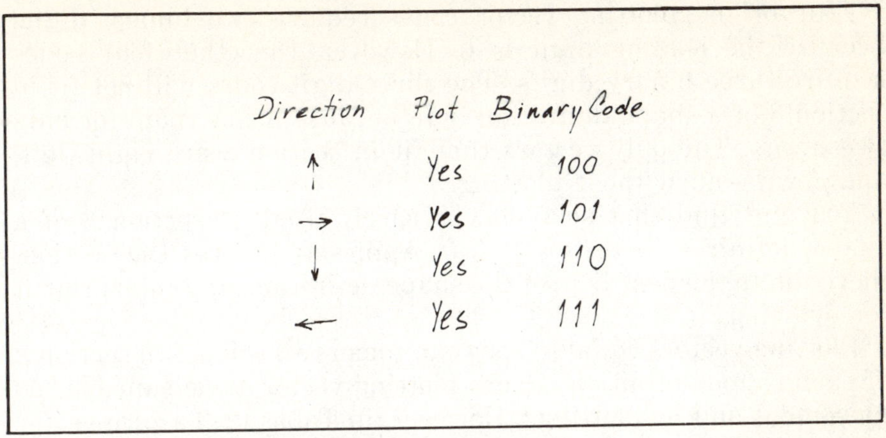

Figure 12-13. Coding plotting vectors by hand

certain Applesoft commands can decode them and draw the shape.

To begin, pick a starting point on the shape you wish to draw. Make a list of the plotting vectors needed to construct the shape, using arrows. List the vectors in order as you go around the shape either clockwise or counterclockwise. Mark any vectors to be plotted but not drawn ("ghost" vectors). For example, starting in the lower left-hand corner, a square has four vectors: up, right, down, and left (Figure 12-13). Write the appropriate binary code next to each vector (use Table 12-3 to translate).

As shown in Table 12-4, every byte of the shape definition contains three sections, each of which may contain a plotting vector. Notice that sections 1 and 2 contain three bits each, while section 3 contains only two bits.

Table 12-4. Shape Table Byte

Bit	Section 3		Section 2			Section 1		
	7	6	5	4	3	2	1	0
M = Movement bit P = Plot/No Plot bit	M	M	P	M	M	P	M	M

Four of the plotting vector codes require two binary digits because the leading digit is 0. However, the other four codes require three binary digits. The three-digit codes will not fit in section 3 of a shape definition byte because it has room for only two digits. The only vectors that fit in section 3 are right, left, and down—all without plotting.

You will find that section 3 is rarely used. If section 3 of a shape definition byte is set to 0, Applesoft ignores the section, moves on to the next byte of the shape definition, and interprets it for drawing.

Plotting vectors equal to zero can mean two things. In section 3 of each shape definition, a zero plotting vector always means "no movement and no plotting." However, in Table 12-3 a zero vector means "move up without plotting." This ambiguity can cause problems in sections 1 and 2 of each shape definition byte, because under certain circumstances Applesoft ignores zero plotting vectors, and in others it performs upward movement without plotting. The rule is as follows: If you intend the zero vector to mean "move up without plotting," do not end the shape definition byte with a zero plotting vector. Applesoft's shape manipulation routines assume that if the most significant portion (section 3) or portions (sections 2 and 3 together) are set to 0, no drawing takes place for any sections set to 0 in the same byte.

If all three sections of a shape definition byte are set to 0, Applesoft interprets this as an "end of shape definition" signal. In fact, you must end each shape definition with a termination byte set to 0. Otherwise, Applesoft will draw past the end of your original shape and will continue drawing until it encounters a zero byte.

You can use the "move up without plotting" vector as long as a different plotting vector follows it in the same byte. For example, section 2 can be set to 0 ("move up without plotting") and if section 3 is set to 01, 10, or 11 (binary), section 2 will be recognized as "move up without plotting." If sections 3 and 2 are set to 0, no movement occurs and Applesoft looks to section 1 of the next byte for the next valid plotting vector.

Armed with this knowledge, you can now arrange the binary-coded plotting vectors for each segment of the shape into groups of two or three. In this way you transpose the three-digit binary plotting vector codes into eight-digit bytes that can be stored in memory. For example, the coded plotting vectors listed in Figure

Memory Location	Plotting Vectors by Section 3	2	1	Binary Codes by Section 3	2	1	Hex Code	Decimal Code
+0	None	→	↑	00	101	100	2C	44
+1	None	←	↓	00	111	110	3E	62
+2	None	None	None	00	000	000	00	0

Figure 12-14. Packing coded plotting vectors into bytes

12-13 fit into three bytes, including the final end-of-shape byte (Figure 12-14).

With the shape packed into binary coded bytes, you can easily convert each byte to hexadecimal and decimal numbers. Appendix J contains binary-to-hexadecimal-to-decimal conversion tables. Notice that the byte values that resulted from coding the plotting vectors by hand are the same as the ones the Shape Coding program computed.

Shape Tables and Directories

At this point the plotting vectors have been coded by the Shape Coding program or by hand into a sequence of numbers. The next step is to create a shape table. A shape table has two parts: the *directory* or *index*, followed by one or more coded shape definitions. Figure 12-15 illustrates shape table organization, and Figure 12-16 shows the shape table for the square.

The directory of a shape table is a series of bytes that describes how many shapes there are in the table and also points to each shape definition in the table. The first byte of the directory contains the total number of shapes in the table. This number ranges from 0 to 255. The second byte is unused and should be set to 0.

The remaining bytes in the directory contain pointers to each shape definition in the table. Each pointer specifies the number of bytes that the shape is offset from the beginning of the directory. In the case of the example square, there is only one shape to

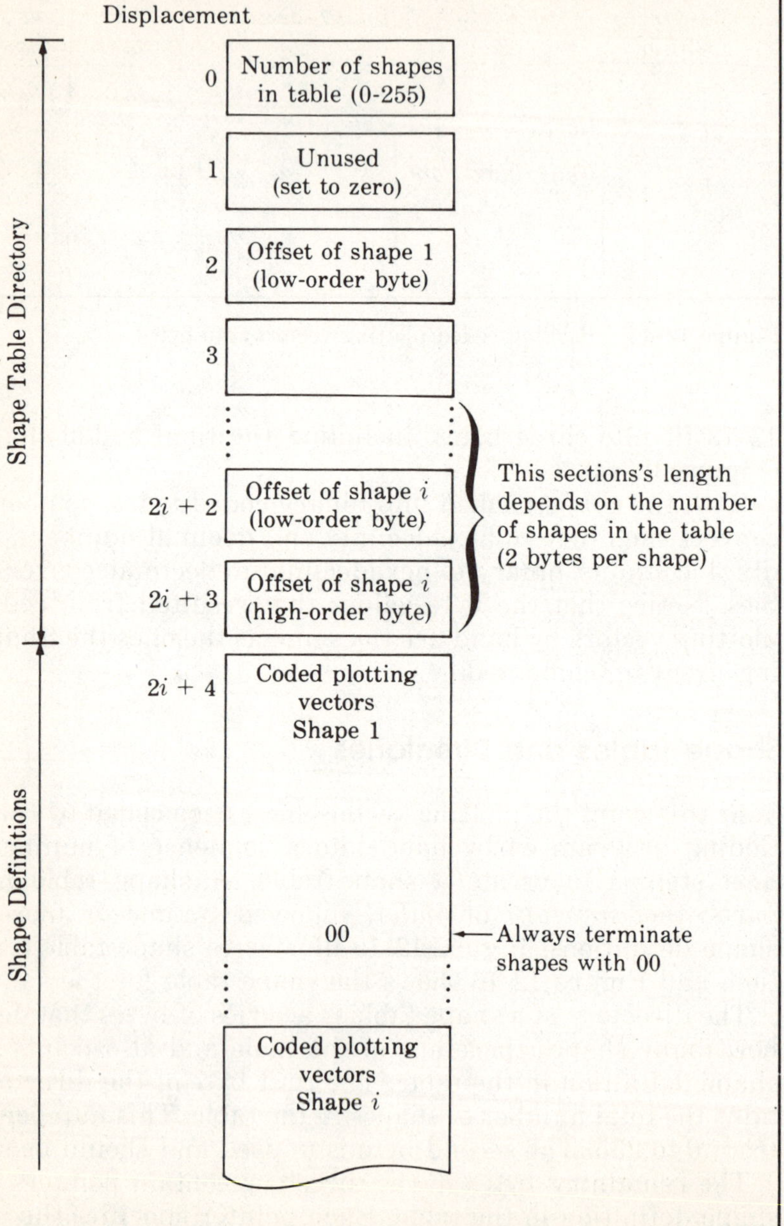

Figure 12-15. Shape table organization

Memory Location	POKE Value	Hexadecimal Value	Interpretation
+0	1	01	Number of shape definitions in the table
+1	0	00	Unused (must be 0)
+2	4	04	Offset of Shape 1 from start of shape table, low-byte
+3	0	00	Offset of Shape 1 from start of shape table, high-byte
+4	44	2C	Shape definition no. 1 starts
+5	62	3E	
+6	0	00	Shape definition no. 1 ends

Figure 12-16. Sample shape table

list in the directory, so the offset of shape 1 from the beginning of the directory is four bytes.

Each shape pointer in the shape table directory occupies two bytes of memory. To calculate the value for the first byte, use the expression SP−INT(SP/256)*256, where variable SP is the number of bytes from the beginning of the directory to the beginning of the shape. To compute the second byte, use INT(SP/256). In the example, SP equals 4, so the first byte computes to 04 and the second byte to 00.

It is a good idea to leave extra bytes at the end of a shape table directory to allow room for pointers to future shape definitions. If you have no room at the end of the directory to allow for expansion, you will have to reorganize the entire shape table in order to insert a new shape pointer. Even though you may only need a directory that holds ten shapes, you should leave unused space at the end of the directory; 20 extra bytes allow for another ten shape pointers, which you can use later. When you want to add another shape to the table, place the new shape definition just after the last shape definition in the table, calculate the offset of the new shape from the beginning of the directory, place the new pointer immediately after the last shape pointer in the directory, and add 1 to the first byte of the directory (which contains the number of shapes in the table).

Storing the Shape Table in Memory

Before you can display coded shapes, you have to put them into the computer's memory. In order to do that, you must decide in what area of memory the shape table will reside. Memory locations 768-975 are generally free for shape tables. Chapter 13 introduces a short machine language subroutine that uses the same area, but no conflict will arise unless you try to put such a subroutine and a shape table into the same part of memory at the same time.

You can use POKE statements to place the shape table in memory. For example, the following series of POKE statements puts the shape table for the square (Figure 12-16) into memory, starting at location 768:

```
]POKE 768,01

]POKE 769,00

]POKE 770,04

]POKE 771,00

]POKE 772,44

]POKE 773,62

]POKE 774,00
```

Since you can put the shape table anywhere in memory where it will fit, you must somehow tell Applesoft where it is. Memory locations 232 and 233 are reserved for that purpose. For example, the following POKE statements tell Applesoft that the shape table starts at memory location 768:

```
]POKE 232,00

]POKE 233,03
```

As with all values that require two memory locations, you can determine what to put in the first location with the expression VALUE−INT(VALUE/256)*256, and the second location with INT(VALUE/256). Here the variable VALUE is the memory location where the shape table begins. Thus the value 768 breaks down to 0 for the first location and 3 for the second location. You can confirm the POKE statements' success with the command PRINT PEEK(233)*256+PEEK(232).

Saving the Shape Table on Disk

If you have invested a lot of time putting together shape tables, it would be a good idea to save your work on disk rather than lose it when you switch off the Apple II. You can use the BSAVE command to save a shape table on disk. Before you can save the shape table, however, you must determine its length. Continuing with the square as an example, look at the number of memory locations it takes up; the total is seven (Figure 12-16). The following example will save the square, assuming you have put it in memory at location 768:

```
]BSAVE SQUARE,A768,L7
```

This BSAVE command creates a binary disk file named SQUARE and copies seven bytes of memory into it. The shape table is now saved on disk, ready for use at a later time. Use your actual shape table name, starting location, and length in place of those shown in the example.

Retrieving a Saved Shape Table

If you recorded the shape table on disk, the BLOAD command will read it back into memory. Here is an example:

```
]BLOAD SQUARE
```

This copies the contents of the file named SQUARE into memory, starting at the location from which the file was saved. If you want the file to go to a different memory location, follow the file name with a comma, the letter A, and the new memory location. The following example puts the shape table at memory location 8000:

```
]BLOAD SQUARE, A8000
```

After copying the shape table into memory with BLOAD, you need to place its starting location in memory locations 232 and 233. As described earlier, you can use POKE statements to do this.

MANIPULATING SHAPES

Applesoft has four shape manipulation commands that draw, erase, and change the orientation of shapes:

- SCALE alters the size of the shape
- DRAW displays the shape on the screen
- XDRAW erases the shape
- ROT rotates the shape.

The shape manipulation commands only work in high-resolution graphics mode. The HCOLOR statement selects the shape color.

Shape Size

You should always set SCALE as a programmed or immediate mode statement before drawing a shape for the first time in a program:

```
]SCALE = 1
```

This statement sets the scaling to draw one point for each plotting vector. If SCALE=5, the Apple II draws five positions for each single plotting vector. You can set SCALE as high as 255 (255 points plotted for each vector). The maximum scale setting is SCALE=0, which plots 256 points for each single plotting vector.

Drawing a Shape

DRAW plots the shape (numbered from 1 to 255) from the shape table in the last color chosen and at the scale and rotation value last set. The following statement plots the first shape definition in the shape table, starting at column 140 and row 96 of the high-resolution display:

```
]DRAW 1 AT 140,96
```

Drawing originates at the column and row coordinates given in the statement. A second DRAW statement option uses an implied starting location:

```
]DRAW 11
```

This statement draws the eleventh shape in the table at the point last plotted by the most recent HPLOT or DRAW statement executed. If the coordinates were not set earlier, Applesoft uses row 0 and column 0 by default.

Important: Applesoft assumes that the shape table is properly located in memory. Before you execute a DRAW statement, make sure the shape table is in memory and that memory locations 232 and 233 point to the beginning of the shape table. If you specify a shape number greater than the number of shapes actually in the table, or if the DRAW statement uses invalid row or column coordinates, drawing does not occur; instead, the error message **?ILLEGAL QUANTITY ERROR** is displayed.

Erasing Shapes

The XDRAW statement allows you to erase a shape without erasing any high-resolution background graphics. Here is an example:

```
]XDRAW 8 AT 90,96
```

The XDRAW statement is identical in format to DRAW; the plotting coordinates can be explicit, as shown in this example, or implicit, as shown in the last DRAW statement example. XDRAW checks the color on the screen at the plotting coordinates and draws a shape in the *complement* of the color found. In the example above, XDRAW occurs at column 90 and row 96 on the screen. Table 12-5 lists the complements of high-resolution colors.

If the coordinates, rotation, and scale are the same as those of a

Table 12-5. XDRAW Colors

If color is	XDRAW color is
Black	White
White	Black
Purple	Green
Orange	Blue
Green	Purple
Blue	Orange

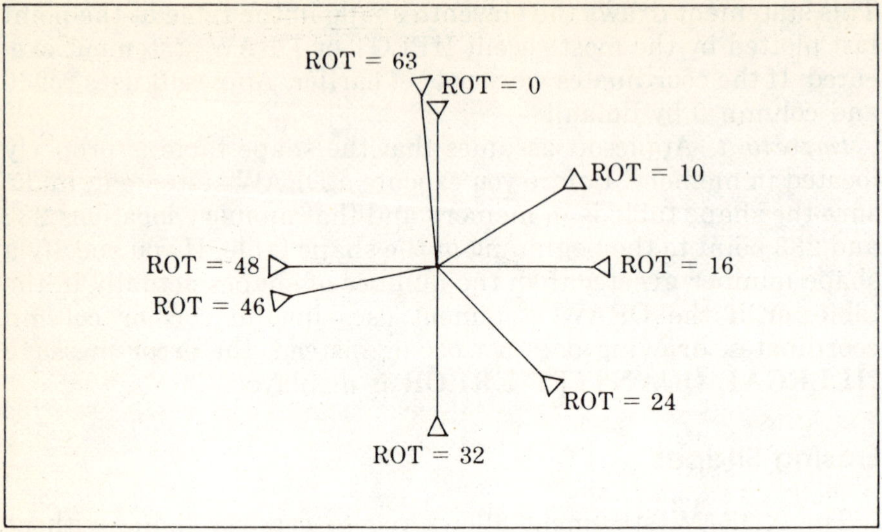

Figure 12-17. Shape rotation

shape already on the screen, XDRAW erases the shape, leaving all surrounding graphics intact.

Rotating a Shape

With the ROT command, you tell Applesoft to rotate subsequent shapes clockwise around the center point of the screen before it draws them. The following statement sets the angle of shape rotation to 90 degrees.

```
]ROT = 16
```

The values for ROT range from 0 to 255, although there are only 64 possible rotation settings, from 0 to 63. Figure 12-17 shows the changes in orientation based on ROT values.

When SCALE is set to 1, ROT rotates shapes in 90-degree increments, which means there are only four meaningful rotations: 0=0 degrees, 16=90 degrees, 32=180 degrees, and 48=270 degrees. Applesoft rounds the rotation value you set to the next lowest ROT increment. All 64 rotational positions are available if SCALE is set to 5 or greater.

Shape Demonstration Programs

One of the simplest yet most rewarding ways to use shapes is in the creation of graphics designs. Starting with just a simple shape like a square, you can create innumerable designs.

You have already done the hardest part: coding the shape table. It is easy to write a program that uses POKE statements to put a shape table in memory. Figure 12-18 lists a program that does this. The program starts by switching to high-resolution graphics mode and eliminating the four-line text window (line 10). Then it establishes the starting memory location of the shape table, in this case location 768 (line 20). Next, the program reads the shape table length from a DATA statement (lines 30 and 80). It uses this length to control the number of iterations in the FOR-NEXT loop that reads the coded shape table from a DATA statement and stores it in memory, one byte at a time (lines 40-70 and 90).

All that remains is to experiment with the Applesoft commands that draw and manipulate shapes. For example, the following program lines, added to Figure 12-18, plot three sizes of squares in random colors and random rotations all over the screen (Figure 12-19).

```
]10 REM ..Remember to add lines 1 to 90
]20 REM   from Figure 12-18, since
]30 REM   they put the shape table in memory
]189 REM
]190 REM ..Display random squares
]191 REM
]200 HCOLOR= RND (1) * 6 + 1: REM ..Any color
]210 S = RND (1) * 3 + 1: REM ..1<=S<=3
]220 SCALE= INT (S) * 10: REM ..10, 20, or 30
]230 ROT= RND (1) * 64: REM ..any angle
]240 X = RND (1) * 280: REM ..any coordinates
]250 Y = RND (1) * 192
]260 DRAW 1 AT X,Y
]270 GOTO 200
```

The program loops endlessly, filling the screen with more and more colored squares. Use CONTROL-C to stop the program, and type the TEXT command to switch the screen back to text mode. The TEXT command will be invisible when you type it, since the program eliminates the text window at the bottom of the screen.

Replace lines 189-270 with the following lines, and a com-

```
1 REM
2 REM ..Put shape table in memory
3 REM
10 HGR: POKE -16302,0: REM ..No text window
19 REM ..Set shape table start location
20 POKE 233,03: POKE 232,00: REM ..768
29 REM ..Put shape table in memory
30 READ L: REM ..Shape table length
40 FOR ML = 768 TO 767 + L
50 READ V: REM ..Read vector
60 POKE ML,V: REM ..Store in memory
70 NEXT ML
80 DATA 7: REM ..Shape table length
89 REM ..Coded shape table follows
90 DATA 1,0,4,0,44,62,0
```

Figure 12-18. POKE Shape Table program

pletely different image appears, although it too is composed of squares. To replace the old program lines, first enter DEL 189,270 to delete the last portion of the program, but keep the

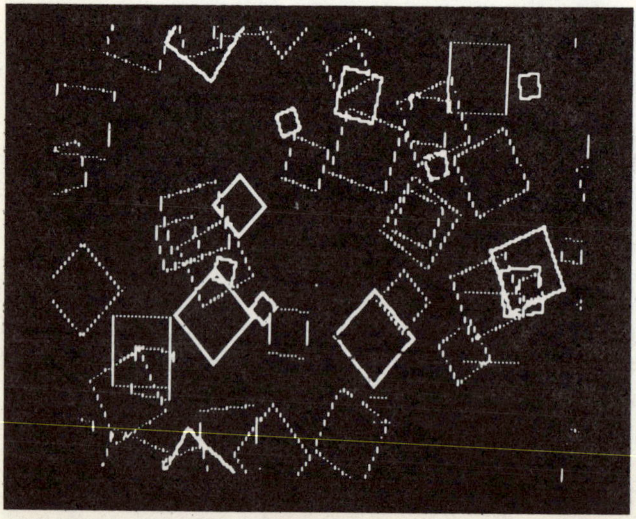

Figure 12-19. Random squares (see Figure 12-18 and text for program listing)

program from Figure 12-18 intact; then type in the new lines 189-310.

```
]10 REM ..Remember to add lines 12 to 90
]20 REM   from Figure 12-18, since
]30 REM   they put the shape table in memory
]189 REM
]190 REM ..Display rosettes using square shape
]191 REM
]200 FOR C = 1 TO 6
]210 HCOLOR= C
]220 REM ..Rotate 100 ways
]230 FOR F = 1 TO 100
]240 ROT= F
]245 REM ..Change size the 1ST 62 times
]250 IF F < 63 THEN SCALE= F
]260 DRAW 1 AT 140,96: REM ..One square
]270 ROT= F + 32: REM ..Rotate 180 degrees
]280 DRAW 1 AT 140,96: REM ..Another square
]290 NEXT F
]300 NEXT C
]310 GOTO 200
```

In the new program, two squares are rotated around the center of the screen, tracing a rosette (Figure 12-20). The program loops

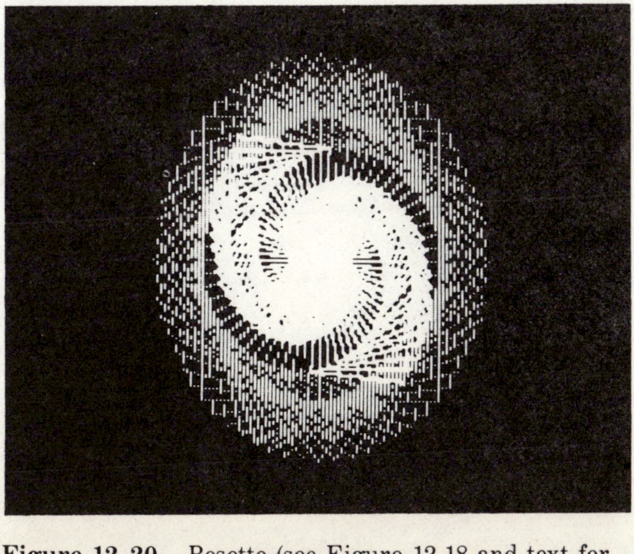

Figure 12-20. Rosette (see Figure 12-18 and text for program listing)

endlessly, changing colors each time it draws the design. Once again, type CONTROL-C to stop the program.

DOUBLE HIGH-RESOLUTION GRAPHICS

The Apple II has another graphics mode, called *double high-resolution,* that combines the 16-color capability of low-resolution mode with the small dots of high-resolution mode. Unfortunately, standard Applesoft BASIC has no commands for using double high-resolution mode. It's possible to use double high-resolution mode by writing assembly language programs, but the methods involved are beyond the scope of this book. Perhaps Applesoft BASIC will support double high-resolution graphics in the future.

Sound 13

The Apple II has a built-in speaker that can make sounds and play music under program control. Earlier chapters showed how to use CONTROL-G or the CHR$ function to direct the speaker to emit its familiar beep. This chapter explains how to go beyond that simple sound to program a variety of tones and vary their length. Also included is a program that plays music, and another that lets you compose your own music.

PROGRAMMING THE SPEAKER IN BASIC

Memory location −16336 is connected to the speaker in such a way that when you read it with a PEEK function, the speaker makes a brief sound. The following example illustrates:

```
]50 A = PEEK(-16336)
]100 END
```

If you listen closely to the speaker as you run this program, you will hear a single click. Run the program a second time and no sound occurs. The first time the Apple II was holding back the speaker cone, and the PEEK(−16336) function caused its release, creating a sound. The second time, the PEEK(−16336) function silently pulled back the speaker cone again. If you run the program a third time, you will hear another click. This is much like picking a guitar: the sound you hear comes not from pulling back on a string, but from letting it go.

To get a tone instead of a single click, you must "pluck" the speaker repeatedly. Try this variation on the last example:

```
]50 A = PEEK(-16336)
]100 GOTO 50
```

This simple loop does nothing but pluck the speaker over and over again, as fast as is possible with BASIC statements. This generates a continuous low-pitched tone. In Applesoft, the frequency is about 70 cycles per second, and in Integer BASIC it is about 250 cycles per second. To stop the program, press CONTROL-C.

Varying the Pitch

Plucking the speaker at a slower rate lowers the pitch of the tone you hear. In programming terms, that means executing the PEEK(−16336) function less often will generate a lower tone. You can make the last program generate a lower-pitched tone by inserting program lines in the middle of the loop, between lines 50 and 100. Any delay in reexecuting the PEEK statement will have an effect. Different BASIC statements execute at different speeds, so how much the pitch goes down depends on the kind of statement you add as well as the number of times it occurs. Here is one approach:

```
]10 INPUT "PITCH, 1 (HIGH) TO 11 (LOW)? ";P
]50 A = PEEK(-16336)
]60 FOR W = 1 TO P
]70 NEXT W
]100 GOTO 50
```

This program uses a FOR-NEXT loop to alter the frequency with which the PEEK(−16336) function plucks the speaker. The value of variable P, which you input from the keyboard, determines how many times the loop iterates. The more times the loop iterates, the longer it takes to finish. The longer the loop takes, the more it retards the frequency of speaker plucking, and the lower the pitch of the resulting tone.

Fixed-Length Tones

All it takes to generate tones of a fixed length instead of continuous tones is another FOR-NEXT loop. Here is an example.

```
]10 INPUT "PITCH, 1 (HIGH) TO 11 (LOW)? ";P
]20 INPUT "LENGTH, 10 (SHORT) TO 200 (LONG)? ";L
]30 FOR D = 1 TO L
]50 A = PEEK(-16336)
]60 FOR W = 1 TO P
]70 NEXT W
]80 NEXT D
]100 GOTO 50
```

This program is just like the previous example, except that variable L determines how long the tone will last. Strictly speaking, pitch also affects length, because lower-pitched notes spend more time in the FOR-NEXT loop on lines 50 and 60 than do high-pitched notes. If you listen closely while you enter the same length for pitch 1 and pitch 11, you will notice that the actual lengths are not identical. This disparity is greatest between notes at opposite ends of the pitch spectrum. To halt the program, press CONTROL-C and then press RETURN.

PROGRAMMING THE SPEAKER IN MACHINE LANGUAGE

As the previous examples show, the range of tones you can get with a BASIC program is quite limited. Machine language can generate much higher tones and also has a wider pitch range. This is possible because machine language is much faster than BASIC, and speed is the key to high notes. The faster the speaker vibrates, the higher the note will be.

A Machine Language Speaker Subroutine

This section presents a speaker subroutine, written in machine language, and explains how the subroutine works. You don't need to know why the subroutine works in order to use it, so you can go on to the next section if you wish to skip the technical details.

It only takes a few machine language instructions to vibrate the speaker and produce tones of different pitch and length. The subroutine in Figure 13-1 shows one approach; the machine language code appears along with its assembly language equivalent to make it easier to understand.

In the Machine Language Speaker subroutine, pitch is determined by the frequency with which the subroutine reads the speaker location, −16336 ($C030), and that is affected by two

```
                          ; PROGRAM: APPLE IIc SPEAKER DRIVER
                          ;
                          ; MEMORY REQUIRED:        27 ($1B) BYTES
                          ; I/O REQUIREMENTS:       SPEAKER AT $C030
                          ; MONITOR SUBROUTINES:    'WAIT' AT $FCA8
                          ; REGISTERS AFFECTED:     A,X,Y,S
                          ; INPUT REQUIREMENTS:     LENGTH OF TONE IN 864
                          ;                         ($360)
                          ;                         PITCH OF TONE IN 865
                          ;                         ($361)
                          ; METHOD:
                          ;   1. LOW VALUE FOR 'PITCH' YIELDS LOW NOTE,
                          ;      HIGH VALUE FOR 'PITCH' YIELDS HIGH NOTE.
                          ;   2. 'RANGE' FACTOR ALSO AFFECTS PITCH.
                          ;   3. COMPENSATES SOMEWHAT FOR PITCH-INDUCED
                          ;      LENGTH DISPARITIES BY REPEATING THE TONE
                          ;      'PITCH' TIMES.
                          ;   4. REPEATS EVERYTHING 'LENGTH' TIMES.
                          ; NOT RELOCATABLE UNLESS REASSEMBLED
                          ;
                          WAIT    =$FCA8          ;MONITOR'S WAIT SUBROUTINE
                          SPEAKR  =$C030          ;SPEAKER LOCATION
                          RANGE   =#4             ;ESTABLISHES PITCH RANGE
                                  *=$360          ;STARTING LOCATION
0360-   00                LENGTH  .BYTE   0       ;LENGTH OF TONE
0361-   00                PITCH   .BYTE   0       ;PITCH OF TONE
                          ;
                          ;
0362-   AC 61 03          TONE    LDY     PITCH
0365-   AE 61 03          Y1      LDX     PITCH
0368-   E8                X1      INX             ;VARIABLE DELAY
0369-   D0 FD                     BNE     X1      ;  USING PITCH NUMBER
036B-   A9 04                     LDA     RANGE   ;FIXED DELAY
036D-   20 A8 FC                  JSR     WAIT    ;  USING RANGE NUMBER
0370-   AD 30 C0                  LDA     SPEAKR  ;PLUCK SPEAKER
0373-   88                        DEY             ;REPEAT, USING INVERSE
0374-   D0 EF                     BNE     Y1      ;  OF PITCH NUMBER
0376-   CE 60 03                  DEC     LENGTH  ;REPEAT ALL, USING
0379-   D0 E7                     BNE     TONE    ;  LENGTH NUMBER
037B-   60                        RTS
```

Assembly Language Instructions

Machine Language Codes (Hexadecimal numbers)

Memory Locations (Hexadecimal numbers)

Figure 13-1. Machine Language Speaker subroutine

things. First, a simple loop creates a delay whose length is inversely proportional to the value of the pitch number in location 865 ($361). In other words, a high pitch number yields a short delay, resulting in a high-pitched tone. The pitch is also affected by a second, fixed delay caused by calling the Machine Language Monitor Wait subroutine. The value in location 876 ($36C) determines the length of the fixed delay, thereby affecting the range of available pitches. The standard value is 4. A higher number would yield lower notes with a narrower pitch range, and a lower number the opposite.

An earlier BASIC example in this chapter demonstrated how a note's pitch can affect its length. This is a serious problem in machine language because of the relatively wide pitch range available. The Machine Language Speaker subroutine compensates somewhat for this variation by holding a tone for a length of time directly proportional to its pitch number. Thus the length of a note is approximately equal to the time spent in the pitch delay loop multiplied by a number inversely proportional to that. For example, pitch 1 and pitch 255 are both held for approximately the same length of time (1*(256−1)=255 and 255*(256−255)=255. However, midrange notes such as pitch 130 are held longer (130*(256−130)=16380). This compensation is not perfect, but is better than none at all. Without the compensation the ratio of longest tone to shortest is 255:1, but with it that ratio is about 64:1. Further improvement would require a longer and more complex machine language subroutine.

The overall tone length is also affected by the value of memory location 864 ($360), which is the tone's length number. It determines the number of times the subroutine repeats itself before ending.

Using the Speaker Subroutine

To use the Machine Language Speaker subroutine from BASIC, you must first put it into memory. It is designed to occupy memory locations 864-891 and will not work in any other location. Those memory locations will be vacant unless you are using them for shape tables or another machine language subroutine. The simplest way to put the subroutine in memory is with a program like this one:

```
]5 REM
]6 REM ..Put speaker subroutine in memory
]7 REM
]10 FOR ML = 864 TO 891
]20 READ MC
]30 POKE ML,MC
]40 NEXT ML
]300 END
]3090 REM
]3091 REM ..Machine Language Speaker Subroutine
code
]3092 REM
]4000 DATA 0,115,172,97,3,174,97,3,232,208,253,169
]4010 DATA 4,32,168,252,173,48,192,136,208,239,206
]4020 DATA 96,3,208,231,96
```

This program contains the machine language instruction codes in DATA statements (lines 4000-4020). It puts those codes in memory locations 864-891 with a FOR-NEXT loop (lines 10-40).

With the subroutine installed in memory, a BASIC program can generate tones of different pitches and frequencies. Use a POKE statement to put a tone length in memory location 864, another POKE statement to put a tone pitch in memory location 865, and a CALL statement to call the subroutine at location 866. Here is an example:

```
]210 INPUT "PITCH, 1 (LOW) TO 255 (HIGH)? ";P
]220 INPUT "LENGTH, 1 (SHORT) TO 255 (LONG)? ";L
]230 POKE 864,L
]240 POKE 865,P
]250 CALL 866: REM ..Play a note
]260 GOTO 210
```

To end this program, press CONTROL-C followed by RETURN.

MUSIC

The speaker subroutine hardly makes an Apple II a sophisticated musical instrument, but it can play 43 notes on the Western chromatic scale, and it can play them as eighth notes, quarter notes, half notes, or whole notes. This is enough to do a credible job with simple melodies.

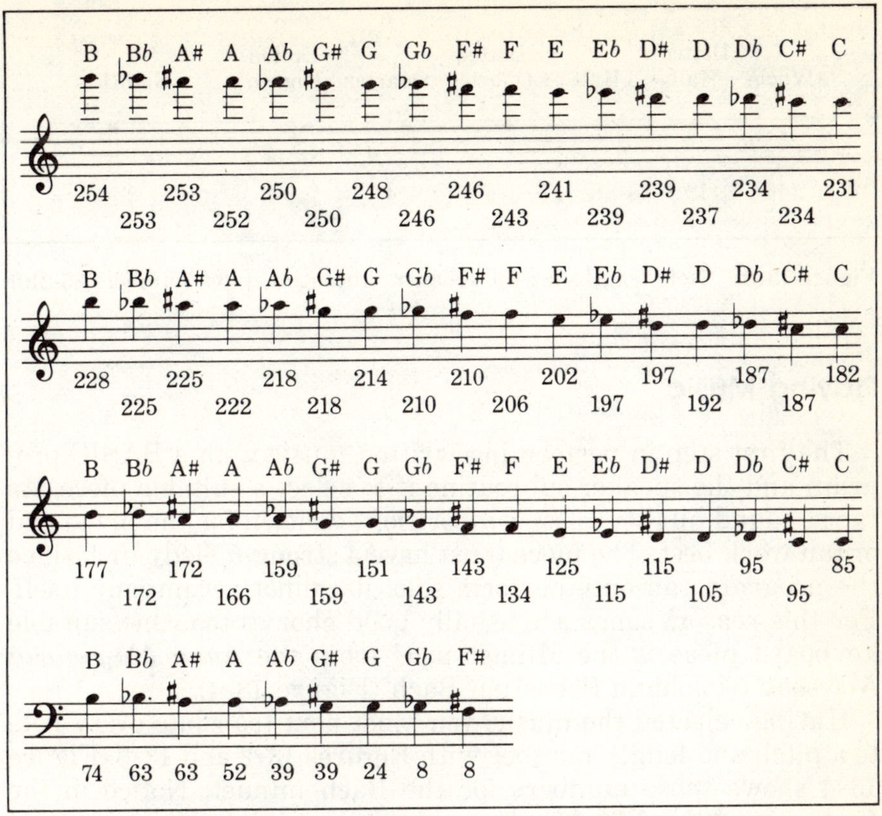

Figure 13-2. The chromatic scale and pitch numbers for the speaker subroutine

A pitch number determines which note will be played from the speaker subroutine's range, which includes most of the notes in the octave below middle C and all of the notes in the three octaves above it (Figure 13-2). Likewise, a length number determines the note's approximate length: whole, half, quarter, or eighth (Figure 13-3). The length is only approximate because the pitch value also affects how long the note is held, as demonstrated earlier in this chapter. You may wish to individually adjust length numbers for pitch numbers below 85 and above 210. For example, length number 3 may sound more like an eighth note when the pitch number is 214 or higher.

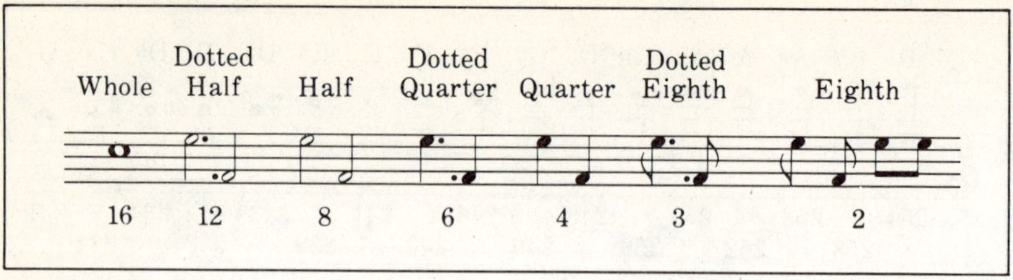

Figure 13-3. Note lengths for the speaker subroutine (pitch numbers 85-210)

Playing Music

The first step in performing written music with a BASIC program and the speaker subroutine is to select a suitable piece. As far as sound quality goes, compositions written for the piano and organ work best. The piece must have a strong melody line, since the program can only perform solo; it cannot accompany itself. For this reason, songs are usually good choices too. One suitable keyboard piece is the Minuet in G from the *Anna Magdalena Notebook* by Johann Sebastian Bach (Figure 13-4).

Having selected the music, you must next translate every note to a pitch and length number with Figures 13-2 and 13-3. Figure 13-4 shows those numbers for the Bach minuet. Notice in the first part of the fifth line how the pitch numbers above 210 use length numbers that are slightly longer than normal, thereby compensating for the length variations owing to pitch.

A long but simple BASIC program will play the Bach minuet or any other piece (Figure 13-5). It starts with a FOR-NEXT loop that reads the machine language code for the speaker subroutine from DATA statements and puts the codes in memory (lines 10-40 and lines 4000-4020). From more DATA statements it reads the title and composer of the tune and displays them centered on the screen (lines 100-140 and 5000-5020).

The length and pitch numbers for each note are kept in still more DATA statements, along with the number of notes to be played (lines 6000 and up). To play the tune, the program first reads the number of notes to play (line 200). Then, in a FOR-NEXT loop, it reads the length and pitch for each note (line 220) and calls the speaker subroutine using those values (lines 230-250). An empty FOR-NEXT loop pauses very briefly after each

Figure 13-4. Pitch and length numbers for the Bach minuet

```
5 REM
6 REM ..First put Speaker Subroutine in memory
7 REM
10 FOR ML = 864 TO 891
20 READ MC
30 POKE ML,MC
40 NEXT ML
90 REM
91 REM ..Display title and composer
92 REM
100 HOME
110 READ T$: REM ..Title of tune
120 VTAB 10: PRINT SPC( (40 - LEN (T$)) / 2);T$
130 READ C$: REM ..Composer
140 VTAB 12: PRINT SPC( (40 - LEN (C$)) / 2);C$
190 REM
191 REM ..Play the tune
192 REM
200 READ N: REM ..Number of notes
210 FOR T = 1 TO N
220 READ L,P: REM ..Length and pitch
230 POKE 864,L
240 POKE 865,P
250 CALL 866: REM ..Play a note
260 REM ..Slight pause between notes
270 FOR S = 1 TO 5
280 NEXT S
290 NEXT T
300 END
3090 REM
3091 REM ..Machine Language Speaker
     Subroutine code
3092 REM
4000 DATA 0,115,172,97,3,174,97,3,232,208,253,169
4010 DATA 4,32,168,252,173,48,192,136,208,239,206
4020 DATA 96,3,208,231,96
4990 REM
4991 REM ..Music
4992 REM
5000 DATA MINUET: REM ..Title
5010 DATA J.S. BACH: REM ..Composer
5020 DATA 127: REM ..Number of notes
5080 REM
5081 REM ..Note lengths and pitches,
5082 REM ..measure by measure
5083 REM
5090 REM ..Line 1
```

Figure 13-5. Program to play the Bach minuet (see Figure 13-4)

```
6000 DATA 4,192,2,151,2,166,2,177,2,182
6010 DATA 4,192,4,151,4,151
6020 DATA 4,202,2,182,2,192,2,202,2,210
6030 DATA 4,214,4,151,4,151
6040 REM ..Line 2
6050 DATA 4,182,2,192,2,182,2,177,2,166
6060 DATA 4,177,2,182,2,177,2,166,2,151
6070 DATA 4,143,2,151,2,166,2,177,2,151
6080 DATA 4,177,8,166
6090 REM ..Line 3
6100 DATA 4,192,2,151,2,166,2,177,2,182
6110 DATA 4,192,4,151,4,151
6120 DATA 4,202,2,182,2,192,2,202,2,210
6130 DATA 4,214,4,151,4,151
6140 REM ..Line 4
6150 DATA 4,182,2,192,2,182,2,177,2,166
6160 DATA 4,177,2,182,2,177,2,166,2,151
6170 DATA 4,166,2,177,2,166,2,151,2,143
6180 DATA 12,151
6190 REM ..Line 5
6200 DATA 5,228,3,214,3,222,3,228,3,214
6210 DATA 5,222,2,192,2,202,2,210,2,192
6220 DATA 4,214,2,202,2,210,2,214,2,192
6230 DATA 4,187,2,177,2,187,4,166
6240 REM ..Line 6
6250 DATA 2,166,2,177,2,187,2,192,2,202,2,210
6260 DATA 4,214,4,210,4,202
6270 DATA 4,210,4,166,4,187
6280 DATA 12,192
6290 REM ..Line 7
6300 DATA 4,192,2,151,2,143,4,151
6310 DATA 4,202,2,151,2,143,4,151
6320 DATA 4,192,4,182,4,177
6330 DATA 2,166,2,151,2,143,2,151,4,166
6340 REM ..Line 8
6350 DATA 2,105,2,125,2,143,2,151,2,166,2,177
6360 DATA 4,182,4,177,4,166
6370 DATA 2,177,2,192,4,151,4,143
6380 DATA 12,151
```

Figure 13-5. Program to play the Bach minuet (*continued*)

note is played in order to keep the notes from slurring together (lines 270 and 280). For a legato performance, you could change the loop to iterate once instead of five times. For a staccato performance, you could change the loop to iterate 10 or 15 times. In fact, the number of iterations for this loop could be stored in the DATA statements along with the length and pitch of each note, allowing the program to vary the performance to match the written music more closely.

As written, neither the speaker subroutine nor the BASIC program that plays music has any provision for rests. You may wish to add that feature.

The program listed in Figure 13-6 lets you compose music for the speaker subroutine. You specify each note of your composition

```
1 REM
2 REM ..Music Composer Program
5 REM
6 REM ..Put speaker subroutine in memory
7 REM
10 FOR ML = 864 TO 891
20 READ MC
30 POKE ML,MC
40 NEXT ML
90 REM
91 REM ..Find out what to do
92 REM
100  DIM A(100,2): REM ..Stores the composition
110 HOME
120  INPUT "(E)NTER, (L)ISTEN, (P)RINT,
     (C)HANGE? ";A$
130 IF A$ = "L" OR A$ = "l" THEN GOSUB 1400
140 IF A$ = "P" OR A$ = "p" THEN GOSUB 1600
150 IF A$ = "E" OR A$ = "e" THEN GOSUB 1000
160 IF A$ = "C" OR A$ = "c" THEN GOSUB 1200
170 PRINT
180 GOTO 110
300 END
990 REM
991 REM ..Enter more notes in sequence
992 REM
1000 I = I + 1: REM ..Current end of composition
1010 M = I: REM ..Note number to enter
1020 GOSUB 1800: REM ..Input lenght & pitch
1030 IF P = 0 AND L = 0 THEN I = I - 1: RETURN:
     REM ..Quit?
1040 A(I,1) = P:A(I,2) = L: REM ..Remember note
```

Figure 13-6. Music Composer program

```
1050 GOTO 1000: REM ..Get next note
1190 REM
1191 REM ..Allow changes to composition
1192 REM
1200 PRINT "NOTE TO CHANGE (1 TO ";I;"; 0 ENDS)";
1210 INPUT E
1220 IF E = 0 THEN RETURN
1230 IF E < 1 OR E > I THEN PRINT CHR$ (7);:
     GOTO 1200
1240 M = E: GOSUB 1800: REM ..Input length & Pitch
1250 A(E,1) = P:A(E,2) = L: REM ..Remember
     the change
1260 GOTO 1200
1390 REM
1391 REM ..Listen to the composition
1392 REM
1400 FOR K = 1 TO I
1410 POKE 864,A(K,2)
1420 POKE 865,A(K,1)
1430 CALL 866: REM ..Play a note
1440 NEXT K
1450 RETURN
1590 REM
1591 REM ..Print the composition
1592 REM
1600 PRINT "NOTE"; TAB( 7);"LENGTH";
     TAB( 15);"PITCH"
1610 FOR K = 1 TO I
1620 PRINT K; TAB( 7);A(K,2); TAB( 15);A(K,1)
1630 NEXT K
1640 PRINT
1650 PRINT "PRESS RETURN TO CONTINUE": INPUT Z$
1660 RETURN
1790 REM
1791 REM ..Input one note
1792 REM
1800 PRINT "NOTE NO. ";M;
1810 INPUT " - ENTER LENGTH, PITCH: ";L,P
1820 IF P = 0 AND L = 0 THEN RETURN
1830 IF (P < 0 OR P > 255) OR (L < 1 OR L > 255)
     THEN PRINT CHR$ (7); GOTO 1810
1840 POKE 864,L
1850 POKE 865,P
1860 CALL 866: REM ..Play a note
1870 RETURN
3090 REM
```

Figure 13-6. Music Composer program (*continued*)

```
3091 REM ..Machine Language Speaker
     Subroutine code
3092 REM
4000 DATA 0,115,172,97,3,174,97,3,232,208,253,169
4010 DATA 4,32,168,252,173,48,192,136,208,239,206
4020 DATA 96,3,208,231,96
```

Figure 13-6. Music Composer program (*continued*)

by entering its length and pitch. The program will then play back your composition, let you change individual notes, or print the length and pitch numbers.

When you run the program, you will see the message **(E)NTER, (L)ISTEN, (P)RINT, (C)HANGE?** Your first action will be to enter some notes, so press E and then RETURN.

Next, the message **NOTE NO. 1– ENTER LENGTH, PITCH:** appears. Enter two numbers separated by a comma. The first is the length of the note and the second is the pitch. Both numbers must be between 1 and 255. When you press RETURN after entering these values, the program plays the note. Repeat this process to enter a series of tones (up to 100). To stop entering notes, enter a length and pitch of 0. The program will ask you to specify another action.

If you choose to change entries you have made, the message **NOTE TO CHANGE (1 to 12; 0 ENDS)?** appears, except that where you see the 12 here, the number of the last note you actually entered will appear. Enter the number of the note you want to change. The program will ask you for the length and pitch once more. To end changes for now, enter note number 0, and the program will ask you to specify another action.

When you listen to your composition, the program displays all the notes you have entered so far. It displays them all at once, so if there are more than 22, some will disappear off the top of the screen. You can always freeze and unfreeze the display by pressing CONTROL-S as required.

You may wish to modify the program to print your composition in addition to, or instead of, displaying it. Use the techniques described in Chapter 10. Also, you may wish to add to the progam so it will save the notes you enter in a disk file. Either sequential or random-access programs may suit your needs; see Chapter 11. With your compositions or disk files, another program you write could retrieve one and then play it using the speaker subroutine.

Machine Language Monitor

14

Residing permanently in the Apple II's read-only memory (ROM) is a control program called the *Machine Language Monitor.* The Machine Language Monitor serves as a link between the BASIC interpreter (or another programming language) and many low-level functions that the computer performs, such as displaying a character or drawing a line.

This chapter describes how to use the Machine Language Monitor via keyboard commands. For example, you can use it to put graphics shape tables and machine language subroutines into memory. You can examine memory locations or the microprocessor registers, and change them if you wish. You can also move blocks of data from one part of memory to another and compare one block of memory to another.

In addition to describing the Machine Language Monitor, this chapter explains how to use the Mini-Assembler to enter an assembly language program. However, this chapter does not teach you assembly language programming. For that, read *6502 Assembly Language Programming* by Lance Leventhal (Berkeley: Osborne/McGraw-Hill, 1979) or another 6502 assembly language text.

Accessing the Machine Language Monitor

To transfer control of an Apple IIe or Apple II Plus directly to the Machine Language Monitor, type the command CALL −151. The command prompt changes to an asterisk, reminding you that

BASIC commands will no longer work.

On most standard Apple II machines, the asterisk command prompt appears immediately when you switch on the computer. The Machine Language Monitor is already in control; there is no need to type the CALL −151 command.

Leaving the Machine Language Monitor

On an Apple IIe or Apple II Plus, you can exit the Machine Language Monitor and return control to BASIC by pressing CONTROL-C and then RETURN. After you press RETURN, the BASIC command prompt appears:] for Applesoft or > for Integer BASIC. If there was a BASIC program in memory before you transferred to the Machine Language Monitor, the program and its variables will be unchanged when you return to BASIC, unless you did something with the Machine Language Monitor to change them.

On a standard Apple II, you can exit the Machine Language Monitor by pressing CONTROL-C and then RETURN. But unless the standard Apple II is equipped with an Applesoft Firmware card, CONTROL-C always restarts Integer BASIC. To restart Applesoft if you are using ProDOS or DOS 3.3, type 3D0G and then press RETURN. (That's a zero between the D and the G.) To restart Applesoft that you loaded from cassette, type 0G and press RETURN.

Important: Use the command 0G *only* with cassette-based Applesoft.

Hexadecimal Numbers

The Machine Language Monitor does not use the decimal (base 10) number system you are familiar with. It uses the hexadecimal (base 16) number system instead. Hexadecimal numbers make a convenient shorthand for the binary (base 2) numbers used internally by the Apple II's 6502 microprocessor. You normally count 1, 2, 3, 4, 5, 6, 7, 8, 9, 10, 11, and so on. The Machine Language Monitor counts 1, 2, 3, 4, 5, 6, 7, 8, 9, A, B, C, D, E, F, 10, 11, and so on. The microprocessor counts 0, 1, 10, 11, 100, 101, and so on.

BASIC isolates you from hexadecimal and binary numbers by converting to and from decimal behind the scenes. When you use the Machine Language Monitor, you must learn to think in hexadecimal or use the conversion table in Appendix H.

Loading ProDOS or DOS 3.3

You can load the ProDOS or DOS 3.3 operating system program with a Machine Language Monitor command. On most Apple II systems you simply type a 6, press CONTROL-P, and then press RETURN. This command loads the operating system from drive 1 attached to slot 6, just as the PR#6 command does in BASIC. To load DOS from a drive attached to a different slot, enter that slot number instead of the 6.

Activating the 80-Column Adapter

On an Apple IIe equipped with an 80-column adapter, you can put the computer in active-80 mode with a Machine Language Monitor command. Type a 3, press CONTROL-P, and then press RETURN. This works just like the PR#3 command in BASIC.

EXAMINING MEMORY

The Machine Language Monitor allows you to examine the contents of memory locations one at a time, eight at a time, or a block at a time.

Examining Single Locations

To look at a single memory location from the Machine Language Monitor, type the address (in hexadecimal) of the location and press RETURN, as in this example:

```
*FF69

FF69- A9
*▒
```

When you enter an address, the Machine Language Monitor retains it for future use as a memory location pointer. To change the memory location pointer, simply type a new address. For example, type the following:

```
*300F
```

and the Machine Language Monitor resets the memory location pointer in addition to displaying the contents of location 300F.

Examining Words of Memory

To examine more memory locations starting at the memory location pointer, enter nothing after a Machine Language Monitor command prompt; just press RETURN. For example, suppose you examined location FF69 as in the example above, and at the next command prompt pressed RETURN, as follows:

```
*FF69

FF69- A9
*
 AA 85 33 20 67 FD
*
FF70- 20 C7 FF 20 A7 FF 84
*▒
```

The RETURN key is pressed three times in this example, once on each line that begins with an asterisk command prompt. The first time, the contents of location FF69 are displayed. The second time, the contents of the next seven locations, FF6A through FF6F, appear. The third time, the contents of the next eight locations appear, along with the first address for the group of eight.

Examining Blocks of Memory

You can examine a large block of memory (usually more than eight bytes) in block mode. Type the starting address (in hexadecimal), a period, and the ending address (in hexadecimal), and then press RETURN. Here is an example:

```
*F800.F83F

F800- 4A 08 20 47 F8 28 A9 0F
F808- 90 02 69 E0 85 2E B1 26
F810- 45 30 25 2E 51 26 91 26
F818- 60 20 00 F8 C4 2C B0 11
F820- C8 20 0E F8 90 F6 69 01
```

```
F828- 48 20 00 F8 68 C5 2D 90
F820- F5 60 A0 2F D0 02 A0 27
F838- 84 2D A0 27 A9 00 85 30
*▒
```

If you specify an ending address lower than the starting address, only the contents of the starting address are displayed.

You can specify a block of memory too large to display at once on the screen. In this case, data scrolls off the top of the screen to make room for more at the bottom. You cannot cancel this display without pressing CONTROL-RESET. On most Apple II machines, you can temporarily halt the display by pressing CONTROL-S. Using CONTROL-S freezes output to the screen, giving you a chance to view the screen at your leisure. Press CONTROL-S again to restart the display.

A shortened form of the block-examine command uses the memory location pointer for the starting address of the block. Enter a period followed by the ending address of the block. For instance, if you just looked at memory locations F800 through F83F, as shown in the example above, you can continue examining a block beginning with F840 and ending with F880 as follows:

```
*.F880
F840- 20 28 F8 88 10 F6 60 48
F848- 4A 29 03 09 04 85 27 68
F850- 29 18 90 02 69 7F 85 26
F858- 0A 0A 05 26 85 26 60 A5
F860- 30 18 69 03 29 0F 85 30
F868- 0A 0A 0A 0A 05 30 85 30
F870- 60 4A 08 20 47 F8 B1 26
F878- 28 90 04 4A 4A 4A 4A 29
F880- 0F
*▒
```

EXAMINING THE MICROPROCESSOR REGISTERS

With the Machine Language Monitor, you can inspect the registers in the Apple II's 6502 microprocessor. This is done by pressing CONTROL-E and then RETURN. The next example illustrates the results.

```
*
 A=F6 X=02 Y=00 P=00 S=98
*▒
```

The values displayed are those stored in the Accumulator register (A), Index Register X (X), Index Register Y (Y), Processor Status Register (P), and Stack Pointer (S). The values directly to the right of each equal sign are the latest values of the registers. However, they are not affected by operating the Machine Language Monitor. In other words, the register contents are saved by the Machine Language Monitor and remain unchanged until you either execute your own machine language program or return to BASIC.

ALTERING MEMORY

Altering memory is more complicated than examining it. You must specify which location to alter and you must supply the new data that goes into that location. You can alter a single location, or you can modify a range of consecutive memory locations with one command.

Altering a Single Memory Location

The first step in changing a single memory location is to set the memory location pointer, which is the same pointer used in examining memory. You specify a location to alter the same way you specify a location to examine: type its address (in hexadecimal) and then press RETURN. The Machine Language Monitor responds with the contents of the memory location. For example, the following command line sets the memory location pointer to 1200 hexadecimal:

```
*1200
1200- 44
*▒
```

The next step is to alter the value stored in this location. To do that, type a colon and the two-digit hexadecimal number you want to store at the location you just set (then press RETURN). For example, type

```
*:5F
```

The colon indicates a memory alteration command to the Machine Language Monitor. The 5F is the new data to place at memory location 1200. You can alter memory using one command line instead of two, as shown below:

```
*1200:5F
```

This command line has the same effect on location 1200 as the two separate lines shown previously. The memory location pointer becomes 1200, and the Machine Language Monitor places 5F at that location. The memory location pointer moves to the next highest memory location. If you want to change location 1201 to 7F, for example, type this:

```
*:7F
```

Again, the memory location pointer is increased by 1. Now you can alter memory location 1202 without explicitly entering its address.

Altering a Range of Memory Locations

The Machine Language Monitor lets you change more than one memory location at a time, provided the locations are consecutive. First, you set the memory location pointer. Next, you type a colon and, on the same line, you enter a series of two-digit hexadecimal numbers—one two-digit number for each consecutive location you want to alter. The following example places the numbers 00 through 07 in locations 1200 through 1207:

```
*1200:00 01 02 03 04 05 06 07
```

This example alters eight addresses at once, but you can alter more than 80 with one command. If necessary, the command line wraps around to encompass several display lines.

Checking Memory Alterations

It is good practice to check memory alterations if you want the final product (whether a graphics shape table or a series of machine language instructions) to be accurate. To do this you can use any of the three examine-memory commands discussed earlier in this chapter. The following example checks the alterations made by the previous example:

```
*1200.1207
1200- 00 01 02 03 04 05 06 07
*▒
```

If you spot any mistakes in the memory locations you altered, you can correct them individually without having to reenter all the data. Simply note the address of each incorrect location and alter it again. For instance, suppose you made a mistake entering the fourth number above, at location 1203. You can correct it by typing this:

```
*1203:03
```

ALTERING THE MICROPROCESSOR REGISTERS

The process of altering the microprocessor registers is slightly different from altering memory, since the registers have no addresses. To alter the contents of a register, you first examine them all using CONTROL-E. On the next line, you can change the contents of the registers by typing a colon followed by one to five hexadecimal numbers. Separate the numbers with spaces.

The first hexadecimal number will be the new value of the Accumulator register, the second number will be the new value of Index Register X, the third number the value of Index Register Y, the fourth the value of the Processor Status Register, and the fifth the new value of the Stack Pointer. You must enter values for all registers up to and including the last register in the series you intend to change. You need not enter values for any registers beyond that.

As an example, say you want to change Index Register Y while leaving all other registers intact. First, examine the registers with CONTROL-E:

```
*
 A=FF X=02 Y=00 P=00 S=98
*▒
```

(These register contents are just examples.)

To change Index Register Y to 8A without changing any other registers, type the existing values of the Accumulator register and Index Register X, followed by the new value for Index Register Y. Don't type values for the last two registers and they will be unchanged.

```
*: FF 02 8A
```

Verify that the change is correct by using CONTROL-E to examine the registers once again.

STORING MEMORY CONTENTS ON DISK AND TAPE

The Machine Language Monitor allows you to use a cassette recorder to save the contents of a block of memory on tape. With the ProDOS and DOS 3.3 operating systems, you can store memory contents even more quickly and reliably on disk. In order to save memory on disk, you have to leave the Machine Language Monitor temporarily and use BASIC commands.

Saving Memory on Tape

The Machine Language Monitor's write-memory command saves a block of memory on tape. You specify the beginning and ending addresses of the memory block you want to save. The following example illustrates:

```
*360.366W
```

This command tells the Machine Language Monitor to write the contents of memory on the cassette recorder, starting at memory location 360 (hexadecimal) and ending with memory location 366.

When you enter the command to write memory, don't press RETURN until you have pressed the cassette recorder's RECORD button and you can see the tape moving. If the cassette you are using is at the beginning of the tape, let it run for at least five seconds before pressing RETURN. This allows the nonmagnetic leader tape to pass through the recorder. The write-memory command does not check for the presence of an operating tape recorder and usable tape.

When you press RETURN, the Machine Language Monitor command prompt disappears from the screen and the computer sends a ten-second reference tone to the recorder. The Machine Language Monitor uses this tone later as a locking-on signal during the read-memory command, as described in the next section. When the write-memory command finishes, the Apple II speaker beeps once and the Machine Language Monitor command prompt reappears on the screen.

The write-memory command enables you to record from one byte to 64K bytes (65,536 bytes) on tape. The Machine Language Monitor sends data through the cassette output port at a rate of approximately 210 characters per second (based on a 16,384-byte move in 77.5 seconds, after the reference tone).

Retrieving Data From Cassette Tape

The read-memory command enables you to transfer data from the cassette recorder into the Apple II's memory. You specify the starting address and the ending address. The following example illustrates:

```
*360.366R
```

This command reads data from cassette tape into memory, starting at memory location 360 (hexadecimal) and ending at 366.

The read-memory command waits for a reference tone from the cassette recorder and locks up the computer until it encounters the tone. So before you press PLAY on the cassette recorder, make sure you position the tape to where the reference tone begins. You can tell the difference between the reference tone and actual data on the tape by listening to it. Unplug the cable from the earphone jack to listen to the tape using the cassette recorder's speaker. The reference tone is a steady, medium-pitched hum. Actual data sounds like random noise or static.

Be sure to adjust the cassette recorder playback volume before using the read-memory command. The procedure for adjusting the volume is explained in Chapter 2.

Error Conditions in the Read-Memory Command

The Machine Language Monitor listens to the cassette recorder for at least 3.5 seconds before expecting data from it. This allows the Machine Language Monitor to lock onto the reference tone. If the tape contains less than 3.5 seconds of this tone, the Machine Language Monitor loses the beginning of the data transmission from the cassette, resulting in a checksum error. Should this happen, you will hear a beep from the Apple II speaker and see the message **ERR** on the screen. To check the cause of the error, you can time the reference tone. To do that, rewind the tape to the beginning of the tone, unplug the cable from the recorder's earphone jack, and depress the PLAY button. Note when the tone starts and stops. If it is less than 3.5 seconds long, you must write memory to the tape again. You probably forgot to move past the nonmagnetic leader tape at the beginning of the cassette before recording.

Reading more or less data into memory from cassette than was originally saved on the tape usually causes an error message to appear on the screen. As a general rule, you should only read in as much memory as you wrote to the cassette in the first place.

Saving Memory on Disk

The BSAVE command saves a block of memory on disk. First you must leave the Machine Language Monitor and return to BASIC using CONTROL-C or one of the methods described at the beginning of this chapter. Then you can type a BSAVE command. Here is an example:

```
]BSAVE SHAPE.TABLE,A$360,L6
```

This command creates a disk file named SHAPE.TABLE. The parameter A$360 designates the starting address of the block of memory to write, and the dollar sign prefix means the number is hexadecimal. The parameter L6 specifies the length of the block of memory to write, in this case 6 bytes. You can use hexadecimal or decimal numbers for the address and length parameters.

Retrieving Memory From Disk

The BLOAD command retrieves data from a disk file and loads it into memory. To use the BLOAD command, you must leave the Machine Language Monitor and return to BASIC using CONTROL-C or one of the methods described at the beginning of this chapter. Then you can type a BLOAD command. Here is an example:

```
]BLOAD SHAPE.TABLE,A$360
```

This example loads the file named SHAPE.TABLE from the disk currently in use and puts the data directly into memory, starting at address 360 (hexadecimal). This command also accepts a decimal address. The starting address parameter is not necessary if you want the file contents to start at the same location they were saved from. You need only specify an address if it differs from the BSAVE starting address. A length parameter is also optional. If no length is specified, the operating system checks the length of the disk file and terminates the transfer of data automatically.

MOVING AND COMPARING BLOCKS OF MEMORY

The Machine Language Monitor has a move-memory command that copies a block of data from one part of memory to another. It also has a compare-memory command that reports any discrepancies between two blocks of memory. When used with the Machine Language Monitor's read-memory and write-memory commands, these new commands allow you to verify the success of a write-memory command.

The Move-Memory Command

In order to move data from one part of memory to another, you must specify where you want to move memory to, where you want to move memory from, and the last address you want moved. As with other Machine Language Monitor commands, all addresses are hexadecimal numbers. Here is an example:

```
*1200<2000.2100M
```

This example moves data to address 1200 from the block starting at location 2000 and ending at location 2100. The implied length of the block moved is 101 bytes hexadecimal (257 bytes decimal). The original contents of addresses 2000 through 2100 remain undisturbed.

Filling Memory

The move-memory command can also be used to fill consecutive memory locations with a repeated set of values. For example, with two commands you could place a zero value in the entire block of memory starting with address 1D00 and ending with 1DFF. To begin, you make the first block location zero, as follows:

```
*1D00:00
```

Next you copy the first block location to all the rest of the block locations with one move-memory command. The following example shows how:

```
*1D01<1D00.1DFEM
```

You specify a destination starting address that is one greater than the last byte of the pattern (in this example it is 1D01). Set the source starting address to the beginning of the pattern (1D00 in this case), and set the source ending address to the last byte that you want filled (1DFF) minus the length of the pattern you want to fill memory with (1DFE).

This example fills locations 1D01 through 1DFF with the contents of location 1D00, which contains 00. To move the first byte, the Machine Language Monitor moves data from location 1D00 to location 1D01 first, moving 00 into location 1D01. To move the second byte, the Machine Language Monitor moves 00 from location 1D01 to location 1D02. Similarly, the contents of 1D02 are moved to 1D03, and so on, until the contents of location 1DFE are moved into location 1DFF.

You can also fill memory with a pattern that is more than one byte long. For example, to fill from 1D00 through 1DFF with the four-byte pattern 00 5E 7F FF, you first alter four bytes of memory starting at address 1D00:

```
*1D00:00 5E 7F FF
```

This sets the pattern. Now you can fill successive memory locations with the pattern, as follows:

```
*1D04<1D00.1DFBM
```

Note that the destination starting address occurs one byte after the end of the pattern, the source starting address points to the beginning of the fill pattern, and the source ending address points to the last address to fill minus the length of the pattern (1DFF − 04 = 1DFB in hexadecimal arithmetic).

The Verify-Memory Command

The Machine Language Monitor verify-memory command compares two blocks of memory, noting differences. It looks much like the move-memory command. You specify where the first block starts and where the second block starts and ends. Here is an example:

```
*32D0<0.CV
```

This example instructs the Machine Language Monitor to start comparing data at location 32D0 with location 0, and to continue the comparison until address 32DC is compared with location 000C. Notice that no leading zeros are needed for addresses in a Machine Language Monitor command line.

If the Machine Language Monitor encounters a byte in the first block that is not the same as its counterpart in the second block, it displays the address from the first block and its value, and then the value at the same relative address in the second block. For example, suppose you moved memory from locations 0000 through 000C to locations 32D0 through 32DC, as follows:

```
*32D0<0.CM
```

You could visually check the move-memory operation by displaying the source and destination blocks.

```
*0.C
0000- 4C 3C D4 4C 3A DB 00 00
0008- FF FF 4C 99 E1
*32D0.32DC
32D0- 4C 3C D4 4C 3A DB 00 00
32D8- FF FF 4C 99 E1
```

Now suppose you altered location 32D8 from its present value (FF) to 5A, and then verified the two blocks.

```
*32D8:5A
*32D0<0.CV
0008-FF (5A)
```

In this example, the Machine Language Monitor compares the two blocks of memory, byte by byte, and finds a discrepancy between location 32D8 and location 0008. The value at location 0008 is FF, but the value at location 32D8 is 5A.

Verifying a Write-Memory Command

The verify-memory command is especially useful if you save memory contents onto cassette tape or disk. By saving a portion of memory and then loading it back at a different location, you can verify that memory was saved properly. The following example illustrates with cassette commands:

```
*2000.20FFW
*2100.21FFR
*2000<2100.21FFV
*▒
```

This example writes data from memory onto cassette tape, starting at location 2000 and ending at location 20FF. Then it reads the same data back, but, but locations 2100 through 21FF. Finally, it verifies locations 2000 through 20FF with locations 2100 through 21FF. Since no discrepancies are displayed, you can be sure that the write-memory operation was successful.

To verify memory saved on disk, the same general procedures apply. First, you return to BASIC (with CONTROL-C) and type a BSAVE command. Next, you type a BLOAD command, but specify a different starting address than you used with BSAVE. Then you switch to the Machine Language Monitor and type a verify-memory command. Here is an example:

```
*
]BSAVE MEM.DATA,A$2000,L$100
]BLOAD MEM.DATA,A$2100
]CALL -151

*2000<2100.21FFV
*▒
```

If no discrepancies occur, you can be sure that memory was properly saved onto disk.

THE GO COMMAND

The Machine Language Monitor has a command that transfers control of the Apple II to a program at a location you specify. Here is an example:

```
*3D0G
```

This example instructs the Machine Language Monitor to jump to location 3D0 in memory and execute the machine language instruction it finds there. The letter G at the end of the command line stands for "Go." Transferring control to the instruction at location 3D0 restarts BASIC with the ProDOS or DOS 3.3 operating system.

The address is optional; if no address is entered, the Machine Language Monitor uses its memory location pointer as the assumed address.

USING THE PRINTER

If your Apple II connects to a printer via a serial or parallel accessory card, you can use the printer for output from the Machine Language Monitor. To divert all output from the screen to a printer, type the slot number of the accessory card that controls the printer, press CONTROL-P, and then press RETURN. To reselect the screen for output, use slot number 0 with the CONTROL-P command. The printer command works in exactly the same way as the PR# command in BASIC.

When using this command, be sure the slot you select has an accessory card in it. If no accessory card exists in the slot you specify, the Apple II will lock up. The only way to recover from this condition is to press CONTROL-RESET.

THE KEYBOARD COMMAND

You can direct the Machine Language Monitor to accept input from a device other than the Apple II keyboard. To do that, type the slot number for the new input device, press CONTROL-K, and then press RETURN. To return control to the Apple II keyboard, use slot number 0 with CONTROL-K.

CHANGING DISPLAY STYLE

To view Machine Language Monitor output on the screen with inverse characters, enter the inverse video command, I. To cancel inverse style, enter the normal video command, N. Neither of these commands needs any additional parameter other than the letter I or N.

HEXADECIMAL ARITHMETIC IN THE MACHINE LANGUAGE MONITOR

The Machine Language Monitor can perform hexadecimal addition and subtraction. To perform addition, enter a hexadecimal addend followed by a plus sign and a hexadecimal augend. If the result is greater than FF, the Machine Language Monitor truncates the most significant digit and displays the low-order eight bits of the result, as shown in this example:

```
*7F+8A
=09
```

To perform subtraction, enter the minuend followed by a minus sign and the subtrahend. As with addition, both numbers must be hexadecimal. If the result is less than zero, the Machine Language Monitor displays the one's complement result, as shown below:

```
*0A-2D
=DD
```

USER-DEFINABLE MACHINE LANGUAGE MONITOR COMMAND

By entering CONTROL-Y in response to a Machine Language Monitor prompt, you invoke a special user-definable command. The Machine Language Monitor automatically jumps to location

3F8 when CONTROL-Y is entered. There is enough room at location 3F8 for one machine language jump instruction. If you have a special machine language program somewhere in memory, CONTROL-Y could initiate a jump to it via location 3F8.

The example below shows how to use CONTROL-Y to restart Applesoft on a standard Apple II without typing the 3D0G command. First, you need to know the format of a machine language jump instruction. It takes three bytes. The first byte is the instruction code, 4C. The next two bytes are the address to jump to, with a twist: you must specify the last byte of the address first. Here's an alter-memory command that sets up a jump instruction to address 3D0:

```
*3F8:4C D0 03
```

Now pressing CONTROL-Y and RETURN will restart Applesoft, just as CONTROL-C does on an Apple IIe or Apple II Plus. Reset the user-definable command by placing a different jump instruction at address 3F8.

THE MINI-ASSEMBLER

The Apple II has a built-in program called the *Mini-Assembler* that spares the assembly language programmer the torture of translating to machine language by hand. The Mini-Assembler resides with Integer BASIC in ROM. It is called "mini" because you have to specify memory locations with addresses, rather than mnemonic labels as in a full assembler. Also, each assembly language instruction you enter is immediately translated into machine language. The principal problem here is that you cannot insert or delete instructions with a text editor prior to translation by a full assembler. The principal advantage of the Mini-Assembler is that you can enter machine instructions directly into the Apple II, while still keeping the convenience of assembly language mnemonic instructions.

Although this chapter describes the Mini-Assembler and tells how to use it, it does not explain assembly language programming concepts. Nor does the chapter cover the entire 6502 instruction set, which is the assembly language the Apple II uses. If you don't understand terms such as *assembly, operands*, and *mnemonics*, stop right now. Learn assembly language programming techniques and the 6502 instruction set first. Then finish reading this chapter.

The Mini-Assembler works only with the assembly language

instructions of the 6502 microprocessor found in a standard Apple II, an Apple II Plus, and an original Apple IIe. The 65C02 microprocessor found in an Enhanced Apple IIe recognizes all the 6502 instructions and more, but the Mini-Assembler does not work with the additional 65C02 instructions.

Accessing the Mini-Assembler

The entry point address of the Mini-Assembler program is at location F666. To start it from the Machine Language Monitor, enter the following command:

```
*F666G
```

From Integer BASIC (or Applesoft on some machines), enter the following immediate mode command:

```
>CALL -2458
```

When you first start the Mini-Assembler, the Apple II's speaker beeps once. The command prompt for the Mini-Assembler is an exclamation point (!).

The Mini-Assembler is not always available on an original Apple IIe. On an original Apple IIe, the Mini-Assembler is a supplement to the Integer BASIC interpreter, but not to the Applesoft interpreter. Thus, on the Apple IIe, you must use an INT command from Applesoft before you can start the Mini-Assembler. Since Integer BASIC is only available with the DOS 3.3 operating system, the Mini-Assembler is not available with the ProDOS operating system on an original Apple IIe. None of these restrictions apply to an Enhanced Apple IIe.

Machine Language Monitor Commands In the Mini-Assembler

Except on an Enhanced Apple IIe, you can execute Machine Language Monitor commands while you are using the Mini-Assembler. Immediately after the Mini-Assembler command prompt (!), enter a dollar sign followed by the Machine Language Monitor command. The example below shows how to examine memory contents from the Mini-Assembler:

```
!$1CFF

1CFF- FD
!▒
```

This feature saves you the time spent switching back and forth between the Mini-Assembler and the Machine Language Monitor. You can enter any Machine Language Monitor command while in the Mini-Assembler just by entering the dollar sign as the first character of input. In fact, you will use this feature to leave the Mini-Assembler. Again, this feature is not available on an Enhanced Apple IIe.

Leaving the Mini-Assembler

To leave the Mini-Assembler, use one of the Machine Language Monitor commands (described at the beginning of this chapter) with a dollar sign prefix. To get back to the Machine Language Monitor, branch to location FF69 with an $FF69G command.

Typing a dollar sign followed by CONTROL-C will put you in BASIC on an Apple II Plus and some standard Apple II machines. On a standard Apple II not equipped with an Apple II Firmware card, use CONTROL-C for Integer BASIC, $3D0G for disk-based Applesoft, or $0G for cassette-based Applesoft.

On an Enhanced Apple IIe, you must press CONTROL-RESET to leave the Mini-Assembler.

Instruction Formats

There are six instruction formats used in programming the 6502 microprocessor. These formats accommodate the microprocessor's eleven addressing modes. They are described below.

Absolute or *direct* addressing requires only the one- or two-byte address of an operand in memory. Here is an example:

```
! AND 303A
```

The Mini-Assembler does not require a dollar sign before hexadecimal addresses; it assumes that all addresses used are in base 16.

Immediate addressing mode specifies the actual value to be used as an operand, as in this example:

```
! LDA #04
```

Note that a number sign (#) is the first character of the operand. This indicates that the value of the operand is to be used literally.

Without the number sign, the Mini-Assembler interprets the operand as an address, not a literal value.

Note also the confusing use of the term "immediate." Do not confuse immediate addressing in assembly language with immediate execution in BASIC. The actions are quite different. The terms are commonplace, so we will use them despite the ambiguity.

Indexed addressing adds the contents of the X or Y register to an address you specify and uses the sum as the address that the instruction references. Here is an example:

```
! CMP 36F,X
```

Pre-indexed indirect addressing indicates that the sum of a number and the contents of a register (both specified in the instruction) form the address of a memory location in the first 256 bytes of memory. This location and the one after it together contain the address of the memory location to be used as the operand in the instruction. Here is an example:

```
! AND (F0,X)
```

Post-indexed indirect addressing looks at an address specified in the instruction for another address, to which it adds the contents of a register specified in the instruction, forming the final address of the data to be used by the instruction. Here is an example:

```
! OR (22),Y
```

Indirect addressing is a bit more straightforward than indexed addressing. Here is an example:

```
! JMP (22FE)
```

Here, the JMP instruction does not branch directly to location 22FE. Instead, it branches to the two-byte address contained in locations 22FE and 22FF.

Typing Errors

The Mini-Assembler detects errors that you make when you enter an assembly language instruction. It displays the error by beeping once and redisplaying the instruction with a caret (^) under the first incorrect character in the instruction.

USING THE MINI-ASSEMBLER

The Mini-Assembler maintains a location counter separate from the Machine Language Monitor's memory location pointer. When you enter an assembly language instruction, the Mini-Assembler calculates the length of its machine language equivalent (1, 2, or 3 bytes) and increments the location counter automatically. You need to set the location counter before you enter any instructions.

You can set the location counter as part of the first assembly language statement you enter. Here is an example:

```
!8DB0:LDA  #04
```

Directly after the Mini-Assembler command prompt, type the starting address for the assembly language code you are about to enter, type a colon and the first assembly language instruction, and then press RETURN. You do not have to enter a new location counter value for the next instruction.

For subsequent instructions, type a blank space and enter the next instruction. This example illustrates:

```
! JSR FB1E
```

A Sample Session

This section explains Mini-Assembler operation in step-by-step detail. The object of this sample session is to create a small program that uses the Apple II game control inputs and the onboard speaker to create sounds. This program reads values from paddle 0 and paddle 1 using the built-in Machine Language Monitor subroutine PREAD (at location FB1E). The value of paddle 0 determines the interval between clicking the speaker (0=shortest delay, FF=longest delay), and the value of paddle 1 determines another interval, related inversely to paddle 0 (0=longest interval, FF=shortest interval). The program begins at location 1D00 and uses location 1CFF to store the reading from paddle 0.

When you enter each line of the assembly language program, the Mini-Assembler overlays the line you entered with the current location counter value, operation code, and operand in machine language form (also known as *object code*), along with the instruction mnemonic you entered. Here is an example.

```
1D00-   A2 00         LDX   #$00
```

The location counter appears at the beginning of the assembled line, followed by a dash. After that comes the operation code (A2 for this LDX instruction), followed by the last byte of the instruction. In the case of three-byte instructions (those that use a two-byte address), the low-order byte appears before the high-order byte. Finally, the instruction mnemonic appears.

The annotated sample session appears in Figure 14-1. Note that in the figure, each line produced by the Mini-Assembler appears below the line you enter to generate it. In practice, the Mini-Assembler displays its output over the top of your typed input.

After entering an assembly language program, you should save it on disk or cassette as described earlier in this chapter. You should also check the program for accuracy. The best way to do this is to list the program, preferably in assembly language format. You will need to use the Machine Language Monitor to do so.

To run the program, branch to location 1D00. Use the G command in the Machine Language Monitor, or CALL 7424 from BASIC. Fiddle with the game controls and see how they affect the speaker. To end the program, press CONTROL-RESET.

DISASSEMBLED LISTINGS

The Machine Language Monitor has a command you can use to list machine language instructions in assembly language format, even if the Mini-Assembler is not available. The command L, for list, *disassembles* 20 machine language instructions into assembly language statements and displays them on the screen or any other output device you select. The list command uses the location counter as a pointer to the next instruction to disassemble. Therefore, if you just enter L after entering the program above, disassembly will start with address 1D1D.

It is a good idea to set the location counter when using the list command. Here is a disassembled listing of the sound program:

```
*1D00L

1D00-   A2 00         LDX   #$00
1D02-   20 1E FB      JSR   $FB1E
```

```
! 1D00:LDX #$00 ←—Set location counter and enter first instruction

1D00-     A2 00            LDX    #$00
!   JSR FB1E ←—All numbers are hexadecimal ($ prefix unnecessary)

1D02-     20 1E FB         JSR    $FB1E
! STY  1CFF

1D05-     8C FF 1C         STY    $1CFF
! INX

1D08-     E8               INX
! JSR  FB1E

1D09-     20 1E FB         JSR    $FB1E
! LDA  C030

1D0C-     AD 30 C0         LDA    $C030
1 DEC  1CFF

1D0F-     CE FF 1C         DEC    $1CFF
1 BNE  1D0C ←—Mini-Assembler computes the relative jump (F8)

1D12-     D0 F8            BNE    $1D0C
1 LDA  C030

1D14-     AD 30 C0         LDA    $C030
! INY

1D17-     C8               INY
! BNE  1D14

1D18-     D0 FA            BNE    $1D14
! JMP  1D00

1D1A-     4C 00  1D        JMP    $1D00
!
```

Figure 14-1. A sample session with the Mini-Assembler

```
1D05-    8C FF 1C     STY    $1CFF
1D08-    E8           INX
1D09-    20 1E FB     JSR    $FB1E
1D0C-    AD 30 C0     LDA    $C030
1D0F-    CE FF 1C     DEC    $1CFF
1D12-    D0 F8        BNE    $1D0C
1D14-    AD 30 C0     LDA    $C030
```

```
1D17-   C8          INY
1D18-   D0 FA       BNE   $1D14
1D1A-   4C 00 1D    JMP   $1D00
1D1D-   9F          ???
1D1E-   4E A5 12    LSR   $12A5
1D21-   A4 96       LDY   $96
1D23-   A3          ???
1D24-   D0 A4       BNE   $1CCA
1D26-   EF          ???
1D27-   A4 62       LDY   $62
1D29-   A2 70       LDX   #$70
*!■
```

In this case, the last eight disassembled instructions are immaterial, since the program ends at address 1D1A.

Note that the list command is a Machine Language Monitor feature, independent of the Mini-Assembler. By entering L ($L from the Mini-Assembler) and pressing RETURN without setting the location counter, you direct the Machine Language Monitor to disassemble the next 20 instructions it finds after those just listed.

COMBINING MACHINE LANGUAGE AND BASIC

In some cases BASIC is not powerful enough to perform all of the functions you may need in a program. This is one reason why programmers resort to assembly language subroutines in their BASIC programs. This section shows how to reference these subroutines from a BASIC program.

By weaving assembly language programs in with a BASIC program, you can create as many problems as you intended to solve. Where in memory are you going to put the assembly language programs? The Apple II's memory contains four large reserved areas, two for text and low-resolution graphics and two for high-resolution graphics. The operating system and the Applesoft interpreter may take up memory too. Locating a program where it will not cause problems is dependent on memory size and the model of Apple II you use.

The Machine Language Monitor is your best source for assembly language subroutines for three reasons: first, since it is in ROM, you don't need to worry about finding space; second, the Machine Language Monitor routines have already been debugged;

and third, the intrinsic routines do not take up any additional memory. The useful Machine Language Monitor subroutines are listed in Appendix G.

Incorporating the Subroutine

If you decide to use a Machine Language Monitor subroutine in a BASIC program, first be sure there is no BASIC equivalent for it. This will save you the trouble of making a program more complicated than necessary. Next, check whether the assembly language subroutines need parameters passed from the BASIC program. If you have to set values in the microprocessor registers before executing the subroutine, or if the result of a subroutine resides in a register after execution, you will have to use extra assembly language instructions to interface with BASIC. Most Machine Language Monitor subroutines need no parameters from BASIC; those that do frequently have a BASIC equivalent anyway.

Once you know which subroutine to use, you may want to document it in a way that makes the meaning clear. For instance, CALL −936 clears the text screen and places the cursor in the upper left-hand corner of the screen. One way of making the CALL statement more descriptive is to set a variable at the beginning of the program, as follows:

```
>10 CLSCREEN = -936
```

and to reference it later in the program:

```
>1510 CALL CLSCREEN
```

This makes the context of the CALL statement clearer to someone who has to read it, but it does add one statement to the program. These finer elements of style will make your program easier to read and debug.

Problems to Avoid

If you have an editor/assembler for the Apple II, it is easy to relocate programs by resetting the origin point and reassembling. However, if you write a machine language subroutine with the Mini-Assembler, and the subroutine is designed to be used with BASIC, you may run into problems that force you to rewrite the subroutine for versions of the Apple II with different memory sizes. This will happen if you use memory locations used by the operating system, the graphics areas, or the Applesoft interpreter. Try to use Machine Language Monitor subroutines wherever possible.

If you program in Applesoft, always use the USR function instead of the CALL statement if you have to pass parameters to and from the subroutine. Locations 9D through A3 store the value of the parameter passed by USR, and you can use this area for parameters to pass back to BASIC. Use the POKE statement to put a JMP instruction in locations 10 through 12 (0A through 0C hexadecimal). These locations must contain a JMP instruction to the beginning of the machine language subroutine invoked by USR.

Summary of Commands, Statements, and Functions

A

This appendix serves as a one-stop reference for all commands, statements, and functions used in the BASIC programming environment. It includes the following items:

- Editing commands and keystrokes
- ProDOS commands
- DOS 3.3 commands
- Applesoft commands, statements, and functions
- Integer BASIC commands, statements, and functions
- Immediate and programmed mode restrictions
- Derived mathematical functions
- Reserved command words.

EDITING COMMANDS

When the Apple II is in immediate mode, you can edit anything displayed on the screen. You can reexecute commands or change program lines. Table A-1 lists the keystrokes you can use in escape mode to move the cursor around the screen. Table A-2 lists the keystrokes that delete and copy displayed characters. Table A-3 summarizes how to insert, delete, or replace whole program lines. Table A-4 summarizes the program line renumbering commands available for Applesoft programs after you run the DOS 3.3 RENUMBER program.

Table A-1. Cursor Movement Keystrokes

Keystroke	Cursor Moves One Position	Available on: IIe	II Plus	Standard
←	Left	Yes	No	No
→	Right	Yes	No	No
↓	Down	Yes	No	No
↑	Up	Yes	No	No
J*	Left	Yes	Yes	No
K*	Right	Yes	Yes	No
M*	Down	Yes	Yes	No
I*	Up	Yes	Yes	No
ESC,A**	Right	Yes	Yes	Yes
ESC,B**	Left	Yes	Yes	Yes
ESC,C**	Down	Yes	Yes	Yes
ESC,D**	Up	Yes	Yes	Yes

*Works only in escape mode. To enter escape mode, press the ESC key. To leave it, press the ESC key again.

**Press the ESC key, release it, then press the second key.

Table A-2. Deleting and Recopying Characters

Keystroke	Effect
→	Moves cursor forward, recopying characters passed over
←	Backspaces the cursor, deleting characters passed over without erasing them from the screen
CONTROL-X	Cancels the current line
ESC,E	Deletes from cursor to end of line
ESC,F	Deletes from cursor to end of text window
ESC,@	Clears text window and moves cursor home

Table A-3. Editing Whole Program Lines

Action	Procedure
Add	Type new line with new line number; line number determines sequence in program
Change	Display line with LIST command; use editing commands in Tables A-1 and A-2
Delete	Type line number and press RETURN key, or use DEL command
Renumber*	Run RENUMBER program before loading or typing your program; see Table A-4 for commands
Replace	Type new line with old line number

*Does not work with ProDOS or Integer BASIC.

Table A-4. Renumbering Applesoft Program Lines (DOS 3.3 only)

Command*	Effect
&	Renumber the entire program, using an increment of 10 between line numbers
&S*line*,E*line*, F*line*,I*increment*	Renumber part of the program, starting with the line number listed after S, ending with the line number listed after E, using the first new line number listed after F, and using an increment between line numbers listed after I. The S, E, F, and I clauses are all optional and can be listed in any combination and any order.
&H	Put the program into a holding area of memory
&M	Merge the program lines in the holding area of memory with the program in the main program memory

*These commands only work after running the RENUMBER program. The FP, HIMEM, and MAXFILES commands all disable renumbering until you rerun the RENUMBER program.

Table A-5. Applesoft Restrictions

Programmed Mode Only	
DATA DEF FN GET INPUT	ONERR GOTO READ RESUME

COMMANDS AND STATEMENTS

All ProDOS, DOS 3.3, Applesoft, and Integer BASIC commands and statements are listed here together, in alphabetical order. This appendix includes syntax definitions and functional descriptions; for examples in context, refer to Chapters 2 through 14.

Immediate and Programmed Modes

Most Applesoft and Integer BASIC statements can be used in either immediate mode or programmed mode. Tables A-5 and A-6 list the exceptions.

All ProDOS and DOS 3.3 commands can be used in immediate mode or programmed mode, except the data file commands APPEND, OPEN, POSITION, READ, and WRITE, which are allowed only in programmed mode. ProDOS and DOS 3.3 com-

Table A-6. Integer BASIC Restrictions

Programmed Mode Only	Immediate Mode Only	
END FOR GOSUB INPUT NEXT RETURN	AUTO CLR CON DEL HIMEM: LOAD	LOMEM: MAN NEW RUN SAVE

mands in programmed mode must be issued indirectly, as part of a PRINT statement string, the first character of which is ASCII code 4 (CHR$(4) or CONTROL-D).

Nomenclature and Format Conventions

This appendix uses a standard scheme for presenting the general form of each statement and function. The following is a list of the punctuation, capitalization, and other mechanical conventions used.

{ }	Braces indicate a choice of items; one of the enclosed items must be present; braces do not appear in an actual statement.
[ ]	Brackets indicate that the enclosed parameter is optional; brackets do not appear in an actual statement.
...	Ellipses indicate that the preceding item can be repeated; ellipses do not appear in actual statements.
line numbers	A programmed mode statement has an implied line number.
other punctuation	All other punctuation marks—commas, semicolons, quotation marks, and parentheses—must appear as shown.
UPPERCASE	Uppercase words and letters must appear exactly as shown.
italics	Generic terms are italicized. The programmer supplies the exact wording or value, according to the definitions for generic terms listed in the next section.

Generic Term Definitions

The following italicized generic terms are used in statement and function definitions. Any italicized terms not listed here are peculiar to the statement in which they appear and will be defined in the text that describes that statement.

B*byte*	The number of bytes, between 0 and 65535, ahead of the current file pointer position. If the number specified is past the end of a sequential-access file or past the end of a random-access record, an error results.
col	Low-resolution graphics column number; a numeric expression that has a value between 0 and 39.
colh	High-resolution graphics column number; a numeric expression that has a value between 0 and 279.
const	Any numeric or string constant.
D*n*	A disk drive number that must be specified as D1 or D2.
expr	Any numeric, string, relational, or logical (Applesoft only) constant, variable, or expression; any valid combination thereof.
expr$	Any string constant, variable, or expression.
exprnm	Any numeric constant, variable, or expression.
F*field*	The number of fields, between 0 and 65535 (32767 with DOS 3.3), ahead of the current file pointer position. If the number specified is past the end of a sequential-access file or past the end of a random-access record, an error results. A carriage return character marks the end of every field.
filename	Any DOS 3.3 file name.
line	Any BASIC program line number.
$line_i$	One of many BASIC program line numbers.
memadr	A numeric expression, variable, or constant that evaluates to any memory address. Memory addresses may range from −32767 to 32767, or from 0 to 65535, where −32767 is the same as 32769, −32766 equals 32770, and so on to −1, which equals 65535.
memloc	Any memory location specified by an integer constant between 0 and 65535 (decimal) or $0 and $FFFF (hexadecimal). Hexadecimal constants are identified by a dollar sign ($) prefix.

pathname	A full or partial ProDOS pathname, which in combination with the current ProDOS prefix specifies the path to a ProDOS file or directory from the volume directory.
R*record*	The record number in a random-access file.
R*field*	Same as F*field*, but must be between 0 and 32767 with DOS 3.3.
row	Low-resolution graphics row number; a numeric expression that has a value between 0 and 47.
rowh	High-resolution graphics row number; a numeric expression that has a value between 0 and 191.
S*n*	Slot number for input or output; must be S0, S1, S2, S3, S4, S5, S6, or S7.
T*type*	One of the file-type codes listed in Table A-7.
var	In Integer BASIC, any numeric or string variable. In Applesoft, any numeric, integer, or string variable.
varnm	Any numeric variable name.

Table A-7. ProDOS File-Type Codes

Abbreviation	File Type
DIR	Directory
TXT	Human-readable letters, digits, and symbols (ASCII code)
BAS	Applesoft BASIC program
VAR	Applesoft BASIC variables
BIN	Machine code or data
REL	Machine code that can be loaded anywhere in memory
$F*n*	User- (programmer-) defined type number *n*; *n* is an integer from 1 to 8
SYS	System program or data

var(*sub*)	In Integer BASIC, any subscripted numeric variable. In Applesoft, any subscripted integer, numeric, or string variable.
V*n*	An identifying DOS 3.3 disk volume number between V0 and V255.

APPEND (ProDOS)

Opens a ProDOS file, positions to the end of the file, and issues a WRITE command.

Format: APPEND *pathname* [,T*type*] [,L*length*] [,D*n*] [,S*n*]

If the named file does not exist, ProDOS creates the file. If the file is already open, an error occurs. APPEND allocates a 1024-byte buffer in memory for the file. Half the buffer is for input and half is for output. If there is too little memory available for the buffer, an error occurs. The CLOSE command closes a file.

As many as eight files can be open at once. Note that the command EXEC opens a file automatically and closes it when it's done.

After an APPEND statement is executed, all PRINT statements send characters to the named file. Other characters that would normally appear on the screen also go to the disk file, including error messages. However, the question mark or prompt message displayed by an INPUT statement is not sent to the disk file. The next ProDOS command, including CHR$(4), disables this aspect of the APPEND command, but does not close the file (unless it is the CLOSE command).

The T*type* option can be used to specify a file type other than text. If T*type* is used, the file must exist as named.

The L*length* option specifies the record length of a random-access file. If the length is absent and the file exists, ProDOS uses the length with which the file was created; if the file does not exist, ProDOS uses a record length of 1.

D*n* and S*n* can be specified in any order. If D*n* or S*n* is omitted, the ProDOS prefix specifies the drive and slot.

This is a ProDOS command, requiring PRINT and CHR$(4) in programmed mode.

APPEND cannot be used in immediate mode.

APPEND (DOS 3.3)

Opens a DOS 3.3 file (see OPEN) and positions the file pointer at the end of the file.

Format: APPEND *filename* [,D*n*] [,S*n*] [,V*n*]

A memory buffer of 595 bytes is allocated for the text file specified. The file must be a sequential file. The WRITE command can now be used to store information on the file, starting at the first unused byte. This will be immediately following the last character in the file unless there are unused bytes in the middle.

With DOS version 3.2.1 and earlier versions, APPEND does not always start at the first unused byte in the file (often the end of the file). Instead, it starts at the beginning of the file. (This is not a problem on an Apple IIe.) To make sure this doesn't happen, your program should always write an end-of-file marker before closing a file it has written to. The short machine language subroutine in Table A-8 does the trick. With POKE, put it into memory anywhere there are five free bytes (locations 768 through 772 are OK unless you are using them for something else). Then call the subroutine (use CALL) just before closing the file.

If the file does not exist on drive D*n* of slot S*n*, the **FILE NOT FOUND** error message is displayed. If the disk in drive D*n* of slot S*n* is not volume V*n*, the **VOLUME MISMATCH** error

Table A-8. Machine Language Fix for DOS 3.2.1 APPEND

MACHINE LANGUAGE		6502 ASSEMBLY LANGUAGE	
Decimal	**Hexadecimal**	**Instruction**	**Comments**
169	A9	LDA $0	The Monitor routine at $FDED outputs the character in register A ($0 in this case) to the currently selected output device, the disk.
0	0		
76	4C	JMP $FDED	
237	ED		
253	FD		

results. Volume number V0 will match any disk. If the file is already open, APPEND closes and reopens it (see CLOSE).

D*n*, S*n*, and V*n* can be specified in any order. If D*n* or S*n* is omitted, the last-referenced drive or slot is used. Volume number V0 is used if V*n* is absent.

APPEND is a DOS 3.3 command, requiring PRINT and CHR$(4) or CONTROL-D in programmed mode.

APPEND cannot be used in immediate mode.

AUTO

Sets automatic line numbering mode in Integer BASIC.

Format: AUTO *line* [,*increment*]

Line numbers are automatically displayed each time you press RETURN, starting with *line*, and increasing each time by *increment*, which defaults to 10 if not specified. Type CONTROL-X to erase an automatic line number. Automatic line numbering resumes unless MAN is entered on the next line (see MAN).

AUTO can be used only in immediate mode.

AUTO is not available in Applesoft.

BLOAD (ProDOS)

Retrieves a binary image from a ProDOS disk and stores it in a specified area of the Apple II memory.

Formats: BLOAD *pathname* [,A*memloc*] [,B*byte*] [,E*memloc*] [,T*type*] [,D*n*] [,S*n*]
BLOAD *pathname* [,A*memloc*] [,B*byte*] [,L*length*] [,T*type*] [,D*n*] [,S*n*]

The A*memloc* option specifies where in memory to start storing the binary image. If the memory location is absent, ProDOS uses the location from which the image was saved. The B*byte* option specifies which byte in the file to start transferring from. Anything earlier in the file is ignored.

The E*memloc* option specifies the last memory location to fill from the file. Instead of specifying the endpoint in memory, you can specify the length of the file with the L*length* option. If no endpoint or length is specified, the entire file is transferred to memory.

The T*type* option specifies the file type. If the file type is not specified, the file must be type BIN (binary).

D*n* and S*n* can be specified in any order. If D*n* or S*n* is omitted, the ProDOS prefix specifies the drive and slot.

This is a ProDOS command, requiring PRINT and CHR$(4) in eprogrammed mode.

BLOAD (DOS 3.3)

Retrieves a binary file from a DOS 3.3 disk and stores it in the specified section of memory.

Format: BLOAD *filename* [,A*memloc*] [,D*n*] [,S*n*] [,V*n*]

If the A*memloc* option is absent, the specified file is placed in memory beginning at the memory location from which the file was saved (see BSAVE). If the option is present, the file goes into memory at *memloc*.

If the file does not exist on drive D*n* of slot S*n*, the **FILE NOT FOUND** error message is displayed. If the disk in drive D*n* of slot S*n* is not volume V*n*, the **VOLUME MISMATCH** error results.

D*n*, S*n*, and V*n* can be specified in any order. If D*n* or S*n* is omitted, the last-referenced drive or slot is used. V0 is used if V*n* is absent.

This is a DOS 3.3 command, requiring PRINT and CHR$(4) or CONTROL-D in programmed mode.

BRUN (ProDOS)

Retrieves a machine language program from a ProDOS disk, stores it in a specified area of memory, and executes it.

Formats: BRUN *pathname* [,A*memloc*] [,B*byte*] [,E*memloc*] [,D*n*] [,S*n*]

BRUN *pathname* [,A*memloc*] [,B*byte*] [,L*length*] [,D*n*] [,S*n*]

The file must be type BIN (binary) and must contain a 6502 machine language program. After loading the program, ProDOS executes a machine language jump (JMP in 6502 assembly language) to the starting memory location. If the machine language program ends with a return-from-subroutine instruction (RTS in 6502 assembly language), Applesoft and ProDOS regain control of the Apple II.

The A*memloc* option specifies where in memory to start storing the binary image. If the location is absent, ProDOS uses the location from which the image came. The B*byte* option specifies which byte in the file to start transferring from. Anything earlier in the file is ignored.

The E*memloc* option specifies the last memory location to fill from the file. In the alternative format, the L*length* option tells how many bytes to transfer. Any bytes beyond the specified length are ignored. If no endpoint or length is specified, the entire file is transferred to memory.

D*n* and S*n* can be specified in any order. If D*n* or S*n* is omitted, the ProDOS prefix specifies the drive and slot.

This is a ProDOS command, requiring PRINT and CHR$(4) in programmed mode.

BRUN (DOS 3.3)

Retrieves a machine language program from a DOS 3.3 disk, stores it in the specified section of memory, and executes it.

Format: BRUN *filename* [,A*memloc*] [,D*n*] [,S*n*] [,V*n*]

The file must be type B (binary) and must contain a 6502 machine language program. After loading the program, DOS 3.3 executes a machine language jump (JMP in 6502 assembly language) to the starting memory location. If the machine language program ends with a return-from-subroutine instruction (RTS in 6502 assembly language), Applesoft and DOS 3.3 regain control of the Apple II.

The A*memloc* option specifies where in memory to start storing the binary image. If the location is absent, DOS uses the location from which the image came. A machine language program may work properly at only one memory location. Check carefully for instructions that are address-dependent before loading to a new memory location.

If the file does not exist on drive D*n* connected to slot S*n*, the **FILE NOT FOUND** error message is displayed. If the disk in drive D*n* of slot S*n* is not volume V*n*, the **VOLUME MISMATCH** error results.

D*n*, S*n*, and V*n* can be specified in any order. If D*n* or S*n* is omitted, the last-referenced drive or slot is used. V0 is used if V*n* is absent.

This is a DOS 3.3 command, requiring PRINT and CHR$(4) or CONTROL-D in programmed mode.

BSAVE (ProDOS)

Saves part of the Apple II's memory as a binary image on a ProDOS disk file.

Formats: BSAVE *pathname*,A*memloc*,E*memloc* [,B*byte*] [,T*type*] [,D*n*] [,S*n*]

BSAVE *pathname*,A*memloc*,L*length* [,B*byte*] [,T*type*] [,D*n*] [,S*n*]

The A*memloc* parameter specifies the memory address of the first byte at which to start storing the binary image. The B*byte* parameter specifies which byte in the file to start saving at.

The E*memloc* parameter specifies the last location in memory to fill in the file. In the alternative format, the L*length* option tells how many bytes to transfer to the disk.

The T*type* option specifies the file type. If the file type is not specified, the file must be type BIN (binary).

If there is no file as specified, a file is created and the memory image is saved in it. If a file of the type specified exists as named, the memory image is saved in it. If a file of a different type exists as named, an error message appears.

Warning: Be careful to type the correct *pathname*. If you inadvertently type a wrong name, and that name exists, ProDOS replaces the information that the file contains with the specified memory image—without giving you a warning.

D*n* and S*n* can be specified in any order. If D*n* or S*n* is omitted, the ProDOS prefix specifies the drive and slot.

This is a ProDOS command, requiring PRINT and CHR$(4) in programmed mode.

BSAVE (DOS 3.3)

Saves part of the Apple II's memory as a binary image on a DOS 3.3 disk file.

Format: BSAVE *filename* ,A*memloc* ,L*length* [,D*n*] [,S*n*] [,V*n*]

The A*memloc* parameter specifies the starting address of the memory section to save. The L*length* parameter specifies the number of bytes to save. The length must be an integer between 0 and 32767 (decimal). It may be either a decimal or hexadecimal constant. Hexadecimal constants are identified by a dollar sign ($) prefix.

If the disk in drive D*n* of slot S*n* is not volume V*n*, the **VOLUME MISMATCH** error results.

D*n*, S*n*, and V*n* can be specified in any order. If D*n* or S*n* is omitted, the last-referenced drive or slot is used. V0 is used if V*n* is absent.

This is a DOS 3.3 command, requiring PRINT and CHR$(4) or CONTROL-D in programmed mode.

CALL

Branches to a machine language subroutine at a specified location.

Format: CALL *memadr*

CALL can be used with subroutines that you write yourself, as well as with various built-in subroutines that are listed in Appendix G.

CAT (ProDOS)

Displays a list 40 characters wide of all files in a specified ProDOS directory.

Format: CAT [*pathname*] [,D*n*] [,S*n*]

For each file, CAT lists the following (from left to right):

1. An asterisk if the file is locked
2. Name
3. Type (Table A-7 lists type codes)
4. Number of 512-byte blocks used
5. Last date modified (usually no date).

For the whole directory, CAT reports the total number of 512-byte blocks, the number free, and the number used.

If you omit the *pathname*, ProDOS uses the current prefix.

D*n* and S*n* can be specified in any order. If D*n* or S*n* is omitted, the ProDOS prefix specifies the drive and slot.

This is a ProDOS command, requiring PRINT and CHR$(4) in programmed mode.

CATALOG (ProDOS)

Displays a list 80 characters wide of all files in a specified ProDOS directory.

Format: CATALOG [*pathname*] [,D*n*]

For each file, CATALOG lists the following (from left to right):

1. An asterisk if the file is locked.
2. Name.
3. Type (Table A-5 lists type codes).
4. Number of 512-byte blocks used.
5. Last date and time modified (usually no date or time).

6. Date and time created (usually no date or time).
7. Number of bytes used, or for random-access files, the number that would be used if every record (from record number 0 to the highest record number in the file) were used.
8. Loading address of a binary file or record length of a random-access file. This item not included for any other type of file.

For the whole directory, CATALOG reports the total number of 512-byte blocks, the number free, and the number used. If you omit the *pathname*, ProDOS uses the current prefix.

D*n* and S*n* can be specified in any order. If D*n* or S*n* is omitted, the ProDOS prefix specifies the drive and slot.

CATALOG is a ProDOS command, requiring PRINT and CHR$(4) in programmed mode.

CATALOG (DOS 3.3)

Displays a list of all files on a DOS 3.3 disk.

Format: CATALOG [,D*n*] [,S*n*]

CATALOG prints the volume number of the disk, followed by a list of files on the disk. For each file, CATALOG prints a code letter indica.0ting the type of file, the number of sectors required to store the file, and the name of the file. An asterisk appears to the left of the file type if the file is locked. The file types and their codes are as follows:

I Integer BASIC Program
A Applesoft Program
T Text File
B Binary (Machine Language) File
R Relocatable created by BSAVE
S Reserved for future use.

If a file length exceeds 255 sectors, the file length is displayed modulo 255; that is, 0 is printed if the file length is 256, 1 if it is 257, and so on.

D*n* and S*n* can be specified in any order. If D*n* or S*n* is absent, the last-referenced drive or slot is used.

This is a DOS 3.3 command, requiring PRINT and CHR$(4) or CONTROL-D in programmed mode.

CHAIN (ProDOS)

Loads and runs an Applesoft program from a ProDOS disk without clearing the values of any variables or arrays.

Format: CHAIN *pathname* [,@*line*] [,D*n*] [,S*n*]

The program specified by *pathname* is loaded from disk and then run. The program replaces any program previously in the Apple II's memory. All variables and arrays retain their values, and any open files remain open. If no program exists as named, an error message appears and the existing program, variables, and files will be untouched.

The @*line* option indicates the line number at which the program is started. If the specified line number does not exist, the next-higher line number is used.

D*n* and S*n* can be specified in any order. If D*n* or S*n* is omitted, the ProDOS prefix specifies the drive and slot.

This is a ProDOS command, requiring PRINT and CHR$(4) in programmed mode.

CHAIN (DOS 3.3)

Loads and runs an Integer BASIC program from a DOS 3.3 disk, without clearing the values of any variables or arrays.

Format: CHAIN *filename* [,D*n*] [,S*n*] [,V*n*]

If the file does not exist on drive D*n* of slot S*n*, the **FILE NOT FOUND** error message is displayed. If the disk in drive D*n* of slot S*n* is not volume V*n*, the **VOLUME MISMATCH** error results.

D*n*, S*n*, and V*n* can be specified in any order. If D*n* or S*n* is omitted, the last-referenced drive or slot is used. V0 is used if V*n* is absent.

This is a DOS 3.3 command, requiring PRINT and CHR$(4) or CONTROL-D in programmed mode.

CLEAR

This Applesoft statement assigns 0 to all numeric variables and numeric array elements. CLEAR also assigns a null value to all string variables and string array elements.

Format: CLEAR

Executing this statement is equivalent to turning the Apple II off and then back on, and reloading the program into memory. A program will continue to run following CLEAR, provided the effects of the CLEAR statements do not adversely affect program logic.

For Integer BASIC, use CLR.

CLOSE (ProDOS)

Closes one or all open ProDOS disk files.

Format: CLOSE [*pathname*]

Closing a file writes anything being held in the file buffer to the disk file and then releases the file buffer. You must close any file you have opened to avoid losing information it contains.

Specifying a *pathname* closes only the named file. CLOSE without a *pathname* closes all open files, except a controlling EXEC file (if any).

This is a ProDOS command, requiring PRINT and CHR$(4) in programmed mode.

CLOSE (DOS 3.3)

Closes one or all open DOS 3.3 disk files.

Format: CLOSE [*filename*]

Closing a file writes anything being held in the file buffer to the disk file and then releases the file buffer. You must close any file you have opened to avoid losing information it contains.

Specifying a *filename* closes only the named file. CLOSE without a *filename* closes all open files, except a controlling EXEC file (if any).

With DOS 3.2.1 and earlier versions, a sequential file will occasionally exactly fill a sector as it is closed. Under these conditions, a subsequent APPEND will occur at the beginning of the file rather than at the end. To forestall this, call the short machine language subroutine in Table A-8 just before the CLOSE statement. You can use POKE statements to put the subroutine anywhere there are five free bytes (for example, locations 768 through 772 unless they are otherwise used). This is not necessary on an Apple IIe.

This is a DOS 3.3 command, requiring PRINT and CHR$(4) or CONTROL-D in programmed mode.

CLR

This Integer BASIC command assigns 0 to all numeric variables and array elements and assigns a null value to strings.

Format: CLR

This command also undimensions all arrays and strings. You can still print array values after executing a CLR statement, as long as no variables have been assigned values in the interim.

CLR can be used only in immediate mode.

For Applesoft, use CLEAR.

COLOR=

Sets the color for low-resolution graphics.

Format: COLOR= *exprnm*

Until the next COLOR statement, all PLOT, VLIN, and HLIN statements will be in the color specified. The color codes are listed in Table 12-1. The *exprnm* must have a value in the range 0 to 255; real values are converted to integers. Values greater than 15 repeat the colors shown in Table 12-1 (0, 16, and 32 are black, and so on). COLOR = 0 if not previously specified.

COLOR has no effect if used in high-resolution graphics mode. When used in text mode, COLOR is one factor in determining which character is placed on the screen by a PLOT instruction. For a detailed description of this feature, see PLOT.

CON

This Integer BASIC command resumes program execution at the next instruction after a halt.

Format: CON

CON operates after execution has been halted by CONTROL-C, and sometimes after CONTROL-RESET. If there is no interrupted program, CON simply locks up the system. A program cannot be continued after it is interrupted by CONTROL-C during an INPUT statement.

If a program line has been changed or added or an error message generated since program execution was halted, CON will sometimes work, but may produce an error message or lock up the system.

CON can be used only in immediate mode.

For Applesoft, see CONT.

CONT

This Applesoft command resumes execution at the next instruction after a halt.

Format: CONT

CONT operates after execution has been halted by STOP, END, or CONTROL-C. If an INPUT statement is interrupted by CONTROL-C, the program cannot be continued. If there is no interrupted program, if a program line has been changed or added, or if an error message has been generated since program execution was halted, CONT will produce the message **?CAN'T CONTINUE ERROR**.

For Integer BASIC, see CON.

CREATE (ProDOS)

Creates a ProDOS file or directory.

Format: CREATE *pathname* [,T*type*] [,D*n*] [,S*n*]

The T*type* parameter specifies the type of file to create. If it is absent, a directory is created.

D*n* and S*n* can be specified in any order. If D*n* or S*n* is omitted, the ProDOS prefix specifies the drive and slot.

This is a ProDOS command, requiring PRINT and CHR$(4) in programmed mode.

— (DASH Command; ProDOS)

Loads and runs a program of any type—Applesoft, machine language, or EXEC—from a ProDOS disk.

Format: — *pathname* [,D*n*] [,S*n*]

The so-called Dash command does the same thing as a RUN, BRUN, or EXEC command, depending on the type of file you name. It works with file types BAS, BIN, TXT, and SYS.

If the file you specify is found, the previous program is erased from memory before the named program is loaded and executed. If the file is not found, an error message appears and any existing program is untouched.

D*n* and S*n* can be specified in any order. If D*n* or S*n* is omitted, the ProDOS prefix specifies the drive and slot.

This is a ProDOS command, requiring PRINT and CHR$(4) in programmed mode.

DATA

Creates a list of values to be assigned by READ statements in an Applesoft program.

Format: DATA *const* [,*const*...]

DATA statements may appear anywhere in a program; they need not be executed to be accessed by a READ command.

The DATA statement specifies numeric and string constants. String constants are usually enclosed in quotation marks, but the quotation marks are necessary only if the string contains blanks (spaces), commas, or colons. A quotation mark cannot be represented in a DATA statement *const*.

One or more of the *const* parameters can be null (that is, nothing but blanks). A null *const* is assigned as zero to a numeric variable; a null string (" ") is assigned to a string variable.

You will receive no error message if you enter a DATA statement in immediate mode, but the elements will not be accessible to a READ command.

DATA is not available in Integer BASIC.

DEF FN

The DEF FN statement allows special-purpose functions to be defined and used within Applesoft programs.

Format: DEF FN*name* (*dummy*)=*exprnm*

The *name*, which must conform to the rules for numeric variable names, identifies the function.

The function is defined by *exprnm*. The *dummy* is a dummy variable name that can (and usually does) appear in *exprnm*. Its use in a DEF FN statement has no effect on another variable with the same name elsewhere in the program.

The function is subsequently invoked using FN*name*. At that time, the value of the dummy variable *dummy* is specified by a numeric expression, variable, or constant. The values of all other variables in *exprnm* must be defined before FN*name* is used. (See also FN in the Functions section of this appendix.)

The entire DEF FN statement must appear on a single program line. However, a previously defined function can be included in *exprnm*, so that user-defined functions of any desired complexity can be developed. A user-defined function cannot, however, invoke itself directly or indirectly (that is, by referring to a function that eventually refers to it).

If the *name* appears in more than one DEF FN statement, the most recently used definition is used.

This statement is not available in Integer BASIC.

The DEF FN statement is illegal in immediate mode. However, a user-defined function that has been defined by executing a DEF FN statement since the last NEW, CLR, or LOAD command can be referenced in an immediate mode statement.

DEL

Eliminates specified program lines.

Format: DEL *line1, line2*

All program lines greater than or equal to *line1* and less than or equal to *line2* are removed from the program currently in memory. If *line1* does not exist, the deletion starts at the next-higher line number. If *line2* does not exist, the deletion ends at the next-lower line number.

DEL must be followed by two line numbers that are separated by a comma. Neither line number can be negative, and the second line number must be greater than or equal to the first. If the line numbers are identical, one line (at most) is deleted.

DEL may only be used in immediate mode in Integer BASIC.

If DEL is used in programmed mode (legal only in Applesoft), the indicated deletions take place and the program halts. CONT will not continue the program in this case.

DELETE (ProDOS)

Erases a file from a ProDOS disk.

Format: DELETE *pathname* [,D*n*] [,S*n*]

The file specified by the *pathname* is removed from the disk directory. An open or locked file cannot be deleted. If the *pathname* specifies a directory, the directory must be empty. The volume directory cannot be deleted, even if it is empty. An error message appears if the file does not exist as specified.

D*n* and S*n* can be specified in any order. If D*n* or S*n* is omitted, the ProDOS prefix specifies the drive and slot.

This is a ProDOS command, requiring PRINT and CHR$(4) in programmed mode.

DELETE (DOS 3.3)

Erases a file from a DOS 3.3 disk.

Format: DELETE *filename* [,D*n*] [,S*n*] [,V*n*]

The file with the specified name is removed from the disk.

If the file does not exist on drive D*n* of slot S*n*, the **FILE NOT FOUND** error message is displayed. If the disk in drive D*n* of slot S*n* is not volume V*n*, the **VOLUME MISMATCH** error results.

D*n*, S*n*, and V*n* can be specified in any order. If D*n* or S*n* is omitted, the last-referenced drive or slot is used. V0 is used if V*n* is absent.

This is a DOS 3.3 command, requiring PRINT and CHR$(4) or CONTROL-D in programmed mode.

DIM (Applesoft)

Reserves space in memory for Applesoft arrays.

Format: DIM *var*(*sub*[,*sub*...]),*var*(*sub*[,*sub*...])...]

The Applesoft DIM statement identifies arrays with one or more dimensions as follows:

$var(sub_i)$	Single-dimension array
$var(sub_i,sub_j)$	Two-dimension array
$var(sub_i,sub_j,sub_k\ldots)$	Multiple-dimension array

Applesoft allows three types of arrays: integer, real, and string. Each element of an array is of the type specified by the variable name for the array. The number of dimensions in an array is determined by the number of subscripts in the DIM statement. When an array is referenced, each subscript must fall within the range 0 through *sub*, where *sub* is the corresponding subscript of the same variable in the DIM statement.

The number of dimensions in an array is limited by the amount of memory available. The maximum number of dimensions an array can have is 88, and this is only possible when most of the subscripts are 0. A DIM statement with 89 or more subscripts, or one that otherwise exceeds memory limitations, will produce the message **?OUT OF MEMORY ERROR**.

If you attempt to use an array with a subscript that is out of range or one with the wrong number of subscripts, the message **?BAD SUBSCRIPT ERROR** will appear.

If an array is referenced before a DIM statement for that array has been executed, Applesoft assigns a default value of 10 to each subscript. The array is thereafter treated as if a DIM statement with a subscript of 10 for each dimension had been executed.

An array can never be dimensioned twice, even if it has been dimensioned by default. If you attempt to dimension an array that has already been dimensioned, you will be presented with the message **?REDIM'D ARRAY ERROR**.

DIM (Integer BASIC)

Reserves space in memory for Integer BASIC arrays and strings.

Format: DIM *var* (*sub*) [,*var*(*sub*)...]

Only numeric arrays of one dimension and simple string variables may be dimensioned in Integer BASIC. When an array is dimensioned, space is set aside in memory for the number of elements equal to *sub* plus 1. They are numbered 0 through *sub*. Element 0 of an array is identical to the simple variable of the same name that is, A(0)=A.

DIM statements declare the maximum lengths of string variables. In this case *sub* is the string length.

Every subscript *sub* must be between 1 and 255 in a DIM statement. Aside from this, the maximum allowable dimensions are limited by available memory.

If you reference an array using a subscript greater than the largest subscript declared in the DIM statement for that array, the message ***** RANGE ERR** occurs. If you attempt to use more characters in a string than it was dimensioned for, the message ***** STRING ERR** is displayed.

DIM does not clear the elements of Integer BASIC arrays when it is executed. Therefore, you must initialize every array (that is, set it to zero) after dimensioning it. String variables, on the other hand, always have a null value after first being dimensioned.

DRAW

This Applesoft statement draws a high-resolution graphics shape on the screen.

Format: DRAW *exprnm* [AT *colh, rowh*]

The shape identified by the integer value of *exprnm* is drawn in the color determined by the last-executed HCOLOR statement. The scale and rotation of the shape must be set by SCALE and ROT commands before the DRAW statement is executed.

DRAW starts drawing the shape at the location given by the integer values of numeric expressions *colh* and *rowh*. If you do not specify a location in the DRAW statement, the shape starts at the last point plotted by the last-executed DRAW, XDRAW, or HPLOT command.

The shape number specified (*exprnm*) must be between 0 and the number of shapes in the shape table (which must not exceed 255).

This statement is not available in Integer BASIC.

DSP

Displays the changing values of a specified variable as an Integer BASIC program progresses.

Format: DSP *var*

The value of variable *var* and the current line number are displayed whenever the value of that variable changes. This display may interact with your program's output, rendering one or both illegible. RUN cancels all DSP instructions. Use CON or GOTO when you are debugging with DSP in immediate mode.

To turn off DSP, use NO DSP.

DSP is not available in Applesoft.

END

Causes a program to halt.

Format: END

No message is displayed. In Integer BASIC, END must be the last statement executed or the warning ***** NO END ERR** is displayed. END is optional in an Applesoft program.

END cannot be used in immediate mode in Integer BASIC.

EXEC (ProDOS)

Treats a sequential-access ProDOS text file as a substitute for the keyboard.

Formats: EXEC *pathname* [,F*field*] [,D*n*] [,S*n*]
EXEC *pathname* [,R*field*] [,D*n*] [,S*n*]

A text file to be used with EXEC consists of some combination of Applesoft commands, Applesoft program lines, and ProDOS commands. When EXEC is executed, the first line of the specified file is read from the disk. If the first line is a command, it is executed immediately. If it is a program line, it is added to memory, just as if you had entered it directly from the keyboard. If a keyboard INPUT statement is executed while an EXEC file is open, the response is taken from the EXEC file.

An EXEC file can be used to enter an entire program, list it, run it, save it on disk, change it, or to do anything else that can be done from the keyboard. You can even use an EXEC file to create and execute a second EXEC file.

The F*field* option specifies a number of command lines (carriage return characters) to be skipped from the beginning of the file. The R*field* option does exactly the same thing.

When the last line in the file has been used, the EXEC file is automatically closed. When an EXEC command is encountered in a controlling EXEC file, the original, controlling, file is closed and any further commands in it are ignored. The new EXEC file is opened and used instead.

D*n* and S*n* can be specified in any order. If D*n* or S*n* is omitted, the ProDOS prefix specifies the drive and slot.

This is a ProDOS command, requiring PRINT and CHR$(4) in programmed mode.

EXEC (DOS 3.3)

Treats a sequential-access DOS 3.3 text file as a substitute for the keyboard.

Format: *Format:* EXEC *filename* [,R*field*] [,D*n*] [,S*n*] [,V*n*]

A text file to be used with EXEC consists f some combination of BASIC commands, BASIC program lines, and DOS 3.3 commands. When EXEC is executed, the first line of the specified file is read from the disk. If the first line is a command, it is executed immediately. If it is a program line, it is added to memory, just as if you had entered it directly from the keyboard. If a keyboard INPUT statement is executed while an EXEC file is open, the response is taken from the EXEC file.

An EXEC file can be used to enter an entire program, list it, run it, save it on disk, change it, or to do anything else that can be done from the keyboard. You can even use an EXEC file to create and execute a second EXEC file.

The R*field* option specifies a number of command lines (carriage return characters) to be skipped from the beginning of the file.

When the last line in the file has been used, the EXEC file is automatically closed. When an EXEC command is encountered in a controlling EXEC file, the original, controlling, file is closed and any further commands in it are ignored. The new EXEC file is opened and used instead.

If the file does not exist on drive D*n* of slot S*n*, the **FILE NOT FOUND** error message is displayed. If the disk in drive D*n* of slot S*n* is not volume V*n*, the **VOLUME MISMATCH** error results.

D*n*, S*n*, and V*n* can be specified in any order. If D*n* or S*n* is omitted, the last-referenced drive or slot is used. V0 is used if V*n* is absent.

This is a DOS 3.3 command, requiring PRINT and CHR$(4) or CONTROL-D in programmed mode.

FLASH

This Applesoft statement switches to flashing character style.

Format: FLASH

All output from subsequently executed PRINT statements will alternate between white characters on a black background and black characters on a white background. Error messages are similarly affected. However, any previously displayed characters are unaffected.

FLASH works by slightly altering the standard ASCII codes. Any flashing characters sent to a DOS 3.3 disk will be saved with incorrect codes. When those codes are read back in, the wrong characters will result.

This statement is not available in Integer BASIC. Flashing characters are not available when the 80-column adapter is active.

FLUSH (ProDOS)

Writes the contents of one or more ProDOS file buffers to the disk.

Format: FLUSH [*pathname*]

Flushing a file forces all characters waiting in the file's buffer in memory to be written to the file on disk, and it updates the directory that contains the file. If you specify a file, its buffer is the only one written. If you do not specify a file, the buffers of all open files are written.

This is a ProDOS command, requiring PRINT and CHR$(4) in programmed mode.

FN

Listed in the Functions section of this appendix. See also DEF FN.

FOR

Starts a loop that repeats a set of instructions until an automatically incremented variable attains a certain value.

Format: FOR *varnm* = $exprnm_1$ TO $exprnm_2$ [STEP $exprnm_3$]

When FOR is first executed, the *varnm* is assigned the value of $exprnm_1$. The statements following FOR are executed until a NEXT statement is reached. The *varnm* is then incremented by $exprnm_3$ (or by 1 if the STEP clause is not present). After that, the new value of *varnm* is compared to the value of $exprnm_2$. The sense of the comparison depends on the sign of $exprnm_3$. If the sign is positive and the new value of *varnm* is less than or equal to $exprnm_2$, execution loops back to the statement just after the FOR. The same thing happens if the sign of $exprnm_3$ is negative and the new value of *varnm* is greater than or equal to $exprnm_2$. On the other hand, execution continues with the instruction that follows the NEXT if *varnm* is greater than $exprnm_2$ ($exprnm_3$ positive) or less than $exprnm_2$ ($exprnm_3$ negative). Because the comparison occurs after incrementing *varnm*, the instructions between FOR and NEXT are always executed at least once.

In Integer BASIC *varnm* must be an integer variable. In Applesoft *varnm* must be a real variable. It can never be a string variable.

The start, end, and increment values are determined from

exprnm$_1$, *exprnm*$_2$, and *exprnm*$_3$ only once, on the first execution of the FOR statement. If you change these values inside the loop, it will have no effect on the loop itself. You can change the value of *varnm* within the loop. This lets you terminate a FOR-NEXT loop before the end value is reached. To do so, set *varnm* to the end value (*exprnm*$_2$), and on the next pass the loop will terminate itself. Do not start the loop outside a subroutine and then terminate it inside the subroutine.

FOR-NEXT loops may be nested. Each nested loop must have a different variable name. Each nested loop must be wholly contained within the next outer loop; at most, the loops can end at the same point. Integer BASIC allows 16 levels of FOR-NEXT nesting, while Applesoft allows just 10.

FOR may be used in immediate mode, but only in Applesoft. The entire loop must be entered on one line. If NEXT is not present, the loop will execute once.

FP

Switches from Integer BASIC to Applesoft (not available with ProDOS).

Format: FP [,D*n*] [,S*n*] [,V*n*]

The source of the Applesoft interpreter depends on what kind of Apple II you have and what accessories are installed:

- With an Apple IIe or Apple II Plus, the interpreter is in read-only memory (ROM), no matter what options may also exist.
- If you have the Applesoft firmware card installed, FP obtains the language from it regardless of the switch setting on the card.
- With the Apple Language System installed, FP takes Applesoft from it.
- On any other Apple II, FP looks for Applesoft on the specified (or current) disk. If it does not exist there, the message **LANGUAGE NOT AVAILABLE** is displayed.

FP erases any BASIC program currently in memory.

If the file does not exist on drive D*n* of slot S*n*, the **FILE NOT FOUND** error message is displayed. If the disk in drive D*n* of slot S*n* is not volume V*n*, the **VOLUME MISMATCH** error results.

D*n*, S*n*, and V*n* can be specified in any order. If D*n* or S*n* is omitted, the last-referenced drive or slot is used. V0 is used if V*n* is absent.

Use FP only in immediate mode.

FRE (ProDOS)

The ProDOS FRE command removes string values left in memory by previous Applesoft programs.

Format: FRE

Like the FRE( ) function, the FRE command clears unused strings from the string storage area, but it is much faster. Unused string values are also cleared from memory when you switch off the Apple II, of course.

This is a ProDOS command, requiring PRINT and CHR$(4) in programmed mode.

GET

This Applesoft statement accepts a single character from the keyboard or other input device without echoing it to the screen.

Format: GET *var*

Execution pauses until a key is pressed or a character is input from some other device. When *var* is a string variable, the character entered is assigned to that variable. If CONTROL-@ is entered, the null string is assigned to the variable.

GET is not often used with a numeric variable. When it is, entry of one of the digits 0 through 9 assigns that value to the variable. Entry of a plus sign, minus sign, comma, colon, CONTROL-@, space, E, or period assigns a value of zero to the variable. Entering any character other than those just listed results in the message **?SYNTAX ERROR**, and the program stops.

GET cannot be used in immediate mode.
GET is not available in Integer BASIC.

GOSUB

Causes the program to branch to the indicated line. When a RETURN statement is executed, the program branches back to the instruction immediately following the GOSUB.

General Format: GOSUB *line*

Additional Integer BASIC Format: GOSUB *exprnm*

The GOSUB statement calls a subroutine. The subroutine's entry point must occur on line number *line*. A subroutine's entry point is the beginning of the subroutine in a logical sense; that is to say, it is the line containing the statement (or statements) that are executed first. The entry point need not necessarily be the subroutine line with the smallest line number.

In Integer BASIC a numeric expression is allowed in place of the line number. If *exprnm* does not evaluate to an existing line number, the message ***** BAD BRANCH ERR** is displayed. This form of GOSUB enables you to simulate the ON-GOSUB instruction, which is not available in Integer BASIC.

Upon completing execution, the subroutine branches back to the line following the GOSUB statement. The subroutine uses a RETURN statement in order to branch back in this fashion.

A GOSUB statement may occur anywhere in a program, and as a result, a subroutine may be called from anywhere in the program.

Subroutines may be nested; that is to say, subroutines may be called from within subroutines. Twenty-five levels of nesting are allowed in Applesoft; that means 24 GOSUB statements may be executed before the first RETURN statement. The limit in Integer BASIC is 16 GOSUB statements.

Normally you must exit from a subroutine with a RETURN statement, not with a GOTO statement. In Applesoft, though, you can use a GOTO statement to branch out of a subroutine if you first execute a POP statement.

GOSUB cannot be used in immediate mode in Integer BASIC.

GOTO

Unconditionally causes program execution to branch to the line indicated.

General Format: GOTO *line*

Additional Integer BASIC Format: GOTO *exprnm*

Program execution immediately continues with the first instruction in the line number indicated. If the line number does not exist, the message **?UNDEF'D STATEMENT ERROR** is displayed by Applesoft. The message *** **BAD BRANCH ERR** is displayed by Integer BASIC.

In Integer BASIC a numeric expression is allowed in place of the line number. If *exprnm* does not evaluate to an existing line number, the message *** **BAD BRANCH ERR** is displayed. This form of computed GOTO enables you to simulate the ON-GOTO statement, which is not available in Integer BASIC.

GR

Converts the screen to low-resolution graphics mode (40 × 40), leaving four lines for text at the bottom of the screen.

Format: GR

The graphics portion of the screen is cleared to black, the cursor is moved to the text window, and COLOR is set to 0 (black).

If executed while HGR is in effect, GR behaves normally. However, if HGR2 is in effect, you will be left looking at page 2 of low-resolution graphics and text. This can be confusing, as the screen will usually be filled with garbage, and nothing you type will appear on the screen. To return to normal mode, type TEXT. Be sure to use TEXT in your programs before switching from HGR2 to GR.

You can switch to full-screen (40 × 48), low-resolution graphics with the statement POKE −16302,0 after executing GR. Anything you subsequently type in immediate mode will show up as color dots on the last four lines of the display screen, but will still execute properly. POKE −16302,0 sets full-screen graphics; POKE −16301,0 restores the text window.

HCOLOR=

This Applesoft statement sets the color for plotting in high-resolution graphics mode.

Format: HCOLOR= *exprnm*

Until the next HCOLOR statement, all HPLOT and DRAW statements will be executed in the color specified. The color codes are listed in Table 12-2. The value of *exprnm* must be in the range 0 through 7. Values outside this range produce an **?ILLEGAL QUANTITY ERROR** message. A high-resolution graphics plot executed before the first HCOLOR statement may be any color.

HCOLOR does not affect low-resolution graphics. An HCOLOR statement that is executed while the Apple II is not in high-resolution graphics mode does not affect the color of the next high-resolution graphics plot.

HCOLOR is not available in Integer BASIC.

HGR

This Applesoft statement converts the screen to high-resolution graphics mode (280 × 160), with a four-line text window at the bottom.

Format: HGR

Page 1 of high-resolution screen memory is displayed. The low-resolution (text) screen memory is unaffected, but only the lowest four lines are visible. The cursor is not moved into this four-line text window, and you might not be able to see it until you have typed several lines after executing HGR. The graphics portion of the screen is cleared to black. HCOLOR is left unchanged by this command.

You can switch to full-screen (280 × 192) high-resolution graphics with the statement POKE −16302,0 after executing HGR. Any immediate mode commands you enter subsequently will not be visible but will still execute properly. POKE −16301,0 restores the text window.

On Apple II systems with less than 32K bytes of memory, you

cannot use HGR and DOS 3.3 at the same time since they will try to use the same area of memory. Furthermore, the Applesoft interpreter from disk or cassette occupies part of high-resolution graphics page 1 memory. Thus you cannot use HGR on a standard Apple II with disk-based or cassette-based Applesoft.

If your program is extremely long, it might extend into high-resolution page 1. You can guard against this with the command HIMEM: 16384 or HIMEM: 8192, which will keep your program out of high-resolution graphics page 1. These commands also significantly reduce the amount of memory available to your BASIC program.

HGR is not available in Integer BASIC.

HGR2

Converts the screen to full-screen, high-resolution graphics mode (280 × 192). Page 2 of high-resolution screen memory is displayed.

Format: HGR2

The low-resolution (text) screen memory is unaffected. Although you cannot see what you type, any command that you enter will be executed. The screen is cleared to black. HCOLOR is not affected by this command.

Page 2 of screen memory is not available if your Apple II has less than 24K of memory. On 24K systems, set HIMEM: to 16384 before you use HGR2 to protect your program and variables from your graphics, and vice versa. You cannot use HGR2 and DOS 3.3 concurrently unless your system has at least 36K of memory.

You cannot establish a text window with POKE −16301,0. This will display low-resolution graphics page 2 while your immediate mode commands go into page 1 and hence are invisible (although they execute correctly).

HGR2 is not available in Integer BASIC.

HIMEM:

Sets an upper boundary on memory available to BASIC programs, including variable storage.

Format: HIMEM: *exprnm*

HIMEM: establishes the highest location in read/write memory (RAM) available to your BASIC program and variables. ProDOS or DOS 3.3 resides above HIMEM: if either is present. With the HIMEM: statement you can set aside additional space for machine language subroutines and high-resolution graphics shape tables. You can also protect the high-resolution graphics screen memory area of RAM.

Each additional file buffer you reserve by opening another ProDOS file lowers HIMEM: another 1024 bytes. With DOS 3.3, each additional file buffer you reserve with the MAXFILES command lowers HIMEM: by 595 bytes. If your Applesoft program uses strings, their values are stored starting at the resulting location of HIMEM:, working downwards.

The value of *exprnm* must be in the range −65535 through 65535 (−32767 through 32767 in Integer BASIC), or an error message occurs. You should not set HIMEM: higher than the maximum memory location available. If you do, some of your variable storage might end up in nonexistent memory. If you set HIMEM: lower than LOMEM: or if you do not leave enough memory to run your program, an error message occurs.

You can see the current value of HIMEM: by using PEEK(116) * 256 + PEEK(115) in Applesoft, or PEEK(77) * 256 + PEEK(76) in Integer BASIC.

HIMEM: is not affected by NEW, RUN, or CLEAR.

HIMEM: can only be used in immediate mode in Integer BASIC.

HLIN

Draws a horizontal line on the screen in low-resolution graphics mode.

Format: HLIN col_1, col_2 AT *row*

The line is drawn from col_1 to col_2 in the *row* specified. The color is determined by the COLOR statement last executed. If the screen is in text mode, or the text window is present and *row* is greater than 39, HLIN will draw a line of characters on the screen in the text window where the graphics dots would be plotted. The characters used are determined by previously executed

COLOR statements; see the PLOT statement for particulars.

In Integer BASIC, col_1 must be less than or equal to col_2 or the message *** **RANGE ERR** is displayed.

HOME

This Applesoft statement clears the display screen and positions the cursor at the upper left-hand corner of the text window.

Format: HOME

In Integer BASIC, use CALL −936.

HPLOT

This Applesoft statement places a dot or draws a line of color on the high-resolution graphics screen.

Formats: HPLOT *colh,rowh*

HPLOT TO *colh,rowh*

HPLOT $colh_1$,$rowh_1$ TO $colh_2$,$rowh_2$ [TO $colh_3$, $rowh_3$...]

The first form of the command places a dot of color on the screen at the specified location. The color of the dot is determined by the HCOLOR statement last executed.

The second form of the command draws a line of color from the last dot plotted to the coordinates *colh* and *rowh*. If there has been no dot plotted since the last HGR or HGR2 command, nothing will be plotted. The color of the line is determined by the HCOLOR statement last executed.

The third form of the command also draws a line of color, and the line may have more than one segment. The line is first drawn from $colh_1$ and $rowh_1$ to $colh_2$ and $rowh_2$. The next line segment is then drawn from $colh_2$ and $rowh_2$ to $colh_3$ and $rowh_3$, and so on. There can be any number of coordinates, as long as they all fit on one program line. The color of the line (all segments) is determined by the HCOLOR statement last executed.

Any portion of a line or dot that lies within the text window will not be visible. However, if you switch to full-screen graphics with the command POKE −16302,0, any line or point plotted previously in the text window will become visible.

You must always execute an HGR or HGR2 statement before an HPLOT. Otherwise you may destroy your program or variables.

Not available in Integer BASIC.

HTAB

This Applesoft statement positions the cursor to the specified column on the current display line.

Format: HTAB *col*

The cursor moves right or left to the column specified by the value of *col*, without erasing any displayed characters. Columns are numbered from 1 to 40 (left to right). Except on an Enhanced Apple IIe, use POKE 36, *col*, greater than 40 for column numbers. HTAB works the same way with printers.

In Integer BASIC, use the TAB statement.

IF-THEN (Applesoft)

Conditionally causes the program to execute the indicated instruction or branch to the designated line.

Formats: IF *expr* THEN *statement* [:*statement*...]
IF *expr* THEN GOTO *line*

In the first format of the IF-THEN statement, the *expr* specifies a condition which, if true, causes every *statement* that follows THEN on the same program line to be executed. If the specified condition is false, control passes to the first statement on the next program line and any *statements* following the THEN are not executed.

In the second format (the conditional branch format), the program branches to line number *line* if the condition is true. Otherwise execution continues with the first statement on the next program line after the IF-THEN.

If an unconditional branch is one of many *statements* following THEN, the branch must be the last *statement* on the line, and it must have the GOTO *line* format. If the unconditional branch is not the last *statement* on the line, the *statements* following the unconditional branch can never be executed.

The most common type of expression used with IF-THEN is a relational expression. If string expressions are compared using relational operators, the ASCII codes (listed in Appendix E) for the characters involved determine the relative values of the strings. Strings are compared character by character until a mismatch occurs. Then the string with the higher ASCII code in the mismatch position is considered greater. If no mismatch occurs, the longer string is greater. Execution of more than two or three IF-THEN statements in which *expr* is a string expression during the course of a program generates the message **?FORMULA TOO COMPLEX ERROR**.

The expression may also be a numeric expression. If the value of the expression is not zero, the condition is considered true. If the value of the expression is zero (false), execution continues at the first statement on the next-higher program line.

Applesoft has problems if the last nonspace character preceding THEN is the letter A. The A is combined with the T to form the reserved word AT. You can avoid this problem by enclosing some or all of the expression (including the troublesome A) in parentheses.

IF-THEN (Integer BASIC)

Conditionally causes the program to execute the indicated instruction or branch to the designated line.

Formats: IF *expr* THEN *statement*
IF *expr* THEN [GOTO] *line*

In the first form of the IF-THEN statement, the *expr* specifies a condition which, if true, causes the *statement* following the THEN to be executed. If the condition is false, the statement immediately following the IF-THEN statement is executed; the *statement* that follows THEN is not executed in this case.

In the second format of the IF-THEN statement (the conditional branch format), the *expr* specifies a condition which, if true, causes the program to branch to the indicated line number.

Relational expressions are the most common type of *expr* used with IF-THEN. String values can only be compared for equality or nonequality in Integer BASIC. The *expr* can also be a numeric expression. In this case, the *expr* is considered true if it has a nonzero value. The *expr* cannot be a string expression (that is, anything that evaluates to a string value) in Integer BASIC.

If a FOR-NEXT loop follows the THEN, the loop must be completely contained on the IF-THEN *line*. Additional IF-THEN statements may appear following the THEN as long as they are completely contained on the original IF-THEN *line*. However, a logical expression is clearer than nested IF-THEN statements.

IN#

Switches input to a specified input device.

General Format: IN# *slot*
Additional ProDOS Format: IN# A*memloc*

The general IN# format is the most common. It redirects the input of subsequent INPUT or GET statements to a device attached to one of the numbered accessory card slots.

The additional ProDOS IN# format also redirects input of subsequent INPUT or GET statements. Instead of a slot number, it specifies the memory location of a program that controls an input device (called a *device driver*). Table A-9 lists the memory locations of standard ProDOS input device driver programs.

This ProDOS or DOS 3.3 command requires PRINT and CHR$(4) or CONTROL-D in programmed mode.

Table A-9. Standard ProDOS Input Device Drivers

Number	Memory Location	Device
0	47182*	Keyboard
1	49408	Slot 1 (Serial or parallel adapter)
2	49664	Slot 2 (Serial or parallel adapter)
3	49920	Slot 3 or IIe Auxiliary slot (80-column adapter)
4	50176	Slot 4 (Mouse)
5	50432	Slot 5 (Disk drives)
6	50688	Slot 6 (Disk drives)
7	50944	Slot 7

*64795 if ProDOS is disabled.

INIT

Initializes a DOS 3.3 disk.

Format: INIT *filename* [,D*n*] [,S*n*] [,V*n*]

The program currently in memory is saved on the disk under the *filename* given. This program becomes the greeting program, and it is run automatically whenever this disk is booted. The disk is assigned the volume number specified by the INIT command. If no volume number is specified, the disk is assigned a volume number of 254.

If the file does not exist on drive D*n* of slot S*n*, the **FILE NOT FOUND** error message is displayed.

D*n*, S*n*, and V*n* can be specified in any order. If D*n* or S*n* is omitted, the last-referenced drive or slot is used.

INIT may only be used in immediate mode.

INPUT (Applesoft)

Accepts character entry from the keyboard or another input device, evaluates it, and assigns the value or values entered to the variable or variables specified.

Format: INPUT [“*prompt*”;] *var* [,*var* ...]

INPUT can request values for any combination of numeric and string variables. A question mark is normally displayed as a cue to begin entry at the current cursor location. Applesoft suppresses the question mark if the optional *prompt* is present.

The optional *prompt* is a string constant. If it is present, it will be displayed just before the first variable is input; it is not repeated for each variable in the list. No question mark is displayed after the *prompt*. Note that the *prompt* is followed by a semicolon in an Applesoft INPUT statement.

Generally speaking, when a single Applesoft INPUT statement calls for more than one value, you can enter each one on a separate line, ending each value with the RETURN key. Optionally, you can enter more than one value on a single line and separate the values with commas.

If you enter unacceptable characters (for example, letters in a numeric value) a warning message appears and you must reenter the value. Applesoft displays **REENTER** and reexecutes the INPUT statement from the beginning. The cue (question mark or *prompt*) is redisplayed and you must reenter all values for the INPUT statement.

Numeric input must consist only of valid numeric characters. If you simply press RETURN when a numeric variable is to be entered, you receive an error message and must reenter the line. The digits 0 through 9, spaces, and a plus or minus sign are accepted as numeric input. Applesoft also accepts a decimal point, an additional plus or minus sign, and the letter E for entering real values and scientific notation.

In Applesoft, if the first nonspace character of a string entry is a quotation mark, all characters (including commas and colons) up to the next quotation mark or carriage return are assigned to the string variable. If the entry does not begin with a quotation mark, all characters (including quotation marks) up to the next comma, colon, or carriage return are assigned to the variable. If two or more strings are requested by the same INPUT statement, they must be enclosed in quotes and separated by commas. If you simply press RETURN when a string variable is to be entered, the null string (“ ”) is assigned to the variable.

In Applesoft, all characters after a colon in an INPUT response are ignored unless the entry begins with a quotation mark.

INPUT cannot be used in immediate mode.

INPUT (Integer BASIC)

Accepts character entry from the keyboard or another input device, evaluates it, and assigns the value or values entered to the variable or variables specified.

Format: INPUT [*"prompt"*,] *var* [,*var* ...]

INPUT in Integer BASIC requests values for any combination of integer and string variables. If the first variable is an integer, a question mark is displayed at the current cursor location as a cue to begin entry. Integer BASIC suppresses the question mark if a string is the first variable listed.

The optional *prompt* is a string constant. If it is present, it will be displayed just before the first variable is input; it is not repeated for each variable in the list. A question mark is displayed after the *prompt* if an integer variable is to be entered. The *prompt* alone is displayed if a string variable is to be entered. Note that the *prompt* is followed by a comma in Integer BASIC. The *prompt* may not be a string variable or string expression.

When a single INPUT statement calls for more than one integer value in succession, you can enter each one on a separate line; end each value with the RETURN key. Integer BASIC displays a double question mark (??) on each new line as a cue to continue entries for the INPUT statement. Optionally, you can enter more than one integer value on a single line by separating the values with commas.

Numeric input must consist only of valid numeric characters. These are the digits 0 through 9, spaces, and a plus or minus sign. You get an error message if you simply press RETURN when a numeric value is to be entered.

You must enter each string value on a separate line. All characters (except CONTROL-C, CONTROL-M, CONTROL-H, CONTROL-U, and CONTROL-X) that you enter prior to pressing the RETURN key are accepted and assigned to the string variables. The null string (" ") is assigned to the variable if you simply press RETURN when a string value is to be entered. If you enter unacceptable characters (for example, letters in a numeric value), the warning messages ***** SYNTAX ERR** and **RETYPE LINE** appear. You must reenter all values that you entered on the offending line.

INPUT cannot be used in immediate mode.

INT

Switches from Applesoft to Integer BASIC (not available with ProDOS).

Format: INT

Any program currently in memory is erased. If Integer BASIC is not present (for example, on an Apple II Plus without a Language System), the message **LANGUAGE NOT AVAILABLE** is displayed.

Use INT only in immediate mode.

INVERSE

This Applesoft statement switches to inverse character style.

Format: INVERSE

All output from subsequently executed PRINT statements will appear as black characters on a white background. Error messages are similarly affected. However, any previously displayed characters are unaffected.

INVERSE works by slightly altering the standard ASCII codes. Therefore, any inverse characters sent to a DOS 3.3 disk will be saved with incorrect codes. When read back in, the wrong characters will result.

This statement is not available in Integer BASIC. Lowercase inverse characters are not available on most Apple II Plus and standard Apple II machines.

LET=

The assignment statement, LET= or simply =, assigns a value to a specified variable.

Format: [LET] *var*=*expr*

The *var* is assigned the value computed by evaluating the *expr*.

LIST

Displays all or part of the program lines currently in memory.

General Format: LIST *line*$_1$ [,*line*$_2$]
Applesoft Format: LIST [*line*$_1$] $\left\{\begin{matrix}-\\,\end{matrix}\right\}$ [*line*$_2$]

Any portion of the program may be listed. If no line numbers follow LIST, all program lines are displayed. If only *line*$_1$ is specified, only that line is displayed. If both line numbers are specified, the program is listed starting at *line*$_1$ and continuing through *line*$_2$. If *line*$_1$ does not exist, the listing starts at the next-higher line number. If *line*$_2$ does not exist, the listing ends at the next-lower line number. LIST may not be used with variables or expressions in place of the line numbers.

In Applesoft, either a comma (,) or a hyphen (-) may separate the two line numbers.

In Applesoft you can list from the start of the program to a specific line number by putting a comma or hyphen ahead of *line*$_2$ (and omitting *line*$_1$). You can also list from a specific line number to the end of the program by putting a comma or hyphen after *line*$_1$ (and omitting *line*$_2$).

When LIST displays your program, it adds spaces to make the listing more readable. You can eliminate some of the spaces by reducing the text window to a width of 33 with the command POKE 33,33. (POKE 33,40, POKE 33,80 or TEXT restores the text window to full width.)

Program line lengths are limited, but these limits are calculated before the LIST command adds the extra spaces. You can therefore extend the apparent length of your program lines by leaving out spaces when you type the lines in; LIST will make the lines longer. However, lines such as these will be too long to be edited or copied after they have been listed with all the spaces put in.

LOAD (ProDOS)

Loads an Applesoft program from a ProDOS disk.

Format: LOAD *pathname* [,D*n*] [,S*n*]

The named program is loaded from the disk. The program replaces any program previously in memory. All variables and arrays are cleared, and any open files are closed. If no program exists as named, the existing program, variables, and files will be untouched.

D*n* and S*n* can be specified in any order. If D*n* or S*n* is omitted, the ProDOS prefix specifies the drive and slot.

This is a ProDOS command, requiring PRINT and CHR$(4) in programmed mode.

LOAD (DOS 3.3)

Loads a program from a DOS 3.3 disk.

Format: LOAD *filename* [,D*n*] [,S*n*] [,V*n*]

The program with the name *filename* is loaded from the disk. If the LOAD is successful, any program previously in memory is erased.

If the program to be loaded is in Applesoft and the Apple II is currently in Integer BASIC, or vice versa, the Apple II switches to the proper language. This may require loading the language from the specified disk. If the language is not available, the message **LANGUAGE NOT AVAILABLE** is displayed.

If the file does not exist on drive D*n* of slot S*n*, the **FILE NOT FOUND** error message is displayed. If the disk in drive D*n* of slot S*n* is not volume V*n*, the **VOLUME MISMATCH** error results.

D*n*, S*n*, and V*n* can be specified in any order. If D*n* or S*n* is omitted, the last-referenced drive or slot is used. V0 is used if V*n* is absent.

This is a DOS 3.3 command, requiring PRINT and CHR$(4) or CONTROL-D in programmed mode.

LOAD (Cassette)

Loads a program from cassette.

Format: LOAD

Loads the next sequential program from the cassette, replacing any program currently in memory. You must have the cassette recorder running in playback mode when LOAD is executed; the Apple II does not remind you to do this. The Apple II beeps as it starts to load a program and beeps again when it finishes. The second beep is your signal to manually stop the cassette recorder.

In Integer BASIC, you can only use LOAD in immediate mode.

LOCK (ProDOS)

Protects a ProDOS disk file or directory against change.

Format: LOCK *pathname* [,D*n*] [,S*n*]

Once locked, a file cannot be deleted, changed, or renamed until it is unlocked (see UNLOCK). No program can be saved using the name of a locked file. A locked file is indicated in a disk directory listing by an asterisk in front of the file name.

D*n* and S*n* can be specified in any order. If D*n* or S*n* is omitted, the ProDOS prefix specifies the drive and slot.

This is a ProDOS command, requiring PRINT and CHR$(4) in programmed mode.

LOCK (DOS 3.3)

Protects a DOS 3.3 disk file against change.

Format: LOCK *filename* [,D*n*] [,S*n*] [,V*n*]

Once locked, a file cannot be deleted, changed, or renamed until it is unlocked (see UNLOCK). No program can be saved using the name of the locked file. A locked file is indicated in the disk catalog by an asterisk at the left of the file type.

If the file does not exist on drive D*n* of slot S*n*, the **FILE NOT FOUND** error message is displayed. If the disk in drive D*n* of slot S*n* is not volume V*n*, the **VOLUME MISMATCH** error results.

D*n*, S*n*, and V*n* can be specified in any order. If D*n* or S*n* is omitted, the last-referenced drive or slot is used. V0 is used if V*n* is absent.

This is a DOS 3.3 command, requiring PRINT and CHR$(4) or CONTROL-D in programmed mode.

LOMEM:

Sets a lower boundary on the memory available to BASIC programs.

Format: LOMEM: *exprnm*

LOMEM: establishes the lowest location in read/write memory (RAM) available for your BASIC program lines and variables. The operating system and the BASIC interpreter use RAM below LOMEM: for pointers, low-resolution graphics and text screen memory, and so forth. When the Applesoft interpreter is not in ROM, it resides in RAM below LOMEM:. You can set aside additional space for machine language subroutines and high-resolution graphics shape tables with a LOMEM: command.

LOMEM: starts out at memory location 2048, just above the low-resolution graphics area. Loading the Applesoft interpreter into RAM from disk or cassette raises LOMEM: to 12291. Each time you add an Applesoft program line or change an existing line, LOMEM: is adjusted up or down. Erasing an Applesoft program (with NEW) also changes LOMEM:. So if you want to reserve space below your program, you must do so after erasing one program but before loading or typing in a new one.

The value of *exprnm* must be in the range −65535 through 65535 (−32767 through 32767 in Integer BASIC), or an error message will occur.

You can display the current value of LOMEM: with PRINT PEEK(106) * 256 + PEEK(105).

In Applesoft, if LOMEM: is set higher than the current value of HIMEM:, lower than the existing value of LOMEM:, or lower than the highest memory location used by the current operating system or program, the message **?OUT OF MEMORY ERROR** occurs.

LOMEM: can only be used in immediate mode in Integer BASIC.

MAN

Ends automatic line numbering mode in Integer BASIC.

Format: MAN

Automatic line numbering is instituted with AUTO.

Type CONTROL-X to temporarily halt the generation of line numbers, and then enter MAN.

MAN is not available in Applesoft.

MAXFILES

Specifies the maximum number of DOS 3.3 files that may be active at any one time.

Format: MAXFILES *limit*

When executed, MAXFILES sets aside 595 bytes of memory (a file buffer) for each file. MAXFILES is automatically set to 3 when you load DOS 3.3, and it can be increased to a maximum of 16.

All DOS 3.3 commands except MAXFILES, PR#, and IN# use a file buffer while they are executing. If you attempt to execute any DOS 3.3 command when there is no buffer free, the error message **NO BUFFERS AVAILABLE** appears.

MAXFILES resets HIMEM:, and that may erase part of your program or its variable storage. Execute MAXFILES before you run your program. If you use MAXFILES within an Applesoft program, use it as the first statement.

This is a DOS 3.3 command, requiring PRINT and CHR$(4) or CONTROL-D in programmed mode.

MON

Causes DOS 3.3 commands and data flow to be displayed on the screen.

Format: MON [C] [,][I] [,][O]

The three parameters dictate what is displayed. If C is specified, all DOS 3.3 commands are displayed on the screen. If I is specified, all data input to the Apple II from the disk is displayed. If O is specified, all data output from the Apple II to the disk is displayed. These parameters may be used in any combination and in any order. If none of them are present, MON has no effect. MON remains in effect until a NOMON, FP, or INT is executed, the system is restarted, or on some machines, RESET is struck.

This is a DOS 3.3 command, requiring PRINT and CHR$(4) or CONTROL-D in programmed mode.

NEW

Deletes the current program and all variables from memory.

Format: NEW

NEW also resets LOMEM:, but does not affect HIMEM:, COLOR, or HCOLOR.

NEW may only be used in immediate mode in Integer BASIC.

NEXT

Terminates the loop started by a FOR instruction.

General Format: NEXT *varnm* [,*varnm*...]

Additional Applesoft Format: NEXT

When NEXT is executed, loop index variable *varnm* is incremented by an amount specified in the corresponding FOR statement. The program then either continues with the instruction following NEXT or loops back to the corresponding FOR, depending on the parameters set in the FOR statement. See the discussion of FOR earlier in this appendix.

If there is no currently active FOR loop that matches *varnm*, an error will occur. The message **?NEXT WITHOUT FOR ERROR** is displayed by Applesoft; ***** BAD NEXT ERR** is displayed by Integer BASIC.

Multiple variables following NEXT must be listed in the proper order (the last loop initiated must be terminated first), or an error will occur.

In Applesoft you may use NEXT with no identifying variable name. The loop variable defaults to that of the most recently begun FOR loop that is still in effect. NEXT with no variable executes more rapidly than NEXT with a variable.

NEXT may not be used in immediate mode in Integer BASIC. In Applesoft, an immediate mode NEXT may cause a branch to a FOR that was executed in programmed mode and is still active.

NO DSP

Cancels the display of changing values for the specified variable in Integer BASIC.

Format: NO DSP *var*

NO DSP is not available in Applesoft.

NOMON

Ends the display of DOS 3.3 commands or data flow that was initiated by MON.

Format: NOMON [C] [,][I] [,][O]

Each parameter specified cancels part of the display started by MON. If C is specified, DOS 3.3 commands are not displayed. If I is specified, data input to the Apple II from the disk is not displayed. If O is specified, data output from the Apple II to the disk is not displayed. These parameters may be used in any combination and in any order. If MON is not in effect for the parameter or parameters specified or if no parameters are specified, NOMON has no effect.

This is a DOS 3.3 command, requiring PRINT and CHR$(4) or CONTROL-D in programmed mode.

NORMAL

This Applesoft statement switches to normal character style.

Format: NORMAL

All output from subsequently executed PRINT statements will appear as white characters on a black background. However, any previously displayed characters are unaffected.

NORMAL is not available in Integer BASIC.

NO TRACE

Turns off the tracing of program execution that was initiated by TRACE.

Format: NO TRACE

If TRACE is not in effect, NO TRACE has no effect.

ONERR GOTO

Branches to a specified line number when a subsequent error occurs in an Applesoft program.

Format: ONERR GOTO *line*

This command sets a flag that causes the program to branch to the *line* when an error occurs. ONERR GOTO must be executed before the error occurs.

Each type of error has a code number. The code of the most recently occurring error is stored in memory location 222. PEEK(222) retrieves the error codes. The error codes and their messages are listed in Appendix B.

Except on an Enhanced Apple IIc, when an error occurs inside a FOR-NEXT loop or in a subroutine, the pointers and stacks may be disrupted. If your error-handling routine returns to a

Table A-10. Machine Language Fix for ONERR GOTO

MACHINE LANGUAGE		6502 ASSEMBLY LANGUAGE	
Decimal	**Hexadecimal**	**Instruction**	**Comments**
104	68	PLA	Put top byte of stack in Accumulator
168	A8	TAY	And save it in Y index register
104	68	PLA	Put next byte of stack in Accumulator
166	A6	LDX $DF	Use ONERR pointer
223	DF		as stack address
154	9A	TXS	Push saved stack con-
72	48	PHA	tents on 'ONERR'
152	98	TYA	stack (two bytes—
72	48	PHA	from Accumulator and Y register)
96	60	RTS	Return to Applesoft

NEXT or RETURN statement, an error may occur. The Apple II will lock up if there are two GET errors in a row and if the error-handling routine ends with RESUME, not GOTO. In programs that use PRINT statements (or if TRACE is in effect), the 43rd error not arising from an INPUT statement causes a jump to the Monitor. In this situation, if GOTO ends the error-handling routine (instead of RESUME), the 87th INPUT error causes a jump to the Monitor.

To circumvent the problems just described, your program can call the machine language program listed in Table A-10 each time it intercepts an error. Use POKE statements to put the decimal numbers into memory locations 768 through 777 (or any available memory locations). Then use a CALL 768 statement from your error-handling routine.

ONERR GOTO is not available in Integer BASIC and cannot be used in immediate mode.

ON-GOSUB

Provides conditional subroutine calls to one of several subroutines in an Applesoft program, depending on the current value of an expression.

Format: ON *exprnm* GOTO *line* [,*line*...]

The program branches to the first line number when the integer value of the expression is 1, to the second when it is 2, and so on. The next RETURN statement encountered sends the program back to the line following the ON-GOSUB.

The expression must have a value in the range 0 through 255 or the message **?ILLEGAL QUANTITY ERROR** will occur. If the expression evaluates to zero or to a value greater than the number of line numbers listed, program execution continues with the next instruction following the ON-GOSUB.

ON-GOSUB is not available in Integer BASIC. (But refer to GOSUB for an Integer BASIC form of computed GOSUB.)

ON-GOTO

Causes a conditional branch to one of several points in an Applesoft program, depending on the current value of an expression.

Format: ON *exprnm* GOTO *line* [,*line*...]

The program branches to the first line number when the integer value of the expression is 1, to the second when the integer value is 2, and so on.

The expression must have a numeric value in the range 0 through 255, or the message **?ILLEGAL QUANTITY ERROR** will occur. When the expression evaluates to zero or to a value greater than the number of line numbers listed, program execution continues with the next instruction following the ON-GOTO.

ON-GOTO is not available in Integer BASIC. (But see GOTO for an Integer BASIC form of computed GOTO.)

OPEN (ProDOS)

Prepares a ProDOS disk file for accessing.

Format: OPEN *pathname* [,L*length*] [,T*type*] [,D*n*] [,S*n*]

If the named file does not exist, ProDOS creates it. If the file is already open, an error occurs. OPEN allocates a 1024-byte buffer in memory for the file named. Half the buffer is for input and half is for output. If too little memory is available, an error occurs.

As many as eight files can be open at once. Note that the EXEC command opens a file automatically and closes the file when it's done. The CLOSE command closes the file.

The L*length* option specifies the record length of a random-access file. If the length is not specified and the file exists, ProDOS opens the file for sequential access. If the length is not stated and the file does not exist, ProDOS creates a sequential-access file.

The T*type* option can be used to specify a file type other than text. In that case, the file must exist as named.

D*n* and S*n* can be specified in any order. If D*n* or S*n* is omitted, the ProDOS prefix specifies the drive and slot.

This is a ProDOS command, requiring PRINT and CHR$(4) in programmed mode.

OPEN cannot be used in immediate mode.

OPEN (DOS 3.3)

Prepares a sequential or random-access DOS 3.3 disk text file for accessing.

Format: OPEN *filename* [,L*length*] [,D*n*] [,S*n*] [,V*n*]

If the named file does not exist, DOS 3.3 creates it. If the file is already open, it is closed and then reopened. OPEN requisitions one of the 595-byte file buffers in memory for the text file specified. If all buffers are in use, an error occurs.

The L*length* option specifies the record length of a random-access file. The record length must be an integer constant between 1 and 32767. If the option is absent, the file is opened as a sequential file.

If the disk in drive D*n* of slot S*n* is not volume V*n*, the **VOLUME MISMATCH** error results.

D*n*, S*n*, and V*n* can be specified in any order. If D*n* or S*n* is omitted, the last-referenced drive or slot is used. V0 is used if V*n* is absent.

This is a DOS 3.3 command, requiring PRINT and CHR$(4) or CONTROL-D in programmed mode.

OPEN cannot be used in immediate mode.

PDL

Listed in the Functions section of this appendix.

PEEK

Listed in the Functions section of this appendix.

PLOT

Displays a point on the low-resolution graphics screen.

Format: PLOT *col, row*

In low-resolution graphics mode, PLOT places a dot of color on the screen. The color of the dot is determined by the COLOR statement last executed. Column numbers range between 0 and 39. Column 0 is at the left edge of the screen; column 39 is at the right. Row numbers range between 0 and 47. Row 0 is at the top of the screen, and row 47 is at the bottom. A point plotted in rows 40 through 47 will be in the four-line text window unless a POKE −16302,0 has been executed to eliminate the text window.

In text mode or in the text window, PLOT places a character, rather than a dot, on the screen. Since a character occupies the space of two vertically stacked graphics dots, there are two different sets of PLOT coordinates that will cause a character to appear in a given location. To place a particular character on the screen, you must PLOT both halves of the character location. The character that appears is determined by the COLOR statement last executed before each half is plotted.

You can determine which character will be displayed by computing the screen code from the color numbers of the upper and lower points and looking up the screen code in Appendix E. To compute the screen code, multiply the color number of the lower point by 16 and then add the color number of the upper point. For example, if the color of column 10, row 21 is 0 and the color of column 10, row 20 is 1, the screen code is 1 (0*16+1), which is an inverse-style capital A.

POKE

The POKE statement stores a byte of data in a specified memory location.

Format: POKE *memadr*, *byte*

A value between 0 and 255, provided by *byte*, is written into memory at location *memadr*. If the memory location specified exceeds the maximum location in memory (for example, 16383 if you have 16K of memory) or accesses an output device that is not receiving, POKE has no effect.

Use caution with POKE. Some memory locations contain information essential to the Apple II's uninterrupted operation. Changing random memory locations can destroy your program, lock up your system, or clobber your BASIC.

POP

Causes Applesoft to forget the return location for the most recently executed GOSUB statement.

Format: POP

POP effectively changes the most recently executed GOSUB statement into a GOTO statement (retroactively). The next RETURN statement executed will branch to the instruction immediately following the second most recently executed GOSUB. If the total number of POP and RETURN statements executed in a program exceeds the number of GOSUB statements executed, an error message will occur.

POSITION (ProDOS)

Moves the ProDOS disk file pointer the specified number of fields ahead of its current position.

Formats: POSITION *pathname*,F*field*
POSITION *pathname*,R*field*

The F*field* option specifies a number of fields (carriage return characters) to be skipped in the file. The R*field* option does exactly the same thing and is compatible with the DOS 3.3 operating system.

This is a ProDOS command, requiring PRINT and CHR$(4) in programmed mode.

POSITION cannot be used in immediate mode.

POSITION (DOS 3.3)

Moves the DOS 3.3 disk file pointer the specified number of records ahead of its current position.

Format: POSITION *filename* [,R*field*]

If the file is not open when POSITION is executed, it is opened (see OPEN). The R*field* option specifies a number of fields (carriage return characters) to be skipped in the file. If the file is opened by POSITION, the fields are skipped from the beginning of the file. If any unused space is encountered in the file before the specified number of fields are skipped, the message **END OF DATA** occurs.

This is a DOS 3.3 command, requiring PRINT and CHR$(4) or CONTROL-D in programmed mode.

POSITION cannot be used in immediate mode.

PREFIX

Sets or reports the current ProDOS path prefix.

Format: PREFIX [*pathname*] [,D*n*] [,S*n*]

The *pathname* you specify in the PREFIX command will prefix all pathnames (including simple file names) in subsequent ProDOS commands. If a subsequent ProDOS command specifies no pathname or file name, the prefix is used alone. The prefix cannot be longer than 64 characters, including slashes.

To clear the prefix, use PREFIX /.

To see what the current prefix is, type PREFIX with no *path-*

name. In programmed mode, the next INPUT statement after a simple PREFIX command reads the current prefix.

D*n* and S*n* can be specified in any order. If D*n* or S*n* is omitted, the ProDOS prefix specifies the drive and slot.

This is a ProDOS command, requiring PRINT and CHR$(4) in programmed mode.

PR#

Usually used to switch output to a specified output device.

General Format: PR# *slot*

Additional ProDOS Formats: PR# A*memloc*

PR# A*memloc,slot*

The general PR# format is the most common. It redirects the output of subsequent PRINT statements to a device attached to one of the numbered accessory card slots.

The first additional ProDOS PR# format also redirects output of subsequent PRINT statements. Instead of a device number, it specifies the memory location of a program that controls an output device (called a *device driver*). Table A-11 lists the memory locations of standard ProDOS output device driver programs.

Table A-11. Standard ProDOS Output Device Drivers

Number	Memory Location	Device
0	47179*	Display screen
1	49408	Slot 1 (Serial or parallel adapter)
2	49664	Slot 2 (Serial or parallel adapter)
3	49920	Slot 3 or IIe Auxiliary slot (80-column adapter)
4	50176	Slot 4 (Mouse—commands only)
5	50432	Slot 5 (Disk drives)
6	50688	Slot 6 (Disk drives)
7	50944	Slot 7

*65008 if ProDOS is disabled.

The second additional ProDOS PR# format does not redirect output of subsequent PRINT statements. It only assigns the memory location of a device driver program to one of the device numbers.

This ProDOS or DOS 3.3 command requires PRINT and CHR$(4) or CONTROL-D in programmed mode.

PRINT

Outputs characters to the screen or another output device.

Format: PRINT [*expr*][{;|,}...[*expr*]]...]

There are a number of acceptable variations on the PRINT statement. PRINT by itself outputs a carriage return character. When PRINT is followed by one or more expressions, the values of these expressions are printed. The way the values appear depends on their nature and on the use of semicolons or commas between values.

Negative values are preceded by a minus sign; positive values are not preceded by a sign or a blank space. Scientific notation is used in Applesoft for values closer to zero than ±.01 and for any values with more than nine digits in front of the decimal point. String values are displayed just as they are.

Commas and semicolons determine the spacing between printed values. A semicolon causes the next value to print immediately after the value just printed; the values are concatenated with no intervening spaces. A comma causes the next value to print at the next tab location, several spaces over from the last value. Except on an Enhanced Apple IIe, commas do not work reliably for tabbing when the screen is displaying 80-column lines.

In Integer BASIC, tabs are eight characters apart, at columns 1, 9, 17, and so on. If any nonblank character is printed in the space just ahead of a tab (for example, in column 16), that tab stop is inactivated.

Applesoft places tabs 16 characters apart, at columns. Tabs on the display screen are inactivated according to a scheme illustrated in Figure 9-2. For other devices, a tab is inactivated if a nonblank character is printed just ahead of it (for example, in column 32).

If the list of expressions does not end with a comma or semicolon, a carriage return character is output following the last item in the list. If the list ends with a semicolon, the first character printed by the next PRINT statement will print directly following the last character printed by the current PRINT statement, with no intervening spaces. If the list ends with a comma, the next output will be in the first position of the next tab field.

In Applesoft, items may be listed with no intervening commas or semicolons. Output for such items is concatenated as if the items were separated by semicolons. In Integer BASIC, all items must be separated by either a comma or a semicolon.

Applesoft recognizes a question mark (?) as an abbreviation for PRINT. The word PRINT will be spelled out when the program is listed, however.

READ (ProDOS)

Switches to input from a ProDOS disk file.

Format: READ *pathname* [,R*record*] [,F*field*] [,B*byte*]

After a READ statement is executed, all INPUT and GET statements take characters from the named file, starting at the optional record number (random-access files only). The next ProDOS command, including CHR$(4), disables the READ command.

The F*field* option specifies a number of fields (carriage return characters) to be skipped before reading. The B*byte* option specifies a number of bytes (characters) to skip ahead before reading.

This is a ProDOS command, requiring PRINT and CHR$(4) in programmed mode.

READ cannot be used in immediate mode.

READ (DOS 3.3)

Specifies a DOS 3.3 disk file from which subsequent INPUT and GET commands will obtain data.

Format: READ *filename* [,R*record*] [,B*byte*]

If the file specified is not already open, it is opened (see OPEN). All subsequent INPUT and GET statements receive characters from the disk until the next DOS 3.3 command occurs. If the file is not on the disk, the message **FILE NOT FOUND** appears.

The R*record* option specifies the record number of a random-access file. If that option is absent, the file will be read as a sequential-access file. The B*byte* option specifies a number of bytes (characters) to skip ahead before reading. The numbers following B and R must be integer constants between 0 and 32767.

This is a DOS 3.3 command, requiring PRINT and CHR$(4) or CONTROL-D in programmed mode.

This statement may not be used in immediate mode.

READ (Applesoft)

Assigns values from Applesoft DATA statements to variables.

Format: READ *var* [, *var* ...]

A pointer to the list of DATA statement values determines which value to assign to the first variable in the READ statement. At the start of the program and after a RESTORE statement, the pointer points to the first DATA value. As each READ statement variable gets a value, the pointer moves ahead to the next value.

The variables may be of any type but must match the type of the corresponding DATA list values. A numeric value assigned to a string variable causes no problem. A string assigned to a numeric variable causes the message **?SYNTAX ERROR** to be displayed. The line number of the offending DATA statement is announced with the error message.

If READ attempts to assign more variables than there are DATA values, the **?OUT OF DATA ERROR** message appears, with the line number of the offending READ statement.

READ may be executed in immediate mode as long as the program in memory contains enough DATA values. Otherwise, the message **?OUT OF DATA ERROR** occurs. If ProDOS or DOS 3.3 is present, a READ in immediate mode is interpreted as an operating system command, and the message **NOT DIRECT COMMAND** is displayed.

READ is not available in Integer BASIC.

RECALL

Retrieves an Applesoft numeric array from cassette tape.

Format: RECALL *varnm*

Applesoft waits indefinitely until the array is found on the tape; no other instruction can be executed in the meantime. RECALL does not control tape movement nor advise when to start the cassette recorder in playback mode. The Apple II does beep when it starts getting array values, and it beeps again when the array values stop. The array must be dimensioned before the RECALL statement is executed, or the message **?OUT OF DATA ERROR** is generated (see DIM).

You need not use the same array variable name in the RECALL statement as was used in the STORE statement for the same values. You should use an array with the same dimensions as the one that was stored, however. If the array that was stored contains more elements than the recalled array, the message **?OUT OF DATA ERROR** occurs. If the recalled array contains at least as many elements as the stored array but does not have exactly the same dimensions, the message **ERR** is generated, but program execution continues.

If the recalled array has more elements than the stored array, the values in the recalled array will usually be scrambled. There are two exceptions. You may recall into an array that has the same number of dimensions as the stored array, where each dimension except the last is the same size as the corresponding dimension in the stored array. The last dimension may be larger in the recalled array. You may also recall into an array with more dimensions than are in the stored array, if the dimensions that are in the array match the corresponding dimensions in the recalled array (or exceed them, in the case of the last dimension of the stored array).

String arrays cannot be used with RECALL. Recalled numeric values can be converted to string values with the CHR$ function, however.

RECALL is not available in Integer BASIC.

REM

The REM statement allows comments to be placed in the program for documentation purposes.

Format: REM *comment*

The *comment* is any sequence of characters that will fit on the current program line.

Remark statements are reproduced in program listings, but they are otherwise ignored. A REM statement may be placed on a line of its own, or it may be placed as the last statement of a multiple-statement line. REM cannot be placed ahead of any other statements on a multiple-statement line, since all text following the REM is treated as a comment.

RENAME (ProDOS)

Changes the name of a ProDOS disk file without altering the file's contents.

Format: RENAME *old pathname, new pathname* [,D*n*] [,S*n*]

Both the *old pathname* and the *new pathname* must be in the same directory. RENAME cannot move a file from one directory to another; use the STARTUP program on the System Master disk to do that. The file cannot be open or locked. Duplicate file names are not allowed in the same directory. However, a file in one directory can have the same name as another file in a different directory, because their paths are different.

D*n* and S*n* can be specified in any order. If D*n* or S*n* is omitted, the ProDOS prefix specifies the drive and slot.

This is a ProDOS command, requiring PRINT and CHR$(4) in programmed mode.

RENAME (DOS 3.3)

Changes the name of a DOS 3.3 disk file without altering the file contents.

Format: RENAME *old filename, new filename* [,D*n*] [,S*n*] [,V*n*]

The file named *old filename* is found on the disk, and its name is changed to *new filename*. If the file is open, it is closed (see CLOSE). The file is not affected in any other way.

RENAME will readily change the file name to one that already exists on the disk; in fact, it will do this any number of times. You must make sure that there is no file already named *new filename* before RENAME is executed.

If the *old filename* does not exist on drive D*n* of slot S*n*, the **FILE NOT FOUND** error message is displayed. If the disk in drive D*n* of slot S*n* is not volume V*n*, the **VOLUME MISMATCH** error results.

D*n*, S*n*, and V*n* can be specified in any order. If D*n* or S*n* is omitted, the last-referenced drive or slot is used. V0 is used if V*n* is absent.

This is a DOS 3.3 command, requiring PRINT and CHR$(4) or CONTROL-D in programmed mode.

RESTORE (ProDOS)

Reads a set of Applesoft variables and values from a ProDOS disk file.

Format: RESTORE *pathname* [,D*n*] [,S*n*]

RESTORE clears all existing variables and their values from memory and replaces them with variables and values unpacked from the specified disk file. The file must be type VAR. (See also STORE.)

D*n* and S*n* can be specified in any order. If D*n* or S*n* is omitted, the ProDOS prefix specifies the drive and slot.

This is a ProDOS command, requiring PRINT and CHR$(4) in programmed mode.

RESTORE (Applesoft)

Resets the Applesoft DATA list pointer to the beginning of the list.

Format: RESTORE

Subsequent READ statements start at the first DATA value. RESTORE is not available in Integer BASIC.

RESUME

Causes an Applesoft program to resume execution at the beginning of the statement in which an error occurred.

Format: RESUME

RESUME may only be used after an ONERR GOTO branch has been triggered by an error. If RESUME is executed when no error has occurred, the results are unpredictable but generally tragic.

RESUME is not available in Integer BASIC and cannot be used in immediate mode.

RETURN

Causes the program to branch to the statement immediately following the most recently executed GOSUB.

Format: RETURN

The POP statement will obliterate all knowledge of the most recent GOSUB, with the result that RETURN after POP causes a branch to the statement following the next most recent GOSUB.

If more RETURN (and POP) statements than GOSUB statements are executed in a program, an error message will occur.

ROT=

This Applesoft statement sets the orientation of high-resolution shapes drawn by DRAW or XDRAW.

Format: ROT=*exprnm*

ROT=0 draws the shape in the orientation with which it was defined. The shape is rotated 90 degrees clockwise for each increment of 16 in the value of *exprnm*. Thus, ROT=32 draws the shape upside down, and ROT=64 draws the shape in its original orientation. Values for *exprnm* greater than 64 are evaluated modulo 64 (65 is the same as 1, 66 is the same as 2, and so on).

When SCALE has been set to 1, there are only four recognized values for ROT. They are 0, 16, 32, and 48 (and values greater than 63 equivalent to these values). When SCALE=2 there are eight values, when SCALE=3 there are 16 values, and so on up to a maximum of 64 different recognized values. An unrecognized value for ROT will be treated as if it were the next-lower recognized value.

The *exprnm* must have a value in the range 0 through 255 or the message **?ILLEGAL QUANTITY ERROR** will be generated when the ROT command is executed.

ROT is not recognized as a reserved word unless the character "=" is the first nonspace character following the command.

ROT is not available in Integer BASIC.

RUN (ProDOS)

Loads and runs an Applesoft program from a ProDOS disk.

Format: RUN *pathname* [,@*line*] [,D*n*] [,S*n*]

The named program is loaded from the disk and then run. The program replaces any program previously in the Apple II memory. All variables and arrays are cleared, and any open files are closed. If no program exists as named, the existing program, variables, and files will be untouched.

The @*line* option, if present, specifies a line number at which the program is started. If the specified line number does not exist, the next-higher line number is used.

D*n* and S*n* can be specified in any order. If D*n* or S*n* is omitted, the ProDOS prefix specifies the drive and slot.

This is a ProDOS command, requiring PRINT and CHR$(4) in programmed mode.

RUN (DOS 3.3)

Loads and runs a program from a DOS 3.3 disk.

Format: RUN *filename* [,D*n*] [,S*n*] [,V*n*]

The program named *filename* is loaded from the disk and then run. If the load is successful, any program previously in memory is erased.

If the program to be loaded and run is in Integer BASIC and the Apple II is currently in Applesoft, or vice versa, the Apple II switches to the proper language. If necessary, it will load the Applesoft interpreter from the specified disk. If the language is not available, the message **LANGUAGE NOT AVAILABLE** is displayed.

If the file does not exist on drive D*n* of slot S*n*, the **FILE NOT FOUND** error message is displayed. If the disk in drive D*n* of slot S*n* is not volume V*n*, the **VOLUME MISMATCH** error results.

D*n*, S*n*, and V*n* can be specified in any order. If D*n* or S*n* is omitted, the last-referenced drive or slot is used. V0 is used if V*n* is absent.

This is a DOS 3.3 command, requiring PRINT and CHR$(4) or CONTROL-D in programmed mode.

RUN (BASIC)

Executes the program currently in memory, optionally starting at the specified line number.

General Format: RUN [*line*]

If there is no line number *line*, an error occurs.

Additional Integer BASIC Format: RUN *exprnm*

In Integer BASIC, the starting line number can be a numeric expression. This form of RUN may only be used in immediate mode and in Integer BASIC.

SAVE (ProDOS)

Saves an Applesoft program onto a ProDOS disk.

Format: SAVE *pathname* [,D*n*] [,S*n*]

If there is no file as named, a file is created and the program currently in memory is saved in it. If a file of type BAS exists as named, the program is saved in it. If a file of a different type exists as named, an error message occurs.

Warning: Be careful to type the right *pathname*. If you use the wrong name and a file with that name exists, ProDOS replaces the program it contains with the program in memory—with no warning.

D*n* and S*n* can be specified in any order. If D*n* or S*n* is omitted, the ProDOS prefix specifies the drive and slot.

This is a ProDOS command, requiring PRINT and CHR$(4) in programmed mode.

SAVE (DOS 3.3)

Saves the program currently in memory onto a DOS 3.3 disk.

Format: SAVE *filename* [,D*n*] [,S*n*] [,V*n*]

If there is no file as named, a file is created with that name in the language of the current program, and the program currently in memory is saved on it. If there is a file named *filename* in the same language as the current program, the contents of that file are erased and the current program is saved in its place. If the *filename* exists but in a different language or with a different file type, the message **FILE TYPE MISMATCH** will occur.

Warning: Be careful to type the right *filename*. If you use the wrong name and a file with that name exists, DOS 3.3 replaces the program it contains with the program in memory—with no warning.

If the disk in drive D*n* of slot S*n* is not volume V*n*, the **VOLUME MISMATCH** error results.

D*n*, S*n*, and V*n* can be specified in any order. If D*n* or S*n* is omitted, the last-referenced drive or slot is used. V0 is used if V*n* is absent.

This is a DOS 3.3 command, requiring PRINT and CHR$(4) or CONTROL-D in programmed mode.

SAVE (Cassette)

Saves the program currently in memory onto a cassette.

Format: SAVE

This form saves the program currently in memory on cassette tape. You must have the cassette recorder running in RECORD mode when SAVE is executed. The Apple II does not remind you to do this. The Apple II beeps as it starts to save a program and beeps again when it is finished. The second beep is your signal to manually stop the cassette recorder.

SAVE may only be used in immediate mode in Integer BASIC.

SCALE=

This Applesoft statement sets the size of high-resolution graphics shapes drawn by DRAW or XDRAW.

Format: SCALE= *exprnm*

The size of the shape in the shape table is multiplied by the integer value of *exprnm*. Thus, if SCALE=1 the shape will be drawn just as it was defined; if SCALE=2 it will be drawn twice that size, and so on. If SCALE=0 the shape is drawn 255 times the size of the original.

The value of *exprnm* must be in the range 0 through 255 or the message **?ILLEGAL QUANTITY ERROR** will occur when the SCALE command is executed.

SCALE is not recognized as a reserved word unless the character "=" is the first nonspace character following the command.

SCALE is not available in Integer BASIC.

SHLOAD

This Applesoft statement loads a high-resolution graphics shape table from cassette tape.

Format: SHLOAD

The shape table is loaded into memory just below HIMEM: and HIMEM: is set just below the shape table. The starting location of the table is stored in memory locations 232 and 233. In order to save a shape table on tape, you must use the Machine Language Monitor's write-memory command, as described in Chapter 14.

SHLOAD is not available in Integer BASIC.

SPEED

This Applesoft statement changes the rate at which characters are output.

Format: SPEED *exprnm*

The value of *exprnm* establishes the rate at which characters appear on the display screen or other output device. Speeds range from 0 (slowest) to 255 (fastest).

SPEED is not available in Integer BASIC.

STOP

Causes an Applesoft program to halt.

Format: STOP

The Apple II returns to immediate mode. The message **BREAK IN line** is displayed, where *line* is the line number at which the STOP was executed.

STOP is not available in Integer BASIC.

STORE (ProDOS)

Saves all variables and their current values in a ProDOS disk file.

Format: STORE *pathname* [,D*n*] [,S*n*]

The variables and values are saved in a special packed format on the named file. STORE also cleans up the string storage area of memory (like FRE) before writing to disk. (See also RESTORE.)

D*n* and S*n* can be specified in any order. If D*n* or S*n* is omitted, the ProDOS prefix specifies the drive and slot.

This is a ProDOS command, requiring PRINT and CHR$(4) in programmed mode.

STORE (Cassette)

Saves the specified Applesoft array on cassette tape.

Format: STORE *varnm*

STORE does not control tape movement, nor does it advise when to start the cassette recorder in RECORD mode. You must have the cassette recorder running and ready to record when STORE is executed. Your Applesoft program should display advisories (via PRINT statements). The Apple II does beep when it starts saving values, and beeps again when it stops.

You may only STORE numeric arrays. String arrays must be converted to integer values using the ASC function in order to be stored (see also RECALL).

STORE is not available in Integer BASIC.

TAB

This Integer BASIC statement positions the cursor to the specified column on the current display line.

Format: TAB *col*

The cursor moves right or left to the column specified by the value of *col*, without erasing any displayed characters. Columns are numbered from 1 to 40 (left to right). For column numbers greater than 40, use POKE 36, *col*. TAB works the same way with printers.

For Applesoft, use the HTAB statement. See also the TAB function listed in the Functions section of this appendix.

TEXT

Returns the screen to the usual full-screen text mode from any of the graphics modes.

Format: TEXT

The prompt character and cursor are moved to the last line of the screen. If issued in text mode, this is the only result. If the text window has been set to anything other than full-screen, TEXT resets it to full-screen.

TEXT does not clear the screen, or more precisely, does not clear page 1 of low-resolution screen memory. Since the normal text mode uses the same screen memory as low-resolution graphics, executing TEXT while in low-resolution graphics mode will leave the top 20 lines of the screen filled with strange characters.

TRACE

Displays the line number of each statement as it is executed.

Format: TRACE

This debugging aid may cause line numbers to be displayed intermixed with your program's output, rendering one or both illegible. TRACE can only be turned off by NO TRACE.

UNLOCK (ProDOS)

Unlocks a ProDOS disk file or directory, permitting it to be changed.

Format: UNLOCK *pathname* [,D*n*] [,S*n*]

Once unlocked, a file can be deleted, changed, or renamed. No asterisk precedes the name of an unlocked file in a disk directory listing.

D*n* and S*n* can be specified in any order. If D*n* or S*n* is omitted, the ProDOS prefix specifies the drive and slot.

This is a ProDOS command, requiring PRINT and CHR$(4) in programmed mode.

UNLOCK (DOS 3.3)

Unlocks a DOS 3.3 file, permitting it to be changed.

Format: UNLOCK *filename* [,D*n*] [,S*n*] [,V*n*]

Once unlocked, a file can be deleted, changed, or renamed.

If the file does not exist on drive D*n* of slot S*n*, the **FILE NOT FOUND** error message is displayed. If the disk in drive D*n* of slot S*n* is not volume V*n*, the **VOLUME MISMATCH** error results.

D*n*, S*n*, and V*n* can be specified in any order. If D*n* or S*n* is omitted, the last-referenced drive or slot is used. V0 is used if V*n* is absent.

This is a DOS 3.3 command, requiring PRINT and CHR$(4) or CONTROL-D in programmed mode.

USR

Listed in the Functions section of this appendix.

VERIFY

Checks that a DOS 3.3 file can be read.

Format: VERIFY *filename* [,D*n*] [,S*n*] [,V*n*]

If a file can be read, no message is returned. If it cannot, the message **I/O ERROR** is generated. Any type of file may be verified.

If the file does not exist on drive D*n* of slot S*n*, the **FILE NOT FOUND** error message is displayed. If the disk in drive D*n* of slot S*n* is not volume V*n*, the **VOLUME MISMATCH** error results.

D*n*, S*n*, and V*n* can be specified in any order. If D*n* or S*n* is omitted, the last-referenced drive or slot is used. V0 is used if V*n* is absent.

This is a DOS 3.3 command, requiring PRINT and CHR$(4) or CONTROL-D in programmed mode.

VLIN

Draws a vertical line on the screen in low-resolution graphics mode.

Format: VLIN row_1, row_2 AT *col*

The line is drawn from row_1 to row_2 in the column specified by *col*. The color is determined by the COLOR statement last executed. If the screen is in text mode, or if the text window is present and either *row* is greater than 39, some or all of the line will appear as characters instead of graphics dots. The characters used are determined by previously executed COLOR statements (see PLOT for particulars).

In Integer BASIC, row_1 must be less than or equal to row_2 or the message ***RANGE ERR** will be displayed.

VTAB

Positions the cursor to the specified line in the current display column.

Format: VTAB *row*

The cursor moves up or down to the line specified by the value of *row*, without erasing any displayed characters. Rows are numbered from 1 to 24 (top to bottom).

WAIT

Halts an Applesoft program until a particular memory location attains a specified condition.

Format: WAIT *memadr*, $exprnm_1$ [,$exprnm_2$]

WAIT checks all or part of the eight bits of memory location *memadr* for the pattern of ones and zeros specified by the binary value of $exprnm_2$. The binary value of $exprnm_1$ determines which bits of the memory location to consider and which to ignore. If a particular bit of $exprnm_1$ is 1, the corresponding bit of memory location *memadr* is checked. Conversely, WAIT ignores those memory bits that correspond to 0 bits in the binary value of $exprnm_2$.

As long as the significant bits (as determined by $exprnm_1$) of *memadr* are all different from the corresponding bits of $exprnm_2$, the wait continues. The moment any pair of significant bits are the same (either both 0 or both 1), the wait is over and the Applesoft program continues.

If $exprnm_2$ is absent, 0 is used.

WAIT can only be interrupted by CONTROL-RESET (or a power-off). The value of the numeric expressions must be in the range 0 through 255 or the message **?ILLEGAL QUANTITY ERROR** will be generated. If the specified memory location is greater than the maximum location in memory (for example, 32767 if you have 32K of memory) or if the specified location accesses an output device that is not receiving, WAIT will lock up the system until you press CONTROL-RESET.

WAIT is not available in Integer BASIC.

WRITE (ProDOS)

Switches output to a ProDOS disk file.

Format: WRITE *pathname* [,R*record*] [,F*field*] [,B*byte*]

After a WRITE statement is executed, all PRINT statements send characters to the named file, starting at the optional record number (random-access files only). Other characters, including error messages, that would normally appear on the screen also go to the disk file. However, the question mark or prompt message displayed by an INPUT statement is not sent to the disk file. The next ProDOS command, including CHR$(4), disables the WRITE command.

The F*field* option specifies a number of fields (carriage return characters) to be skipped before writing. The B*byte* option specifies a number of bytes (characters) to skip ahead before writing.

This is a ProDOS command, requiring PRINT and CHR$(4) in programmed mode.

WRITE cannot be used in immediate mode.

WRITE (DOS 3.3)

Specifies a DOS 3.3 disk file to which subsequent PRINT statements will send output.

Format: WRITE *filename* [,R*record*] [,B*byte*]

If the file specified is not already open, it is opened (see OPEN). Subsequent PRINT statements save data on the disk until the next DOS 3.3 command occurs. While WRITE is in effect, every character that the Apple II outputs that would normally be sent to the screen is sent to the disk. This includes the question mark generated by INPUT and any error messages. If the file is not on the disk, the message **FILE NOT FOUND** appears.

The R*record* option specifies the record number of a random-access file. If that option is absent, the file will be written to as a sequential-access file. The B*byte* option specifies a number of bytes (characters) to skip ahead before writing. The numbers following B and R must be integer constants between 0 and 32767.

The B*byte* option can be used to write beyond the last character already in the file. This data can later be read, but any attempt to read intervening unused bytes generates the **OUT OF DATA** message.

WRITE is a DOS 3.3 command, requiring PRINT and CHR$(4) or CONTROL-D in programmed mode.

WRITE may not be used in immediate mode.

XDRAW

This Applesoft statement draws a high-resolution graphics shape on the screen, and if used a second time with the same parameters, erases that shape.

Format: XDRAW *exprnm* [AT *colh, rowh*]

Shape number *exprnm* from the shape table is drawn, with each point in the color that is the complement of the color on the screen at that point. White and black are a complementary pair, as are green and blue and the two colors set by HCOLOR values 5 and 6 (see Table 12-5). The scale and rotation of the shape must be set by the SCALE and ROT commands before the XDRAW command is executed.

You use XDRAW instead of DRAW so that you can easily erase a shape you have drawn. Since XDRAW draws in the color complementary to the color that was previously at that point, if you execute two (or four, six, and so on) XDRAW statements with the same parameters, whatever is on the screen will be unchanged.

If you do not specify a location in the XDRAW statement, the shape is drawn starting at the point plotted by the last executed DRAW, XDRAW, or HPLOT command. If you do specify a location, the shape is drawn starting at that point (*colh, rowh*).

The shape number, *exprnm*, must have a value between 0 and the number of shapes in the shape table (which must not exceed 255), inclusive.

This statement is not available in Integer BASIC.

FUNCTIONS

Apple II BASIC functions are described below in alphabetical order. Nomenclature and abbreviations are described at the beginning of this appendix.

Many of the functions are available only in Applesoft. These functions are appropriately identified.

ABS

Computes the absolute value of a number. This is the value of the number without regard to sign.

Format: ABS *exprnm*

ASC

Determines the ASCII code number for a specified character.

Format: ASC (*expr$*)

If the string is longer than one character, ASC returns the ASCII code for the first character in the string. The code returned will not necessarily be the lowest ASCII code (in the range 0 through 127) for that character. When displayed on the screen, the characters generated by ASCII codes between 128 and 255 duplicate those between 0 and 127. However, they are not evaluated as the same character by relational operators such as <, >, and =. They may be treated differently by printers and other output devices as well. If the first character of *expr$* is ASCII code 0, the message **?SYNTAX ERROR** is generated. If *expr$* is a null string, the message **?ILLEGAL QUANTITY ERROR** is produced.

ASCII codes are listed in Appendix E.

ATN

Computes the arctangent of the argument.

Format: ATN (*exprnm*)

Computes the arctangent, in radians, of *exprnm*. The angle returned is in the range $-\pi/2$ through $\pi/2$.

This function is not available in Integer BASIC.

CHR$

Determines the string value of the specified ASCII code.

Format: CHR$ (*exprnm*)

Determines the character represented by the integer value of *exprnm*, interpreted as an ASCII code. You will find a table of ASCII character codes in Appendix E. Use this function to generate characters you cannot produce at the keyboard for controlling external devices and accessories. The value of *exprnm* must be in the range 0 through 255 or the message **?ILLEGAL QUANTITY ERROR** will appear.

This function is not available in Integer BASIC.

COS

Computes the cosine of an angle.

Format: COS (*exprnm*)

Computes the cosine of *exprnm* radians. This function is not available in Integer BASIC.

EXP

Computes *e* raised to a power.

Format: EXP (*exprnm*)

Computes *e* (the base of natural logarithms, 2.71828183) raised to the power *exprnm*. This function is not available in Integer BASIC.

FN

Invokes a previously defined user-defined function.

Format: FN *varnm* (*exprnm*)

The *varnm* is the name of the function. The value of the *exprnm* is assigned everywhere the dummy variable occurs in the function definition, and the resulting expression is evaluated. See DEF FN in the Commands and Statements section of this appendix.

A function may not be recursive; that is, *exprnm* may not refer to FN *varnm* nor to any other function which refers to FN *varnm*.

If you attempt to use FN *varnm* before the DEF FN *varnm* statement has been executed, you will receive the **?UNDEF'D FUNCTION ERROR** message.

This function is not available in Integer BASIC.

FRE

Determines the number of bytes of memory currently available to an Applesoft program.

Format: FRE (*exprnm*)

The memory available is that below the string storage area and above the array storage. If there are more than 32767 bytes of memory available, FRE returns a negative number. Add 65536 to this number to discover the actual amount of memory available.

FRE also clears disused strings from the string storage area. When a string changes value during a program, the old value of the string is left in memory, and the new value is added to the string storage area. Eventually, this might infringe on memory you are using for something else. To prevent this problem, have a statement such as A = FRE (0) executed periodically in programs that use strings extensively.

The value of *exprnm* is not used by FRE, but it will cause an error if it is illegal.

This function is not available in Integer BASIC.

INT

Computes the integer portion of a number.

Format: INT (*exprnm*)

Computes the largest integer less than or equal to the value of *exprnm*. This function is not available in Integer BASIC.

LEFT$

Extracts the leftmost characters of a string.

Format: LEFT$ (*expr$*, *exprnm*)

Extracts the leftmost *exprnm* characters of *expr$*. The *exprnm* must be in the range 1 through 255, and *expr$* may not have more than 255 characters. If *exprnm* is greater than the length of *expr$*, the entire string is returned.

This function is not available in Integer BASIC.

LEN

Determines the length of a string.

Format: LEN (*expr$*)

Counts the number of characters in *expr$*, including all spaces and nonprinting characters. If *expr$* has more than 255 characters (possible only if *expr$* is a string expression involving concatenation), the message **?STRING TOO LONG ERROR** is generated.

LOG

Computes the natural logarithm of a number.

Format: LOG (*exprnm*)

Computes the natural logarithm of *exprnm*. If *exprnm* is zero or negative, returns **?ILLEGAL QUANTITY ERROR**.
This function is not available in Integer BASIC.

MID$

Extracts any specified portion of a string.

Format: MID$ (*expr$* $exprnm_1$ [,$exprnm_2$])

Extracts $exprnm_2$ characters from *expr$*, starting with the character $exprnm_1$. If $exprnm_2$ is absent, MID$ returns the portion of *expr$* from the character $exprnm_1$ through the last character. If the length of *expr$* is less than $exprnm_1$, the null string is returned. If there are fewer than $exprnm_2$ characters in *expr$* after $exprnm_1$, the result is the same as if $exprnm_2$ were absent. The *expr$* must not exceed 255 characters, and $exprnm_1$ and $exprnm_2$ must each be in the range 1 through 255.
This funcion is not available in Integer BASIC.

PDL

Determines the current value of the game control (paddle) specified.

Format: PDL (*exprnm*)

The value returned is an integer between 0 and 255 based on the rotation of paddle number *exprnm*, or the resistance of a device connected to game controller socket *exprnm*. The game controls are numbered 0 through 3. If the paddle number is less than 0 or greater than 255, the message **?ILLEGAL QUANTITY ERROR** is displayed. If the paddle number is between 4 and 255, PDL returns a somewhat unpredictable number between 0 and 255 and may cause various side effects, such as a click from the speaker or a sudden shift in graphics mode.
If two PDL instructions are executed consecutively or nearly consecutively, the second value may be affected by the first.

Make sure that several instructions are executed between PDL functions (an empty FOR-NEXT loop will do).

PEEK

Determines the contents of a memory location.

Format: PEEK (*memadr*)

The value returned is the decimal equivalent of the eight bits at memory location *memadr*. Appendix F lists some useful memory locations.

POS

Determines the column position of the cursor.

Format: POS (*exprnm*)

The expression is a dummy. It is not used and can therefore have any legal value.

POS will return a value between 0 and 39. Character positions begin at 0 for the leftmost character.

This function is not available in Integer BASIC.

RIGHT$

Extracts the rightmost characters of a string.

Format: RIGHT$ (*expr$*, *exprnm*)

Extracts the rightmost *exprnm* characters of *expr$*. The value of *exprnm* must be in the range 1 through 255, and *expr$* may not have more than 255 characters. If *exprnm* is greater than the length of *expr$*, the entire string is returned.

This function is not available in Integer BASIC.

RND

Computes a random number.

Format: RND (*exprnm*)

Computes a random number, the range of which depends on the value of *exprnm* and the version of BASIC.

In Integer BASIC, RND returns a random integer between 0 and *exprnm* − 1. Thus, RND (1) always returns 0, and RND (−2) produces a fifty-fifty mix of 0 and −1. Attempting to use RND (0) causes the message *****>32767 ERR** to be displayed.

In Applesoft, RND always returns a real number greater than or equal to 0 and less than 1. The value returned can be one of three types, depending on the sign of *exprnm*. If *exprnm* is positive, RND returns a different value each time it is used, unless a repeatable sequence has been started.

A repeatable sequence starts when RND is used in Applesoft with a negative *exprnm*. Any particular negative value always starts the same sequence; subsequent positive arguments will return a repeatable sequence of random numbers. A different repeatable sequence is started by each different negative value of *exprnm*. This feature is useful for testing and debugging programs that use RND.

If *exprnm* is 0 in Applesoft, RND returns the random number most recently generated (this is not affected by CLEAR or by NEW).

SCRN

Determines the color code of the low-resolution graphics point with the specified coordinates.

Format: SCRN (*col*, *row*)

If *col* is between 0 and 39, SCRN determines the color code of the graphics point (*col*, *row*). If *col* is between 40 and 47 and *row* is between 0 and 31, SCRN determines the color number of the graphics point (*col* − 40, *row* + 16). If *col* is between 40 and 47 and *row* is between 32 and 47, SCRN returns a number unrelated to anything on the screen.

If SCRN is used while the screen is in high-resolution graphics mode, the number returned is related to the low-resolution graphics area of memory rather than the high-resolution display.

If the screen is in text mode, or the text window is present and the point specified is within it, SCRN returns the color code of half of the character. The color code of the top half of the character is returned if the *row* is even, while that of the bottom half is returned if the *row* is odd. The ASCII code of the character at character position (*a*,*b*) (with *a* between 0 and 39 and *b* between 0 and 23) is returned by the expression SCRN(*a*,2**b*) + 16*SCRN(*a*,2**b*+1). Appendix E compares screen codes and ASCII codes.

SCRN is only recognized as a reserved word if the next non-space character is a left parenthesis.

SGN

Determines whether a number is positive, negative, or zero.

Format: SGN (*exprnm*)

The SGN function returns +1 if *exprnm* is positive, −1 if it is negative, and 0 if it is zero.

SIN

Computes the sine of an angle.

Format: SIN (*exprnm*)

Computes the sine of *exprnm* radians. This function is not available in Integer BASIC.

SPC

Generates a specified number of blank spaces.

Format: SPC (*exprnm*)

The SPC function is used in PRINT statements to print *exprnm* blank spaces. On the display screen, any characters that the cursor passes over are erased.

The SPC function moves right *exprnm* columns from the current column position of the cursor. This is in contrast to a TAB function, which moves to a fixed column as measured from the leftmost column.

This function is not available in Integer BASIC.

SQR

Computes the square root of a positive number.

Format: SQR (*exprnm*)

A negative value of *exprnm* causes the **?ILLEGAL QUANTITY ERROR** message. SQR (*exprnm*) operates faster than (*exprnm*)^(.5).

This function is not available in Integer BASIC.

STR$

Converts a numeric value to a string.

Format: STR$ (*exprnm*)

The value of *exprnm* is converted to a string. The string characters are the same as those that would be printed by a PRINT *exprnm* statement. Therefore, STR$ (2/3) = ".666666667" and STR$ (2468013579) = "2.46801358E+09". If *exprnm* exceeds the limits for real numbers, the message **?OVERFLOW ERROR** is displayed.

This function is not available in Integer BASIC.

TAB

Moves the cursor right to the specified column position.

Format: TAB (*exprnm*)

Use TAB with the PRINT statement to move the cursor to column *exprnm* if *exprnm* is to the right of the cursor's current position. The cursor does not move if *exprnm* is not to the right of the current position. TAB prints blank spaces as it moves the cursor right, thereby erasing anything that was on the screen.

For TAB, columns are numbered from 1 to 40. Except on an Enhanced Apple IIe, use POKE 36, *exprnm* for column numbers greater than 40. TAB works the same way with printers.

See also HTAB (Applesoft) and TAB (Integer BASIC) in the Commands and Statements section of this appendix.

This function is not available in Integer BASIC.

TAN

Computes the tangent of an angle.

Format: TAN (*exprnm*)

Computes the tangent of *exprnm* radians.

This function is not available in Integer BASIC.

USR

Branches to a machine language subroutine, passing values in the floating point accumulator area of memory.

Format: USR *exprnm*

The value of *exprnm* is placed in the floating point accumulator (memory locations 157 through 163, $90 through $A3). Then an assembly language JSR $000A instruction is executed, branching to your subroutine via memory locations 10 through 12 ($0A through $0C). Those locations must contain an assembly language JMP instruction that branches to the starting location of your subroutine. Since USR is a function, it returns a numeric real value. Whatever is in the accumulator when the assembly language subroutine executes an RTS instruction (returning to the Applesoft program) is the value returned.

There are many useful machine language subroutines present in the Machine Language Monitor. They are listed in Appendix G.

See also the CALL statement described in the Commands and Statements section of this appendix. The CALL statement is available in Integer BASIC, but the USR function is not.

VAL

Converts a string to a numeric value.

Format: VAL (*expr$*)

Returns the numeric value represented by *expr$*. If the first character of *expr$* is not a numeric character, zero is returned. Otherwise, *expr$* is taken character by character until an unacceptable character is encountered. The acceptable characters are as follows: the digits 0 through 9, spaces, a decimal point, a leading plus or minus sign, and in the context of scientific notation, an additional plus or minus sign, an additional period, and the letter E.

If *expr$* is a string expression involving concatenation that contains more than 255 characters, the message **?STRING TOO LONG ERROR** occurs. If the numeric value of *expr$* exceeds the limits of real numbers, the message **?OVERFLOW ERROR** occurs.

This function is not available in Integer BASIC.

DERIVED NUMERIC FUNCTIONS

While the following list of derived functions is by no means complete, it does provide some of the most frequently needed formulas. Certain values of x will invalidate some functions—for example, if COS(x)=0, then SEC(x) is nonreal—so your program should check for them.

None of the derived functions will operate in Integer BASIC.

ARCCOS(x) = −ATN(x/SQR(−x*x+1))+1.5707633
  Computes the inverse cosine of x (ABS(x) < 1).

ARCCOT(x) = −ATN(x)+1.5707633
Computes the inverse cotangent of x.

ARCCOSH(x) = LOG(x+SQR(x*x>−1))
Computes the inverse hyperbolic cosine of x (x > = 1).

ARCCOTH(x) = LOG((x+1)/(x−1))/2
Computes the inverse hyperbolic cotangent of x (ABS(x)>1).

ARCCSC(x) = ATN(1/SQR(x*x−1))+(SGN(x)−1)*1.5707633
Computes the inverse cosecant of x (ABS(x) > 1).

ARCCSCH(x) = LOG((SGN(x)*SQR(x*x+1)+1)/x)
Computes the inverse hyperbolic cosecant of x (x > 0).

ARCSEC(x) = ATN(SQR(x*x−1))+(SGN(x)−1)*1.5707633
Computes the inverse secant of x (ABS(x) > = 1).

ARCSECH(x) = LOG((SQR(−x*x+1)+1)/x)
Computes the inverse hyperbolic secant of x (0 < x < = 1).

ARCSIN(x) = ATN(x/SQR(−x*x+1))
Computes the inverse sine of x (ABS(x) < 1).

ARCSINH(x) = LOG(x+SQR(x*x+1))
Computes the inverse hyperbolic sine of x.

ARTCTANH(x) = LOG((1+x)/(1−x))/2
Computes the inverse hyperbolic tangent of x (ABS(x) < 1).

COSH(x) = (EXP(x)+EXP(−x))/2
Computes the hyperbolic cosine of x.

COT(x) = 1/TAN(x)
Computes the cotangent of x (x < > 0).

COTH(x) = EXP(−x)/(EXP(x)−EXP(−x))*2+1
Computes the hyperbolic cotangent of x (x < > 0).

CSC(x) = 1/SIN(x)
Computes the cosecant of x (x < > 0).

CSCH(x) = 2/(EXP(x)−EXP(−x))
Computes the hyperbolic cosecant of x (x < > 0).

LOGa (x) = LOG(x)/LOG(a)
Computes the base a logarithm of x (a > 0, x > 0).

Table A-12. Applesoft Reserved Words and Tokens*

Reserved Word	Token	Reserved Word	Token	Reserved Word	Token
ABS	(212)	HTAB	(150)	REM	(178)
ABD	(205)	IF	(173)	RESTORE	(174)
ASC	(230)	IN#	(139)	RESUME	(166)
AT	(197)	INPUT	(132)	RETURN	(177)
ATN	(225)	INT	(211)	RIGHT$	(233)
CALL	(140)	INVERSE	(158)	RND	(219)
CHR$	(231)	LEFT$	(232)	ROT=	(152)
CLEAR	(189)	LEN	(227)	RUN	(172)
COLOR=	(160)	LET	(170)	SAVE	(183)
CONT	(187)	LIST	(188)	SCALE=	(153)
COS	(222)	LOAD	(182)	SCRN(	(215)
DATA	(131)	LOG	(220)	SGN	(210)
DEF	(184)	LOMEM:	(164)	SHLOAD	(154)
DEL	(133)	MID$	(234)	SIN	(223)
DIM	(134)	NEW	(191)	SPC(	(195)
END	(128)	NEXT	(130)	SPEED=	(169)
EXP	(221)	NORMAL	(157)	SQR	(218)
FLASH	(159)	NOT	(198)	STEP	(199)
FN	(194)	NOTRACE	(156)	STOP	(179)
FOR	(129)	ON	(180)	STORE	(168)
FRE	(214)	ONERR	(165)	STR$	(228)
GET	(190)	OR	(206)	TAB(	(192)
GOSUB	(176)	PDL	(216)	TAN	(224)
GOTO	(171)	PEEK	(226)	TEXT	(137)
GR	(136)	PLOT	(141)	THEN	(196)
HCOLOR=	(146)	POKE	(185)	TO	(193)
HGR	(145)	POP	(161)	TRACE	(155)
HGR2	(144)	POS	(217)	USR	(213)
HIMEM:	(163)	PRINT	(186)	VAL	(229)
HLIN	(142)	PR#	(138)	VLIN	(143)
HOME	(151)	READ	(135)	VTAB	(162)
HPLOT	(147)	RECALL	(167)	WAIT	(181)
				XDRAW	(149)

*Reserved words in Applesoft are tokenized: each word takes up only one byte of program storage. The tokens are listed with each reserved word here. They are also listed in numerical order in Appendix E.

$LOG_{10}(x)$ = LOG(x)/2.30258509
Computes the common (base ten) logarithm of x ($x > 0$).

MODa(x) = INT((x/a−INT(x/a))*a +0.5)*SGN(x/a)
Computes x modulo a: the remainder after division of x by a ($a <> 0$).

Table A-13. Integer BASIC Reserved Words

Reserved Words				
ABS	END	LET	PDL	SAVE
AND	FOR	LIST	PEEK	SCRN
ASC	GOSUB	LOAD	PLOT	SGN
AT	GOTO	LOMEM:	POKE	STEP
AUTO	GR	MAN	POP	TAB
CALL	HIMEM:	MOD	PRINT	TEXT
COLOR=	HLIN	NEW	PR#	THEN
CON	IF	NEXT	REM	TO
DEL	IN#	NOT	RETURN	TRACE
DIM	INPUT	NOTRACE	RND	VLIN
DSP	LEN	OR	RUN	VTAB

SEC(x) = 1/COS(x)
Computes the secant of x ($x <> \pi/2$).

SECH(x) = 2/(EXP(x)+EXP($-x$))
Computes the hyperbolic secant of x.

SINH(x) = (EXP(x)−EXP($-x$))/2
Computes the hyperbolic sine of x.

TANH(x) = (−EXP(x)/EXP(x)+EXP($-x$))*2+1
Computes the hyperbolic tangent of x.

RESERVED WORDS

Applesoft and Integer BASIC interpret every occurrence of certain key words as part of a command, statement, or function. The only exception is when a command, statement, or function is part of text strings enclosed in quotation marks. As a result, it is important to keep reserved words out of your variable names. Watch especially for the short reserved words. If you type a reserved word with embedded blank spaces, Applesoft and Integer BASIC will compress the blanks out and recognize the reserved word. Table A-12 lists Applesoft reserved words and Table A-13 lists Integer BASIC reserved words.

Messages B

This appendix lists the messages that the Apple II may display. Messages are listed alphabetically within each of these categories:

- Applesoft, which prefixes all error messages with a question mark.
- Integer BASIC, which prefixes all error messages with three asterisks.
- The ProDOS operating system, which does not prefix error messages with anything.
- The DOS 3.3 operating system, which does not prefix error messages with anything.

All ProDOS and DOS 3.3 messages and most Applesoft messages have associated error codes. Table B-1 lists the codes in numerical order. When an error causes an ONERR GOTO statement branch to occur, the error code is placed in memory location 222. Use PEEK(222) to retrieve it. Also, the line number where the error occurred will be in memory locations 218 and 219. Use the expression PEEK(219)*256+PEEK(218) to retrieve it.

APPLESOFT ERROR MESSAGES

#110 #120 #130 etc.

When you run a program and a stream of line numbers appears on the display screen, the TRACE command is in effect. Use NOTRACE to turn it off.

Table B-1. Error Codes

Code	Description	Source
0	NEXT without FOR	Applesoft
1	Language not available	DOS 3.3
2	Range error	ProDOS or DOS 3.3
3	No device connected	ProDOS
4	Write protected	ProDOS or DOS 3.3
5	End of data	ProDOS or DOS 3.3
6	Path or file not found	ProDOS or DOS 3.3
7	Path or volume not found	ProDOS or DOS 3.3
8	I/O error	ProDOS or DOS 3.3
9	Disk full	ProDOS or DOS 3.3
10	File locked	ProDOS or DOS 3.3
11	Invalid option or syntax error	ProDOS or DOS 3.3
12	No buffers available	ProDOS or DOS 3.3
13	File type mismatch	ProDOS or DOS 3.3
14	Program too large	ProDOS or DOS 3.3
15	Not direct command	ProDOS or DOS 3.3
16	Syntax error	ProDOS or DOS 3.3
17	Directory full	ProDOS
18	File not open	ProDOS
19	Duplicate file name	ProDOS
20	File busy	ProDOS
21	File(s) still open	ProDOS
22	RETURN without GOSUB	Applesoft
42	Out of data	Applesoft
53	Illegal quantity	Applesoft
69	Overflow	Applesoft
77	Out of memory	Applesoft
90	Undefined statement	Applesoft
107	Bad subscript error	Applesoft
120	Redimensioned array	Applesoft
133	Division by zero	Applesoft
163	Type mismatch	Applesoft
176	String too long	Applesoft
191	Formula too complex	Applesoft
224	Undefined function	Applesoft
254	Bad reponse to an INPUT	Applesoft
255	CONTROL-C has been struck	Applesoft

?BAD SUBSCRIPT ERROR

An array was referenced with the wrong number of subscripts or with one or more subscripts exceeding their dimensions. Error code 107.

BREAK IN 115

Announces the line number at which the program stopped when it executed a STOP statement or when you pressed CONTROL-C to end the program prematurely.

?CAN'T CONTINUE ERROR

An attempt to continue (with the CONT command) was made when no program existed, after a fatal error occurred, or after a change was made to the program.

?DIVISION BY ZERO ERROR

An attempt was made to divide by an expression that evaluates to zero. Error code 133.

?FORMULA TOO COMPLEX ERROR

More than two statements of the form IF *string* THEN were executed. Error code 191.

?ILLEGAL DIRECT ERROR

An INPUT, DEF FN, or a GET command was entered in immediate mode.

?ILLEGAL QUANTITY ERROR

A numeric value is outside the acceptable range for a string function, numeric function, graphics statement, and so forth. Error code 53.

?NEXT WITHOUT FOR ERROR

A NEXT with no matching FOR was executed. A NEXT with no variable name generates this error only if there is no active FOR. Error code 0.

?OUT OF DATA ERROR

More DATA elements were read than are available. Error code 42.

?OUT OF MEMORY ERROR

Can be caused by any of the following: program too large, too many variables, more than ten levels of FOR loop nesting, more than 24 levels of subroutine nesting, more than 36 levels of parentheses nesting, LOMEM: set too high, or HIMEM: set too low. Error code 77.

?OVERFLOW ERROR

Too large or too small a number was input or calculated. The allowable range is approximately −1.7E+38 to 1.7E+38. Error code 69.

?REDIM'D ARRAY ERROR

A DIM statement for a previously dimensioned array was executed. This error most commonly occurs when an array was dimensioned by default. Error code 120.

RETURN WITHOUT GOSUB ERROR

More RETURN statements than GOSUB statements were executed. Error code 22.

?STRING TOO LONG ERROR

An attempt was made to concatenate strings totaling more than 255 characters. Error code 176.

?SYNTAX ERROR

An error in spelling, punctuation, or sequence, or any error not covered by another message has occurred. Error code 16.

?TYPE MISMATCH ERROR

A numeric expression or variable was used where a string should have been used, or vice versa. This error also occurs when the two sides of an assignment statement do not match in type. Error code 163.

?UNDEF'D FUNCTION ERROR

A user-defined function that was never defined was referenced. Error code 224.

?UNDEF'D STATEMENT ERROR

A branch to a nonexistent line number was attempted. Error code 90.

INTEGER BASIC ERROR MESSAGES

***** > 255 ERR**

A value that should be between 0 and 255 is outside that range.

**** > 32767 ERR*

A number greater than 32767 or less than −32767 was entered or calculated.

#110 #120 #130 etc.

When you run a program and a stream of line numbers appears on the display screen, the TRACE command is in effect. Use NOTRACE to turn it off.

#110 A=200 #120 B=300 etc.

A stream of line numbers and variable assignments on the display screen results from DSP statements in the program.

**** 16 FORS ERR*

More than 16 FOR loops are active.

**** 16 GOSUBS ERR*

Seventeen GOSUB statements were executed, accompanied by only 16 RETURN statements.

**** BAD BRANCH ERR*

A branch to a nonexistent line number was attempted.

**** BAD NEXT ERR*

A NEXT with no matching FOR was executed.

**** BAD RETURN ERR*

More RETURN statements than GOSUB statements were executed.

**** DIM ERR*

The same array was dimensioned more than once.

**** MEM FULL ERR*

More memory is needed than is available.

**** NO END ERR*

The last instruction executed in a program was not END.

**** RANGE ERR*

An array was referenced with a subscript less than zero or greater than the array's size, or an argument in an HLIN,

VLIN, PLOT, TAB, or VTAB instruction was outside the prescribed range.

RETYPE LINE

An error was generated by an INPUT response. A diagnostic message is displayed first, and then this directive.

STOPPED AT 110

Announces the line number at which an error just occurred, or where the program stopped when you pressed CONTROL-C to end it prematurely.

*** *STRING ERR*

An illegal string operation was executed.

*** *STR OVFL ERR*

A string was assigned more characters than it was dimensioned for.

*** *SYNTAX ERR*

An error in spelling, punctuation, or sequence, or any error not covered by another error message has occurred.

*** *TOO LONG ERR*

More than 12 parentheses were nested or more than 128 characters were entered in one line.

PRODOS ERROR MESSAGES

DIRECTORY FULL

The volume directory on any disk can hold at most 51 files (and directories). Error code 17.

DISK FULL

An attempt was made to store more information on a disk than it can hold. Error code 9.

DUPLICATE FILE NAME

You tried to create or rename a file using a file name that already exists in the directory. Error code 19.

END OF DATA

An attempt was made to read from a portion of a text file that does not exist. Error code 5.

FILE BUSY

A ProDOS command referenced a file that is still open. Error code 20.

FILE LOCKED

An attempt was made to use APPEND, BSAVE, DELETE, RENAME, SAVE, STORE, or WRITE on a locked file. Error code 10.

FILE NOT OPEN

The file named in a POSITION, READ, or WRITE command was not open. Error code 18.

FILE(S) STILL OPEN

Program execution was suspended with one or more files left open. Error code 21.

FILE TYPE MISMATCH

A ProDOS command has referenced a file that is not of the required type. The CHAIN, LOAD, RUN, and SAVE commands may be used only with Applesoft program files (type BAS). The EXEC command requires a text file (type TXT). The CAT, CATALOG, and PREFIX commands work only with directories (type DIR). The RESTORE and STORE commands require type VAR files. The OPEN and APPEND commands use text files (type TXT) unless the T*type* option is used, in which case the file type must match the option. BRUN requires a binary file (type BIN). The BLOAD and BSAVE commands use binary files unless the T*type* option is used, in which case the file type must match the option. The — command works with type BAS, BIN, TXT, and SYS files. The file named STARTUP in the volume directory must be type BAS, BIN, or TXT. Error code 13.

INVALID OPTION

An option in the last ProDOS command executed is incorrect. Error code 11.

I/O ERROR

An unsuccessful attempt to store data to or retrieve it from a disk was made. Some common causes are that the disk drive door is open, that the disk has not been initialized, that no disk is in the drive, or that the disk is defective. Error code 8.

NO BUFFERS AVAILABLE

Another file buffer was required when all the available file buffers were already in use. Error code 12.

NO DEVICE CONNECTED

No external drive is connected or no disk is in the drive. Error code 3.

NOT DIRECT COMMAND

The following ProDOS commands may be used only in programmed mode: APPEND, OPEN, POSITION, READ, and WRITE. Error code 15.

PATH NOT FOUND

The current prefix and partial pathname together specify a file that does not exist. Error code 6 or 7.

PROGRAM TOO LARGE

A ProDOS command attempted to put a file from the disk in the Apple II memory and found insufficient memory to hold the file. Error code 14.

RANGE ERROR

A parameter used with a ProDOS command is outside of the range specified for that parameter; for example, the D (drive) parameter must be either 1 or 2. This error also occurs when an attempt is made to read past the highest record in a random-access file. Error code 2.

SYNTAX ERROR

A ProDOS command has an error in spelling, punctuation, or sequence. Error code 16.

WRITE PROTECTED

An attempt was made to use SAVE, BSAVE, WRITE, DELETE, APPEND, STORE, or RENAME on a write-protected disk. Error code 4.

DOS 3.3 ERROR MESSAGES

DISK FULL

An attempt was made to store more information on a disk than it can hold. On a full disk this message may occur in place of a more appropriate message (for example, **FILE NOT FOUND**). Error code 9.

END OF DATA

An attempt was made to read from a portion of a text file that has never been written to. Error code 5.

FILE LOCKED

An attempt was made to use SAVE, BSAVE, WRITE, DELETE, or RENAME on a locked file. Error code 10.

FILE NOT FOUND

A file was referenced that does not exist on the disk. This error only occurs if the DOS 3.3 command that referenced the file does not create the file when it is not found. Error code 6.

FILE TYPE MISMATCH

A DOS 3.3 command has referenced a file that is not of the required type. The LOAD, RUN, and SAVE commands may be used only with program files. The CHAIN command may be used only with an Integer BASIC program file. The OPEN, READ, WRITE, APPEND, POSITION, and EXEC commands may be used only with text files. The BLOAD, BSAVE, and BRUN commands may be used only with binary files. Error code 13.

I/O ERROR

An unsuccessful attempt was made to store data to or retrieve it from a disk. Some common causes are that the disk drive door is open, that the disk has not been initialized, that no disk is in the drive, or that the disk is defective. Error code 8.

LANGUAGE NOT AVAILABLE

An attempt to change languages with FP or INT was made when the desired language was not in ROM or on the disk, or an attempt to load or RUN a program was made when the language of the program was similarly unavailable. Error code 1.

NO BUFFERS AVAILABLE

Another file buffer was required when all the available file buffers were already in use. Error code 12.

NOT DIRECT COMMAND

The following DOS 3.3 commands may be used only from within PRINT statements in programmed mode: APPEND, OPEN, POSITION, READ, and WRITE. Error code 15.

PROGRAM TOO LARGE

A DOS 3.3 command has attempted to put a file from the disk into the Apple II's memory and found insufficient memory to hold the file. Error code 14.

RANGE ERROR

A parameter used with a DOS 3.3 command is outside of the range specified for that parameter; for example, the D (drive) parameter must be either 1 or 2. Error code 2 or 3.

SYNTAX ERROR

A DOS 3.3 command has an error in spelling, punctuation, or sequence. Error code 11.

VOLUME MISMATCH

The V (volume) parameter in a DOS 3.3 command does not match the volume number of the disk accessed. Error code 7.

WRITE PROTECTED

An attempt was made to use SAVE, BSAVE, or WRITE on a write-protected disk. Error code 4.

Program Optimization C

The optimal program is the one that, for a given task, runs the fastest and uses the least memory. Of course, this dual goal must be moderated so that the resulting program is still reliable, easy to write, easy to use, easy to read, and easy to change. You will benefit more in the long run by spending your time directly on these aspects of your programs instead of tweaking programs for maximum speed and minimum memory requirements. Still, if you know how to optimize program speed and memory use, you can initially write programs that are efficient and that do not need any fine-tuning after they are running. In this spirit, we present a few ways to write programs that are faster and that use less memory.

Some of the techniques for making a program run faster will make it take more space, while some ways of decreasing space requirements will increase execution time. You will have to decide which is more important in your program.

FASTER PROGRAMS

The most dramatic increase in program speed comes from translating an Applesoft program into machine language. Chapter 13 demonstrated the difference with a machine language subroutine that produces sound (Figure 13-1). Translating a BASIC program to machine language yourself is a chore, but you can buy a *compiler* program that can translate your BASIC program into machine language in a matter of minutes. However, the compiled version of a BASIC program usually requires more memory than the interpreted version.

If you decide to program with Applesoft, there are several other ways to speed up your program. First, use real variables instead of integer variables. Applesoft takes longer to convert an integer value to a real value than it does to fetch the real value in the first place. When such a conversion takes place inside a FOR-NEXT loop, a frequently used subroutine, or a user-defined function, the difference in speed becomes significant.

Avoid using constants (for example, 0, 100, "Y", "ENTER"). Instead, assign the value of the constant to a variable early in your program. Then use the variable where you would have used the constant. This is especially important when you are repeatedly using constant integer values in real expressions. It takes longer to convert a constant to a real value than it does to look up the value of a variable. This technique has the added benefit of making your program easier to change. If you should ever need to change the constant, it will be easier to change the one assignment statement than to hunt down and change every occurrence of the constant.

Use those variables that are referenced often as early in the program execution as possible. Memory space for variables is allocated on a first-come, first-served basis. BASIC will find a variable at the front of the list faster than one at the end of it.

When BASIC encounters an instruction to branch to another line number, it starts looking for that line number at the beginning of the program and searches sequentially through the program until it finds it. Clearly, the lower a line number is in relation to the rest of the lines in the program, the faster BASIC can branch to it. Therefore, assign the lowest line numbers in your program to the most often used subroutines.

Do not include loop index variables with NEXT statements in an Applesoft program. That way, Applesoft does not have to verify whether you specified the correct loop index.

COMPACT PROGRAMS

To shorten the length of a program, use subroutines to avoid duplicate programming for identical sections of the program. This will also go a long way toward improving the readability and reliability of your program, as well as making it easier to change.

Using the zero elements of arrays—for example, X(0), B(0)—will also shorten a program. So will assigning constant values to variable names, and using the variable names in place of the constant values. There are fewer characters in a short variable name than there are in a constant value that has many digits.

Put more than one statement on a program line. Each program line uses five bytes of memory. Note, however, that compound program lines are hard to edit and harder yet to read and understand. Figuring out how to make the program work the first time is bad enough. It is even worse to have to do it time and time again.

Use REM statements judiciously; abbreviate comments if possible. But be careful: the fewer remarks your program has, the harder it will be to undrstand when you come back to it later on. You can buy programs that actually remove all the REM statements from an Applesoft program. If you do that, however, you almost have to keep two versions of your Applesoft program: one with REM statements and one without.

Be thrifty with your use of variables. Each variable requires a certain amount of memory, even if you only use it once. So establish a system of assigning variable names that includes some "scratch" variables that can be used for FOR-NEXT loops, intermediate calculations, and the like. Even "scratch" variables can be overused. Establish standard identities for individual variables (for example, CN$ is the customer name) and groups of variables (for example, all "scratch" variables start with X).

Use INPUT statements and data files instead of assignment statements and DATA statements.

In an Applesoft program, use integer arrays instead of real arrays. Each integer array element takes two bytes of memory, while real array elements require five bytes each. Use the FRE command or FRE function periodically in your program to clean up the string storage area of memory.

Comparing Apple II Models **D**

The Apple IIc, Apple IIe (original and enhanced models), Apple II Plus, and standard Apple II are different in many ways: external and internal physical features, input and output capabilities, hardware, and software. This appendix compares these aspects of the various Apple II models.

EXTERNAL PHYSICAL FEATURES

The Apple IIc and Apple IIe keyboards have 63 keys, while the Apple II Plus and standard Apple II have 52 keys. Seven of the additional keys are control keys: OPEN APPLE, SOLID APPLE, ↑, ↓, SHIFT LOCK, TAB, and DELETE. The Apple IIc and Apple IIe have no REPEAT key as do the standard Apple II and Apple II Plus. Some characters are typed by different keys on the IIc and IIe than on earlier models, namely @, ^, &, (,), *, :, +, =, ", ', and]. Several new characters can be typed on a IIc or IIe keyboard: \, |, [, {, },`, and ~. The RESET key on the IIc and IIe is recessed, and on the IIc, IIe, and II Plus, RESET only works if pressed along with the CONTROL key.

The Apple IIc keyboard has a different "feel" than the keyboards of other models and is better protected against spilled liquids. It can also be switched between conventional typewriter layout (the *QWERTY* keyboard) and a simplified layout (the *Dvorak* keyboard).

The Apple IIc has a button above the keyboard for selecting a display width of 40 or 80 characters. However, the program being run has control over the display width. None of the other models has the width switch.

The Apple IIc has a headphone jack and volume control on the left side and a built-in disk drive on the right side. None of the other models has any of these features built in.

The Apple II, Apple II Plus, and Apple IIe all have a removable cover, which provides access to the inside of the console. This makes it possible for an average user to install accessory cards. The Apple IIc is designed to be opened only for servicing.

The Apple IIe, Apple II Plus, and standard Apple II have sockets on the back panel for attaching a video monitor and cassette recorder. The back panel of the IIe also has a socket for attaching game controls. The Apple IIe has a metal back panel with 12 cutouts that accommodate accessory sockets of different sizes for a wide variety of devices. Seven sockets are built into the back panel of the Apple IIc for attaching a video display, a television, an external disk drive, a mouse or game controls, a printer, and a modem or some other serial device. The Apple II and Apple II Plus have five notches in the back panel for mounting sockets or passing cables through.

INTERNAL PHYSICAL FEATURES

Though the Apple II models work much the same, there are a number of internal physical differences between them. The Apple II and Apple II Plus have eight slots for auxiliary circuit cards so you can plug in a variety of input and output devices. The Apple IIe has seven regular slots and one slot specially designed for an accessory card that enables an 80-column screen display. The Apple IIc has no slots and accommodates no accessory cards; the functions of the most popular accessory cards are built into the Apple IIc.

The standard Apple II, Apple II Plus, and Apple IIe all have an internal socket for attaching three switch inputs, four analog inputs, and four annunciator outputs. For example, two joysticks or two pairs of paddles can be plugged into the socket. The Apple IIe and Apple IIc have a socket on the back panel for making the same attachments, except that the external socket has no annunciator outputs (and only two analog input sockets on the IIc).

The entire power supply is housed inside the Apple II, Apple II

Plus, and Apple IIe. The Apple IIc has an external power transformer.

INPUT AND OUTPUT

All models can display uppercase letters, punctuation, and numbers in normal, flashing, and inverse styles. The Apple IIe and Apple IIc display normal-style lowercase letters. They also have an alternate set of characters that has no flashing style but does include lowercase letters in inverse style.

The Apple IIc and Enhanced Apple IIe alternate character set includes 33 special graphic symbols called *Mousetext* in place of the inverse uppercase letters and symbols @, [,], ., \, ^, and _. The Mousetext symbols have screen codes 64 to 95.

The keyboard on the Apple IIc and Apple IIe can generate all 128 ASCII codes. Unless they are modified, the Apple II Plus and standard Apple II cannot generate lowercase characters and some punctuation symbols. On the Apple IIc and enhanced Apple IIe, commands can be typed in any combination of uppercase and lowercase letters. On other models, all commands must be typed in uppercase letters.

In addition to text, all models can display low-resolution and high-resolution graphics. The Apple IIe and IIc can also display double high-resolution graphics.

All Apple II models except the Apple IIc can use a cassette recorder for program and data storage.

The Apple IIc has a built-in provision for attaching and reading a mouse. The other models require an accessory card in order to use a mouse.

MICROPROCESSOR AND MEMORY

The Apple II and Apple II Plus use a 6502 microprocessor. The original Apple IIe uses a 6502A microprocessor, which is more reliable and has a higher tolerance level than the 6502. The Apple IIc and Enhanced Apple IIe use a 65C02 microprocessor, which is an upgraded version of the 6502 that offers new addressing modes, 27 new instructions, and more. Machine language programs that use these new features will not work on other models. The original Apple IIe can be retrofitted with a 65C02, but the standard Apple II and Apple II Plus cannot.

The Apple IIc has 128K (131,072 bytes) of read/write memory (RAM). The Apple IIe has at least 64K (65,536 bytes) of read/write memory (RAM), and can easily be upgraded to 128K by installing an 80-column adapter that contains another 64K. The Apple II Plus has at least 48K (49,152 bytes) of read/write memory (RAM), and can easily be upgraded to 64K by installing a Language card, which contains another 16K. The memory capacity of standard Apple II models ranges from 4K to 64K.

SOFTWARE

All models come with built-in machine language software in ROM. Each model includes at least some subroutines that handle fundamental tasks such as inputting and outputting characters. These subroutines are called the Machine Language Monitor, or simply the Monitor. On the Apple IIc, Apple IIe, and Apple II Plus, the Machine Language Monitor tries to start a program automatically from the disk when you switch on the computer. The standard Apple II can be retrofitted with this type of Monitor.

In addition to the Monitor, the Apple IIc has built-in programming for dual screen width (40 or 80), the alternate character set, and Mousetext characters. It also has software to control two serial ports, two disk drives, and a mouse. All of this software is part of optional accesory cards on other models.

The Apple IIe has built-in diagnostic software that is activated by pressing CONTROL-SOLID APPLE-RESET.

Pascal versions 1.1 and 1.2 work on all models; version 1.0 works on all models except the Apple IIc and Enhanced Apple IIe.

Applesoft

The Applesoft BASIC interpreter is built into ROM on the Apple IIc, Apple IIe, and Apple II Plus. The standard Apple II has the Integer BASIC interpreter built in.

Several glitches present in the Applesoft interpreter on Apple IIe and Apple II Plus ROMs have been fixed on the Apple IIc and the Enhanced Apple IIe. Now PRINT statement commas, the

HTAB command, the TAB function, and the SPC function all work properly on an 80-column screen.

Operating Systems

ProDOS is the preferred operating system for the Apple IIe, though it can use DOS 3.3 too. The Apple II Plus and standard Apple II can use ProDOS only if they have been retrofitted with 64K RAM and the built-in Applesoft interpreter. (The Integer BASIC interpreter does not work with ProDOS.)

By plugging in an adapter card, you can adapt the Apple IIe, Apple II Plus, and standard Apple II to the CP/M operating system. Another adapter card, plus a special disk drive, allows the use of the MS-DOS operating system. The Apple IIc has no slots, so it cannot be adapted for CP/M or MS-DOS by plugging in a card.

Character Codes And Applesoft Tokens E

The first table in this appendix (Table E-1) shows ASCII codes 0 through 127, the characters they represent, and the keystrokes that generate them. ASCII codes 128 through 255 repeat codes 0 through 127. Table E-2 shows the relationship between ASCII codes and the codes used to represent characters on the screen. The screen codes also carry information about character style: normal, inverse, or flashing.

Table E-3 lists the Applesoft reserved words. Each reserved word takes up only one byte in program memory and is repre-

Table E-1. Characters, Keystrokes, and ASCII Codes

ASCII Code	Display Screen Character		Keystroke	
	Apple IIe	Other Models	Apple IIe	Other Models
0	None	None	CTRL-@	CTRL-@
1	None	None	CTRL-A	CTRL-A
2	None	None	CTRL-B	CTRL-B
3	None	None	CTRL-C	CTRL-C
4	None	None	CTRL-D	CTRL-D
5	None	None	CTRL-E	CTRL-E
6	None	None	CTRL-F	CTRL-F
7	Bell	Bell	CTRL-G	CTRL-G
8	Backspace	Backspace	CTRL-H	CTRL-H
9	None	None	CTRL-I	CTRL-I

Table E-1. Characters, Keystrokes, and ASCII Codes (*continued*)

ASCII Code	Display Screen Character		Keystroke	
	Apple IIe	**Other Models**	**Apple IIe**	**Other Models**
10	Linefeed	Linefeed	CTRL-J	CTRL-J
11	None[†]	None	CTRL-K	CTRL-K
12	None[†]	None	CTRL-L	CTRL-L
13	Return	Return	CTRL-M	CTRL-M
14	None[†]	None	CTRL-N	CTRL-N
15	None[†]	None	CTRL-O	CTRL-O
16	None	None	CTRL-P	CTRL-P
17	None[†]	None	CTRL-Q	CTRL-Q
18	None[†]	None	CTRL-R	CTRL-R
19	None	None	CTRL-S	CTRL-S
20	None	None	CTRL-T	CTRL-T
21	None[†]	Fwd. space	CTRL-U	CTRL-U
22	None[†]	None	CTRL-V	CTRL-V
23	None[†]	None	CTRL-W	CTRL-W
24	None	Cancel line	CTRL-X	CTRL-X
25	None[†]	None	CTRL-Y	CTRL-Y
26	None[†]	None	CTRL-Z	CTRL-Z
27	None	None	ESC	ESC
28	None[†]	None	CTRL-\	None
29	None[†]	None	CTRL-]	CTRL-SHIFT-M
30	None	None	None	CTRL-ˆ
31	None	None	CTRL-SHIFT--	None
32	Space	Space	SPACE BAR	SPACE BAR
33	!	!	SHIFT-1	SHIFT-1
34	"	"	SHIFT-'	SHIFT-2
35	#	#	SHIFT-3	SHIFT-3
36	$	$	SHIFT-4	SHIFT-4
37	%	%	SHIFT-5	SHIFT-5
38	&	&	SHIFT-7	SHIFT-6
39	'	'		SHIFT-7
40	(	(	SHIFT-9	SHIFT-8
41	)	)	SHIFT-0	SHIFT-9
42	*	*	SHIFT-8	SHIFT-:
43	+	+	SHIFT-=	SHIFT-;
44	,	,	,	,
45	-	-	-	-
46	.	.	.	.
47	/	/	/	/
48	0	0	0	0
49	1	1	1	1

†Acts as a display screen control code when the 80-column adapter is active. Table 9-2 lists the control code uses.

Table E-1. Characters, Keystrokes, and ASCII Codes (*continued*)

ASCII Code	Display Screen Character		Keystroke	
	Apple IIe	Other Models	Apple IIe	Other Models
50	2	2	2	2
51	3	3	3	3
52	4	4	4	4
53	5	5	5	5
54	6	6	6	6
55	7	7	7	7
56	8	8	8	8
57	9	9	9	9
58	:	:	SHIFT-;	:
59	;	;	;	;
60	<	<	SHIFT-,	SHIFT-,
61	=	=	=	SHIFT--
62	>	>	SHIFT-.	SHIFT-.
63	?	?	SHIFT-/	SHIFT-/
64	@	@	SHIFT-2	SHIFT-P
65	A	A	SHIFT-A	A
66	B	B	SHIFT-B	B
67	C	C	SHIFT-C	C
68	D	D	SHIFT-D	D
69	E	E	SHIFT-E	E
70	F	F	SHIFT-F	F
71	G	G	SHIFT-G	G
72	H	H	SHIFT-H	H
73	I	I	SHIFT-I	I
74	J	J	SHIFT-J	J
75	K	K	SHIFT-K	K
76	L	L	SHIFT-L	L
77	M	M	SHIFT-M	M
78	N	N	SHIFT-N	N
79	O	O	SHIFT-O	O
80	P	P	SHIFT-P	P
81	Q	Q	SHIFT-Q	Q
82	R	R	SHIFT-R	R
83	S	S	SHIFT-S	S
84	T	T	SHIFT-T	T
85	U	U	SHIFT-U	U
86	V	V	SHIFT-V	V
87	W	W	SHIFT-W	W
88	X	X	SHIFT-X	X
89	Y	Y	SHIFT-Y	Y
90	Z	Z	SHIFT-Z	Z
91	[	[	[	None

Table E-1. Characters, Keystrokes, and ASCII Codes (*continued*)

ASCII Code	Display Screen Character		Keystroke	
	Apple IIe	Other Models	Apple IIe	Other Models
92	\	\	\	None
93	]	]	]	SHIFT-M
94	^	^	SHIFT-6	SHIFT-N
95	_	None	SHIFT--	None
96	`	None	`	None
97	a	A	A	None
98	b	B	B	None
99	c	C	C	None
100	d	D	D	None
101	e	E	E	None
102	f	F	F	None
103	g	G	G	None
104	h	H	H	None
105	i	I	I	None
106	j	J	J	None
107	k	K	K	None
108	l	L	L	None
109	m	M	M	None
110	n	N	N	None
111	o	O	O	None
112	p	P	P	None
113	q	Q	Q	None
114	r	R	R	None
115	s	S	S	None
116	t	T	T	None
117	u	U	U	None
118	v	V	V	None
119	w	W	W	None
120	x	X	X	None
121	y	Y	Y	None
122	z	Z	Z	None
123	{	None	SHIFT-[	None
124	|	None	SHIFT-\	None
125	}	None	SHIFT-]	None
126	~	None	SHIFT-`	None
127	▒	None	DELETE	None

sented by a code, called a token, with a numeric value between 128 and 255. The token replaces the spelled-out reserved word in the Apple II's memory and on the disk. The list is in numerical order by token. Appendix A contains a list of reserved words in alphabetical order.

Table E-2. Screen Codes and ASCII Codes

Screen Codes	ASCII Codes	Alternate Characters	ASCII Codes	Primary Characters
0-31	64-95	Inverse uppercase letters	64-95	Inverse uppercase letters
32-63	32-63	Inverse punctuation and numbers	32-63	Inverse punctuation and numbers
64-95	64-95	Inverse uppercase letters*	64-95	Flashing uppercase letters
96-127	96-127	Inverse lowercase letters	32-63	Flashing punctuation and numbers
128-159	64-95	Normal uppercase letters	64-95	Normal uppercase letters
160-191	32-63	Normal punctuation and numbers	32-63	Normal punctuation and numbers
192-223	64-95	Normal uppercase letters	64-95	Normal uppercase letters
224-255	96-127	Normal lowercase letters	96-127	Normal lowercase letters

*Screen codes 64-95 are also used for Mousetext characters (Apple IIc and Enhanced Apple IIe)

Table E-3. Applesoft Reserved Word Tokens

Token	Reserved Word	Token	Reserved Word	Token	Reserved Word
128	END	164	LOMEM:	200	+
129	FOR	165	ONERR	201	–
130	NEXT	166	RESUME	202	*
131	DATA	167	RECALL	203	/
132	INPUT	168	STORE	204	^
133	DEL	169	SPEED=	205	AND
134	DIM	170	LET	206	OR
135	READ	171	GOTO	207	>
136	GR	172	RUN	208	=
137	TEXT	173	IF	209	<
138	PR#	174	RESTORE	210	SGN
139	IN#	175	&	211	INT
140	CALL	176	GOSUB	212	ABS
141	PLOT	177	RETURN	213	USR
142	HLIN	178	REM	214	FRE
143	VLIN	179	STOP	215	SCRN(
144	HGR2	180	ON	216	PDL
145	HGR	181	WAIT	217	POS
146	HCOLOR=	182	LOAD	218	SQR
147	HPLOT	183	SAVE	219	RND
148	DRAW	184	DEF	220	LOG
149	XDRAW	185	POKE	221	EXP
150	HTAB	186	PRINT	222	COS
151	HOME	187	CONT	223	SIN
152	ROT=	188	LIST	224	TAN
153	SCALE=	189	CLEAR	225	ATN
154	SHLOAD	190	GET	226	PEEK
155	TRACE	191	NEW	227	LEN
156	NOTRACE	192	TAB(	228	STR$
157	NORMAL	193	TO	229	VAL
158	INVERSE	194	FN	230	ASC
159	FLASH	195	SPC(	231	CHR$
160	COLOR=	196	THEN	232	LEFT$
161	POP	197	AT	233	RIGHT$
162	VTAB	198	NOT	234	MID$
163	HIMEM:	199	STEP		

Useful PEEK And POKE Locations F

Each of the memory locations listed in this appendix is expressed as a decimal number less than 32767. Memory locations above 32767 are expressed as negative numbers. There is a positive number that refers to the same location. To get the positive equivalent, add 65536 to the listed negative location (for example, 65536 − 16384 = 49152).

Some of the functions described here may be actuated just by accessing them. This means that any time a PEEK statement accesses the specified memory location, the indicated action takes place. A POKE statement to the specified memory location also triggers the action, but because of the operating characteristics of the microprocessor in the Apple II, a POKE statement actually triggers the action twice. In this case, POKE is the same as two PEEK statements. Usually this makes no difference, but in cases like −16336 (Speaker Click), it does. The value placed in memory by the POKE statement is irrelevant in such address-actuated actions.

TEXT WINDOW AND CURSOR CONTROL LOCATIONS

The memory locations listed in this section enable you to change the dimensions of the text window, to determine the row and column the cursor is in, and to change the cursor's position.

32 Left Margin of the Text Window

Specifies the column of the left text window margin. PEEK returns a value in the range 0 through 39 (for a 40-column display) or 0 through 79 (for an 80-column display). The left edge of the screen is 0. Changing location 32 does not affect the width of the text window, since the left and right margins both move.

If you place a value greater than 39 (on a 40-column display) or 79 (for an 80-column display) into this location, or if the value of this location plus the width of the text window exceeds 40 (or 80), some or all of the output meant for the screen will be put in memory outside the screen area. This could destroy part of your program or other essential data.

33 Text Window Width

Specifies the width of the text window. The value in this location must be in the range 1 through 40, or 1 through 80 if the display width is 80. Changing this location sets the right margin at the column that is the specified number of characters away from the left margin (memory location 32).

A value of zero in this location (that is, a width of zero) can destroy the BASIC interpreter. If you POKE a value greater than 40 (or 80) into this location, or if the value in this location plus the value in location 32 (left margin) exceeds 40 (or 80), some or all of the output meant for the screen will be put in memory outside the screen area. This could destroy part of your program or other essential data.

34 Top Margin of the Text Window

Specifies the top margin of the text window. The value in this location must be in the range 0 through 23; 0 specifies the top row on the screen, 23 the bottom. If you POKE a value greater than 23 into this location, some or all of the output meant for the screen will go into memory outside the screen area, wiping out data that could be important. Do not set the top margin of the text window below the bottom margin.

35 Bottom Margin of the Text Window

Specifies the bottom margin of the text window. The value in this location must be in the range 0 through 23; 0 specifies the top row on the screen, 23 the bottom. If you POKE a value greater than 23 into this location, some or all of the output meant for the screen will go into memory outside the screen area, wiping out data that could be important. Do not set the bottom margin of the text window above the top margin.

36 Horizontal Position of the Cursor

Specifies the current horizontal position of the cursor. PEEK(36) returns a value in the range 0 through 39, or 0 through 79 if the display width is 80. PEEK(36) specifies the cursor's position relative to the left margin of the text window (not necessarily the left edge of the screen). This location can be used to position beyond the right edge of the text window (and subsequently print there with PRINT), but the cursor stays there only long enough to print one character. Do not put a value in this location that, when added to the left screen margin (location 32), exceeds 39, or 79 with an 80-column screen.

PEEK(36) is equivalent to the Applesoft function POS.

37 Vertical Position of the Cursor

Specifies the current vertical position of the cursor. PEEK(37) returns a value in the range 0 through 23, relative to the top of the screen (not the top of the text window). Do not put a value over 23 in this location.

ERROR-HANDLING LOCATIONS

The memory locations in this section report the code of an intercepted error and the line on which it occurred, and enable you to cancel error interception.

216 Error Flag

Indicates whether an ONERR GOTO is in effect. If location 216 has a value of 128 or more, an ONERR GOTO statement has been encountered, and control will branch to the line number specified when an error occurs. Place a value less than 128 in this location to disable a previously executed ONERR GOTO statement.

218 and 219 Error-Causing Line Number

When an error triggers a branch according to an ONERR GOTO statement, these locations specify the line number in which the error occurred. This line number is computed by the expression PEEK(219)*256+PEEK(218).

222 Error Type Code

Specifies which type of error has occurred. The error codes and their descriptions are listed in Appendix B.

KEYBOARD LOCATIONS

The memory locations listed in this section enable you to read a character directly from the keyboard and to reset the keyboard after doing so.

−16384 Character from Keyboard

Reads the keyboard. If the value in this location is greater than 127, a key has been pressed. Determine the ASCII code of the key last pressed by subtracting 128 from PEEK(−16384).

−16368 Keyboard Flag

POKE −16368,0 resets the keyboard strobe so that another character may be read from the keyboard.

SPEAKER OUTPUT LOCATIONS

The memory locations listed in this section enable you to output directly to a cassette recorder or the built-in speaker.

−16352 Cassette Click

Generates a click at the cassette output jack.

−16336 Speaker Click

Generates a click on the internal speaker.

DISPLAY SWITCHES

The memory locations listed in this section control certain switches that determine display screen characteristics. There are no physical switches; instead, there are imaginary switches, called *soft switches*, that you set by accessing certain memory locations with PEEK functions or POKE statements. Every Apple II has four soft switches; each can be set in two different positions. The Apple IIe has an additional soft switch (Figure F-1).

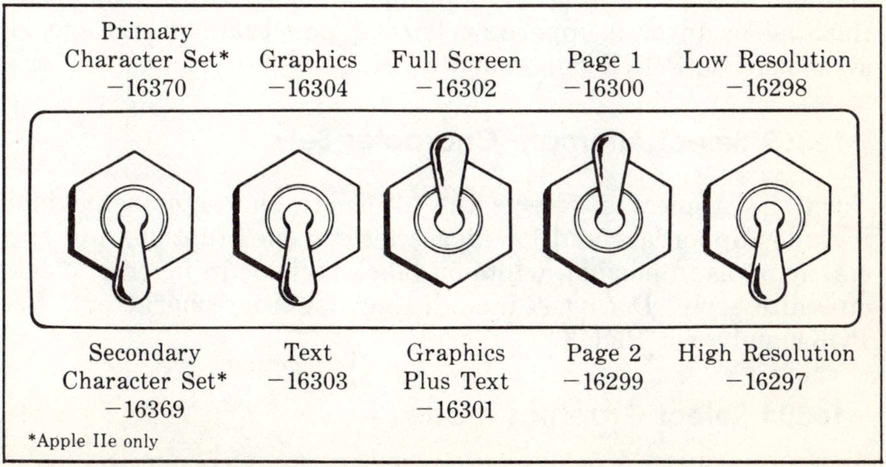

Figure F-1. Display screen soft switch memory locations

Table F-1. Apple IIe Soft Switch Status

Soft Switch Function	Memory *Location*	Status, if PEEK (*Location*) is: <128	>127
Character set	−16354	Primary	Alternate
Screen mode	−16358	Graphics	Text
Text window	−16357	Absent	Present
Screen memory	−16356	Page 1	Page 2
Graphics mode	−16355	Low-resolution	High-resolution

You cannot use the PEEK function to determine a soft switch setting, because the act of accessing the memory location may change the setting. The Apple IIe has additional memory locations that disclose the soft switch settings, as listed in Table F-1. If the PEEK function reports the value in one of these locations to be less than 128, the soft switch is set one way, and if the value is 128 or greater, the soft switch is set the other way.

−16370 Select Primary Character Set

On the Apple IIe, selects the primary character set, which includes uppercase and lowercase letters, punctuation, and special symbols in normal, white-on-black style. Also included are flashing or inverse uppercase letters, punctuation, and special symbols. Use POKE only, not PEEK.

−16369 Select Alternate Character Set

On the Apple IIe, selects the alternate character set, which includes uppercase and lowercase letters, punctuation, and special symbols in normal, white-on-black style or in inverse, black-on-white style. Does not include any flashing characters. Use POKE only, not PEEK.

−16304 Select Graphics Mode

Selects graphics mode. The graphics screen is not cleared to black. The graphics mode may be low- or high-resolution, page 1 or page 2, full-screen graphics or mixed graphics and text. These characteristics are determined by other soft switch memory locations.

−16303 Select Text Mode

Selects text mode. The text may be from either page 1 or page 2, as determined by memory locations −16300 and −16299.

−16302 Select Full-Screen Graphics

Selects full-screen graphics. If the screen is in text mode, this will not be visible until location −16304 is accessed.

−16301 Select Graphics Plus Text

Establishes a four-line text window at the bottom of the screen. If the screen is in text mode, this will not be visible until location −16304 is accessed.

−16300 Select Screen Page 1

Selects graphics or text page 1.

−16299 Select Screen Page 2

Selects graphics or text page 2.

−16298 Select Low-Resolution Graphics

Selects low-resolution graphics. If the screen is in text mode, the effect will not be visible until location −16304 is accessed.

−16297 Select High-Resolution Graphics

Selects high-resolution graphics. If the screen is in text mode, the effect will not be visible until location −16304 is accessed.

VERTICAL BLANKING INTERVAL

The Apple II must continuously refresh the display screen image or the image will fade away. The Apple II refreshes the screen display by reading the contents of the display screen from its memory and broadcasting the data. This refresh cycle occurs automatically, many times each second, so that normally you are not even aware of it. There is even a brief period at the end of each refresh cycle, called the *vertical blanking interval*, during which the Apple II does not broadcast anything.

High-speed programs, usually written in machine language, may be able to change the display screen memory contents while the Apple II is in the process of broadcasting them. The result is an erratic flickering or blinking on the screen. The cure for this is to change the display screen memory only during the vertical blanking interval, when the Apple II is not broadcasting. The vertical blanking interval can be detected on an Apple IIe by checking the value in a memory location.

−16359 Vertical Blanking Signal

As long as PEEK(−16359) is 128 or greater, the Apple II is broadcasting a refresh signal to the display screen. During the brief vertical blanking interval, the value of PEEK(−16359) is less than 128.

GAME CONTROL LOCATIONS

The memory locations in this section can turn game control outputs on or off, sense whether the SOLID APPLE key, OPEN APPLE key, or game control pushbuttons are being pressed or not, and actuate a strobe output. Figure F-2 shows how the game control outputs are manipulated.

The inputs for these locations connect to the game control connector, shown in Figure F-3.

−16296 Annunciator 0 Off

Turns off game control output (annunciator) number 0. The voltage on pin 15 of the game control connector is set to approximately 0 volts (TTL low).

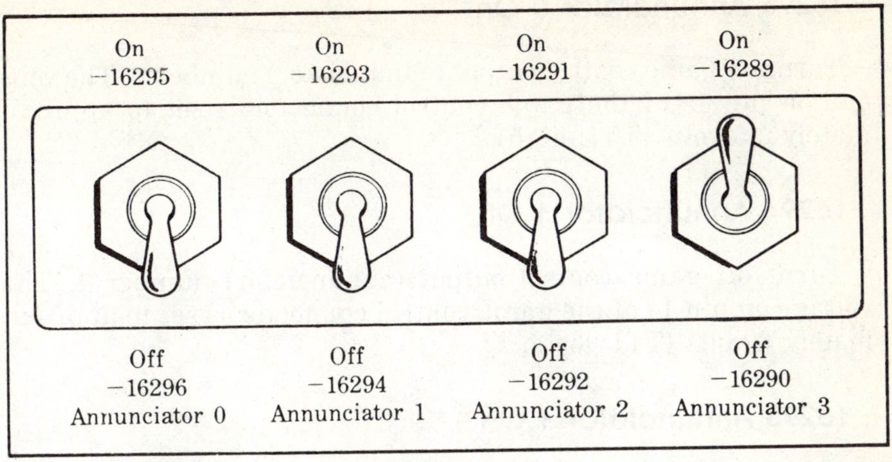

Figure F-2. Game control outputs (soft switches)

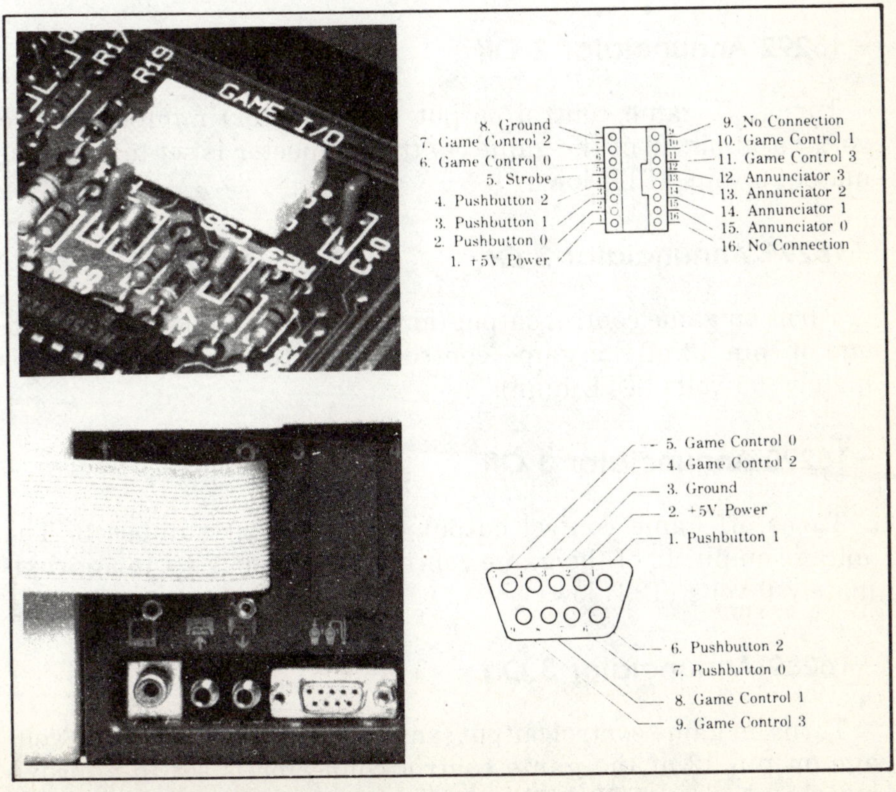

Figure F-3. Game control pin assignments

−16295 Annunciator 0 On

Turns on game control output (annunciator) number 0. The voltage on pin 15 of the game control connector is set to approximately +5 volts (TTL high).

−16294 Annunciator 1 Off

Turns off game control output (annunciator) number 1. The voltage on pin 14 of the game control connector is set to approximately 0 volts (TTL low).

−16293 Annunciator 1 On

Turns on game control output (annunciator) number 1. The voltage on pin 14 of the game control connector is set to approximately +5 volts (TTL high).

−16292 Annunciator 2 Off

Turns off game control output (annunciator) number 2. The voltage on pin 13 of the game control connector is set to approximately 0 volts (TTL low).

−16291 Annunciator 2 On

Turns on game control output (annunciator) number 2. The voltage on pin 13 of the game control connector is set to approximately +5 volts (TTL high).

−16290 Annunciator 3 Off

Turns off game control output (annunciator) number 3. The voltage on pin 12 of the game control connector is set to approximately 0 volts (TTL low).

−16289 Annunciator 3 On

Turns on game control output (annunciator) number 3. The voltage on pin 12 of the game control connector is set to approximately +5 volts (TTL high).

−16287 Read Pushbutton 0

When the pushbutton on game control number 0 or the OPEN APPLE key is being pressed, the value in this location exceeds 127. When it is not being pressed, the value is 127 or less. Pushbutton 0 connects to pin 2 of the internal game control connector.

−16286 Read Pushbutton 1

When the pushbutton on game control number 1 or the SOLID APPLE key is being pressed, the value in this location exceeds 127. When it is not being pressed, the value is 127 or less. Pushbutton 1 connects to pin 3 of the internal game control connector.

−16285 Read Pushbutton 2

When the pushbutton on game control number 2 is being pressed, the value in this location exceeds 127; when it is not being pressed, the value is 127 or less. Pushbutton 2 connects to pin 4 of the internal game control connector.

−16272 Strobe Output

Normally pin 5 of the game control connector is +5 volts. Executing PEEK(−16285) drops it to 0 volts for one-half microsecond. A POKE statement will trigger the strobe twice.

Built-in Subroutines G

The following two tables list a number of useful machine language subroutines available on the Apple II. Table G-1 lists them by general function; it does not provide complete information about each subroutine. Find the entry point listed in Table G-1 in the first column of Table G-2 for additional information, including details on microprocessor registers affected.

Table G-2 lists the subroutines in order by entry point. The third column shows which registers, if any, must contain specific values before the subroutine is executed. The fourth column shows which microprocessor registers are affected by the execution of the subroutine.

Most of these subroutines have an equivalent in a BASIC command, or else can be accessed from BASIC with a single CALL statement. These equivalents appear in Table G-2. Some of the BASIC commands listed are only available in Applesoft; they are marked with an *A*.

Some subroutines, however, have no equivalent in either version of BASIC and cannot be executed by a single CALL because one or more microprocessor registers must be loaded with specific values prior to execution. Different techniques are required to handle this problem in Applesoft and Integer BASIC.

Integer BASIC provides a simple solution. First execute a CALL −182 to save the current values of the registers in RAM. Then, using POKE statements, place the desired values in memory location 69 for the A register, 70 for the X register, and 71 for the Y register. Execute a CALL −193 to load the values into the registers, and call the built-in machine language subroutine.

This technique does not work in Applesoft. Instead, you must write your own machine language subroutine to load the regis-

Table G-1. Built-in Subroutines by Function

	Function	Entry Point
Low-Resolution Graphics	Plot a low-resolution graphics point.	$F800
	Draw a low-resolution horizontal line.	$F819
	Draw a low-resolution vertical line.	$F828
	Clear all 48 low-resolution graphics rows to black (if in text mode, sets to inverse "@").	$F832
	Clear the top 40 low-resolution rows to black (or inverse "@").	$F836
	Increment the current low-resolution graphics color by three.	$F85F
	Set low-resolution graphics color.	$F864
	Read the color of a low-resolution graphics point.	$F871
	Set low-resolution graphics mode, clear screen, and set four-line text window.	$FB40
Input	Wait for keystroke while cursor is flashing, and seed the random number generator at locations $4E and $4F.	$FD1B
	Same as above except that escape codes are also allowed.	$FD35
	Send carriage return to display screen, and then allow input of an entire line of up to 256 characters.	$FD67
Output	Send three blanks to the currently selected output device.	$F948
	Send from 1 to 256 blanks to the currently selected output device.	$F94A
	Send a carriage return and linefeed to the Apple II screen.	$FC62
	Output a character to the currently selected output device.	$FDED
	Output a character to the text window.	$FDF0
Bell Output	Send BELL character (ASCII code 7) to the currently selected output device.	$FBDD
	Beep the onboard speaker for 1/10 second.	$FBE4

Table G-1. Built-in Subroutines by Function (*continued*)

	Function	Entry Point
Bell Output	Print the message ERR and beep the onboard speaker.	$FF2D
	Beep the onboard speaker.	$FF3A
Text Window	Set the Apple II screen to 24 rows by 40 columns.	$FB2F
	Scroll the text window up one line.	$FC70
Cursor Control	Send a backspace character to the screen, updating the cursor position.	$FC10
	Move the cursor up one line. If the cursor is already at the top of the screen, it does not move.	$FC1A
	Move the cursor down one line without changing its horizontal position. Scrolls the text window if the cursor is at the bottom of the screen.	$FC66
Screen Clearing	Clear the text window from the current cursor position to the lower right-hand corner of the screen.	$FC42
	Clear the entire text screen and move the cursor to the upper left-hand corner.	$FC58
	Clear the text from the current cursor position to the end of the line.	$FC9C
Video Mode	Set inverse video mode (black on white).	$FE80
	Set normal video mode (white on black).	$FE84
Print Register Contents	Print Y and X register contents (in the format YYXX) on the currently selected output device.	$F940
	Print A and X register contents (in the format AAXX) on the currently selected output device.	$F941
	Print X register contents on the currently selected output device.	$F944
	Print A register contents on the currently selected output device.	$FDDA

Table G-1. Built-in Subroutines by Function (*continued*)

	Function	Entry Point
Move Register Contents	Restore register contents (valid only if intrinsic routine at $FF4A executed previously).	$FF3F
	Save register contents in reserved page 0 locations.	$FF4A
Misc.	Read status of one paddle.	$FB1E
	Execute a delay loop.	$FCA8
	Return to BASIC, eliminating the program and variables in memory.	$FEB0
	Entry point for the Monitor.	$FF69

ters with the necessary values and then execute an assembly language JSR instruction to the entry point of the built-in machine language subroutine.

Table G-2. Built-in Subroutines by Entry Point

Entry Point	Use	Registers to Load Before Calling	Registers Affected	BASIC Equivalent
$F800	Plot a graphics point on low-resolution page 1.	Place row in A, column in Y.	A	PLOT
$F819	Draw a low-resolution horizontal line.	Row in A, left column in Y, right column at memory location 44.	A,Y	HLIN
$F828	Draw a low-resolution vertical line.	Column in Y, high row in A, low row at memory location 45.	None	VLIN
$F832	Clear all 48 low-resolution graphics rows to black (if in text mode, sets to all "@").	None	A,Y	CALL 1998
$F836	Clear the low-resolution graphics rows, leaving the text window intact.	None	A,Y	GR (see $FB40)
$F85F	Increment the current low-resolution graphics color by 3.	None	A	CALL −1953
$F864	Set low-resolution graphics color.	Color number in A.	A	COLOR
$F871	Read the color of a low-resolution graphics point.	Row in A, column in Y.	A (contains color number)	SCRN
$F940	Print Y and X register contents (in the format YYXX) on the screen or other output device selected.	None	None	CALL −1728
$F941	Print A and X registers (AAXX) as above.	None	None	CALL −1727

[1] Denotes BASIC commands available in Applesoft only.

Table G-2. Built-in Subroutines by Entry Point (*continued*)

Entry Point	Use	Registers to Load Before Calling	Registers Affected	BASIC Equivalent
$F944	Print X register contents.	None	None	CALL −1724
$F948	Send 3 blanks to the currently selected output device (determined by CSW contents).	None	X,A	CALL −1720
$F94A	Send 1 to 256 blanks to the currently selected output device.	Number of blank spaces in A (loading 0 prints 256 blanks).	None	SPC( )[A] CALL −1718
$FB1E	Read status of paddle 0, 1, 2, or 3.	Paddle number in X.	0-FF in Y register. A contents destroyed.	PDL( )
$FB2F	Set the text screen to text mode.	None	A	TEXT
$FB40	Set low-resolution graphics mode, clear screen, and set 4-line text window.	None	A,Y	GR
$FBDD	Send BELL character (ASCII code 7) to the current output device.	None	A,Y	CALL −1059
$FBE4	Beep speaker for 1/10 second.	None	A,Y	CALL −1052
$FC10	Send a backspace character to the screen, updating cursor position.	None	A	CALL −1008
$FC1A	Move the cursor up one line. If already at the top of the screen, cursor does not move.	None	A	CALL −998

[A] Denotes BASIC commands available in Applesoft only.

Table G-2. Built-in Subroutines by Entry Point (*continued*)

Entry Point	Use	Registers to Load Before Calling	Registers Affected	BASIC Equivalent
$FC42	Clear the text window from the present cursor position to the lower right-hand corner of the screen.	None	A,Y	CALL −958
$FC58	Clear the entire text screen and move the cursor to the upper left-hand corner.	None	A,Y	CALL −936
$FC62	Send a carriage return and linefeed to the screen.	None		CALL −926
$FC66	Move the cursor down one line without changing its horizontal position. Scrolls text up one line if cursor is at the bottom of the screen.	None	A,Y	CALL −922
$FC70	Scroll the text window up one line.	None	A,Y	CALL −912
$FC9C	Clear text from the current cursor position to the end of the line. Cursor position remains unchanged.	None	A,Y	CALL −868
$FCA8	Execute a delay loop that is $0.5(5x^2 + 27x + 26)$ microseconds long.	Delay value (x) in A.	A	CALL −856

[A] Denotes BASIC commands available in Applesoft only.

Table G-2. Built-in Subroutines by Entry Point (*continued*)

Entry Point	Use	Registers to Load Before Calling	Registers Affected	BASIC Equivalent
$FD0C	Wait for keystroke; flash cursor while waiting. Seed random number generator at memory locations 78 and 79.	None	Character returned in A. X,Y	CALL −756
$FD35	Same as $FD0C, except that escape codes are also allowed.	None	Character returned in A. X,Y	CALL −715
$FD67	Send carriage return to screen; allow input of an entire line of data, up to 256 characters.	Prompt character at memory location 51.	Y,A. X contains length of entry. Data entered starts at memory location $200.	INPUT
$FDDA	Print the value in the accumulator as two hexadecimal digits.	Data in A.	A	CALL −550
$FDED	Output a character to the currently selected output device.	Character in A.	None	PRINT
$FDF0	Output a character to the text window.	Character in A.	None	PRINT
$FE80	Set inverse video mode (black-on-white text).	None	Y	INVERSE[A] CALL −384
$FE84	Set normal video mode (white-on-black text).	None	Y	NORMAL[A] CALL −380

[A] Denotes BASIC commands available in Applesoft only.

Table G-2. Built-in Subroutines by Entry Point (*continued*)

Entry Point	Use	Registers to Load Before Calling	Registers Affected	BASIC Equivalent
$FEB0	Return to BASIC, eliminating the program and variables in memory.	None	A,X,Y	CALL −336
$FF2D	Print the message ERR and beep onboard speaker.	None	A	CALL −211
$FF3A	Beep the onboard speaker.	None	A	CALL −198
$FF3F	Restore register contents.	None	Register contents restored from these locations: A register: 69 ($45) S register: 72 ($48) X register: 70 ($46) Stack Pointer: 73 ($49) Y register: 71 ($47).	CALL −193
$FF4A	Save register contents in reserved page 0 locations: A register: 69 ($45) S register: 72 ($48) X register: 70 ($46) Stack Pointer: 73 ($49) Y register: 71 ($47).	None	None	CALL −182
$FF69	Entry point for the Monitor.	None	None	CALL −151

[A] Denotes BASIC commands available in Applesoft only.

Conversion Tables H

This appendix contains tables for the following conversions:

- Binary-Hexadecimal Numbers (Table H-1)
- Hexadecimal-Decimal Integers (Table H-2).

Convert binary numbers larger than 1111 to hexadecimal numbers four binary digits at a time, working from right to left. If there are fewer than four binary digits in the leftmost group, add leading zeros. Here is an example:

$$100101_2 = 00100101_2$$

$$2_{16}\ 5_{16}$$

$$25_{16}$$

Convert hexadecimal numbers larger than 0F to binary one digit at a time. Here is an example:

$$67_{16}$$

$$6_{16} \quad 7_{16}$$

$$0110_2 \quad 0111_2$$

$$01100111_2$$

Table H-1. Binary-Hexadecimal Conversion Table

Hexadecimal	Binary
00	0000
01	0001
02	0010
03	0011
04	0100
05	0101
06	0110
07	0111
08	1000
09	1001
0A	1010
0B	1011
0C	1100
0D	1101
0E	1110
0F	1111

Table H-2. Hexadecimal-Decimal Conversion Table

The table below provides for direct conversions between hexadecimal integers in the range 0–FFF and decimal integers in the range 0–4095. For conversion of larger integers, the table values may be added to the following figures:

Hexadecimal	Decimal	Hexadecimal	Decimal
01 000	4 096	20 000	131 072
02 000	8 192	30 000	196 608
03 000	12 288	40 000	262 144
04 000	16 384	50 000	327 680
05 000	20 480	60 000	393 216
06 000	24 576	70 000	458 752
07 000	28 672	80 000	524 288
08 000	32 768	90 000	589 824
09 000	36 864	A0 000	655 360
0A 000	40 960	B0 000	720 896
0B 000	45 056	C0 000	786 432
0C 000	49 152	D0 000	851 968
0D 000	53 248	E0 000	917 504
0E 000	57 344	F0 000	983 040
0F 000	61 440	100 000	1 048 576
10 000	65 536	200 000	2 097 152
11 000	69 632	300 000	3 145 728
12 000	73 728	400 000	4 194 304
13 000	77 824	500 000	5 242 880
14 000	81 920	600 000	6 291 456
15 000	86 016	700 000	7 340 032
16 000	90 112	800 000	8 388 608
17 000	94 208	900 000	9 437 184
18 000	98 304	A00 000	10 485 760
19 000	102 400	B00 000	11 534 336
1A 000	106 496	C00 000	12 582 912
1B 000	110 592	D00 000	13 631 488
1C 000	114 688	E00 000	14 680 064
1D 000	118 784	F00 000	15 728 640
1E 000	122 880	1 000 000	16 777 216
1F 000	126 976	2 000 000	33 554 432

Hexadecimal fractions may be converted to decimal fractions as follows:

1. Express the hexadecimal fraction as an integer times 16^{-n}, where n is the number of significant hexadecimal places to the right of the hexadecimal point.

$$0.\,CA9BF3_{16} = CA9\,BF3_{16} \times 16^{-6}$$

2. Find the decimal equivalent of the hexadecimal integer

$$CA9\,BF3_{16} = 13\,278\,195_{10}$$

3. Multiply the decimal equivalent by 16^{-n}

$$\begin{array}{r} 13\,278\,195 \\ \times\, 596\,046\,448 \times 10^{-16} \\ \hline 0.791\,442\,096_{10} \end{array}$$

Decimal fractions may be converted to hexadecimal fractions by successively multiplying the decimal fraction by 16_{10}. After each multiplication, the integer portion is removed to form a hexadecimal fraction by building to the right of the hexadecimal point. However, since decimal arithmetic is used in this conversion, the integer portion of each product must be converted to hexadecimal numbers.

Example: Convert 0.895_{10} to its hexadecimal equivalent

$$\begin{array}{r} 0.895 \\ \underline{16} \\ (14).320 \\ \underline{16} \\ (5).120 \\ \underline{16} \\ (1).920 \\ \underline{16} \\ (14).720 \end{array}$$

$$0.E51E_{16}$$

Table H-2. Hexadecimal-Decimal Conversion Table (*continued*)

	0	1	2	3	4	5	6	7	8	9	A	B	C	D	E	F
00	0000	0001	0002	0003	0004	0005	0006	0007	0008	0009	0010	0011	0012	0013	0014	0015
01	0016	0017	0018	0019	0020	0021	0022	0023	0024	0025	0026	0027	0028	0029	0030	0031
02	0032	0033	0034	0035	0036	0037	0038	0039	0040	0041	0042	0043	0044	0045	0046	0047
03	0048	0049	0050	0051	0052	0053	0054	0055	0056	0057	0058	0059	0060	0061	0062	0063
04	0064	0065	0066	0067	0068	0069	0070	0071	0072	0073	0074	0075	0076	0077	0078	0079
05	0080	0081	0082	0083	0084	0085	0086	0087	0088	0089	0090	0091	0092	0093	0094	0095
06	0096	0097	0098	0099	0100	0101	0102	0103	0104	0105	0106	0107	0108	0109	0110	0111
07	0112	0113	0114	0115	0116	0117	0118	0119	0120	0121	0122	0123	0124	0125	0126	0127
08	0128	0129	0130	0131	0132	0133	0134	0135	0136	0137	0138	0139	0140	0141	0142	0143
09	0144	0145	0146	0147	0148	0149	0150	0151	0152	0153	0154	0155	0156	0157	0158	0159
0A	0160	0161	0162	0163	0164	0165	0166	0167	0168	0169	0170	0171	0172	0173	0174	0175
0B	0176	0177	0178	0179	0180	0181	0182	0183	0184	0185	0186	0187	0188	0189	0190	0191
0C	0192	0193	0194	0195	0196	0197	0198	0199	0200	0201	0202	0203	0204	0205	0206	0207
0D	0208	0209	0210	0211	0212	0213	0214	0215	0216	0217	0218	0219	0220	0221	0222	0223
0E	0224	0225	0226	0227	0228	0229	0230	0231	0232	0233	0234	0235	0236	0237	0238	0239
0F	0240	0241	0242	0243	0244	0245	0246	0247	0248	0249	0250	0251	0252	0253	0254	0255
10	0256	0257	0258	0259	0260	0261	0262	0263	0264	0265	0266	0267	0268	0269	0270	0271
11	0272	0273	0274	0275	0276	0277	0278	0279	0280	0281	0282	0283	0284	0285	0286	0287
12	0288	0289	0290	0291	0292	0293	0294	0295	0296	0297	0298	0299	0300	0301	0302	0303
13	0304	0305	0306	0307	0308	0309	0310	0311	0312	0313	0314	0315	0316	0317	0318	0319
14	0320	0321	0322	0323	0324	0325	0326	0327	0328	0329	0330	0331	0332	0333	0334	0335
15	0336	0337	0338	0339	0340	0341	0342	0343	0344	0345	0346	0347	0348	0349	0350	0351
16	0352	0353	0354	0355	0356	0357	0358	0359	0360	0361	0362	0363	0364	0365	0366	0367
17	0368	0369	0370	0371	0372	0373	0374	0375	0376	0377	0378	0379	0380	0381	0382	0383
18	0384	0385	0386	0387	0388	0389	0390	0391	0392	0393	0394	0395	0396	0397	0398	0399
19	0400	0401	0402	0403	0404	0405	0406	0407	0408	0409	0410	0411	0412	0413	0414	0415
1A	0416	0417	0418	0419	0420	0421	0422	0423	0424	0425	0426	0427	0428	0429	0430	0431
1B	0432	0433	0434	0435	0436	0437	0438	0439	0440	0441	0442	0443	0444	0445	0446	0447
1C	0448	0449	0450	0451	0452	0453	0454	0455	0456	0457	0458	0459	0460	0461	0462	0463
1D	0464	0465	0466	0467	0468	0469	0470	0471	0472	0473	0474	0475	0476	0477	0478	0479
1E	0480	0481	0482	0483	0484	0485	0486	0487	0488	0489	0490	0491	0492	0493	0494	0495
1F	0496	0497	0498	0499	0500	0501	0502	0503	0504	0505	0506	0507	0508	0509	0510	0511
20	0512	0513	0514	0515	0516	0517	0518	0519	0520	0521	0522	0523	0524	0525	0526	0527
21	0528	0529	0530	0531	0532	0533	0534	0535	0536	0537	0538	0539	0540	0541	0542	0543
22	0544	0545	0546	0547	0548	0549	0550	0551	0552	0553	0554	0555	0556	0557	0558	0559
23	0560	0561	0562	0563	0564	0565	0566	0567	0568	0569	0570	0571	0572	0573	0574	0575
24	0576	0577	0578	0579	0580	0581	0582	0583	0584	0585	0586	0587	0588	0589	0590	0591
25	0592	0593	0594	0595	0596	0597	0598	0599	0600	0601	0602	0603	0604	0605	0606	0607
26	0608	0609	0610	0611	0612	0613	0614	0615	0616	0617	0618	0619	0620	0621	0622	0623
27	0624	0625	0626	0627	0628	0629	0630	0631	0632	0633	0634	0635	0636	0637	0638	0639
28	0640	0641	0642	0643	0644	0645	0646	0647	0648	0649	0650	0651	0652	0653	0654	0655
29	0656	0657	0658	0659	0660	0661	0662	0663	0664	0665	0666	0667	0668	0669	0670	0671
2A	0672	0673	0674	0675	0676	0677	0678	0679	0680	0681	0682	0683	0684	0685	0686	0687
2B	0688	0689	0690	0691	0692	0693	0694	0695	0696	0697	0698	0699	0700	0701	0702	0703
2C	0704	0705	0706	0707	0708	0709	0710	0711	0712	0713	0714	0715	0716	0717	0718	0719
2D	0720	0721	0722	0723	0724	0725	0726	0727	0728	0729	0730	0731	0732	0733	0734	0735
2E	0736	0737	0738	0739	0740	0741	0742	0743	0744	0745	0746	0747	0748	0749	0750	0751
2F	0752	0753	0754	0755	0756	0757	0758	0759	0760	0761	0762	0763	0764	0765	0766	0767

Table H-2. Hexadecimal-Decimal Conversion Table (*continued*)

	0	1	2	3	4	5	6	7	8	9	A	B	C	D	E	F
30	0768	0769	0770	0771	0772	0773	0774	0775	0776	0777	0778	0779	0780	0781	0782	0783
31	0784	0785	0786	0787	0788	0789	0790	0791	0792	0793	0794	0795	0796	0797	0798	0799
32	0800	0801	0802	0803	0804	0805	0806	0807	0808	0809	0810	0811	0812	0813	0814	0815
33	0816	0817	0818	0819	0820	0821	0822	0823	0824	0825	0826	0827	0828	0829	0830	0831
34	0832	0833	0834	0835	0836	0837	0838	0839	0840	0841	0842	0843	0844	0845	0846	0847
35	0848	0849	0850	0851	0852	0853	0854	0855	0856	0857	0858	0859	0860	0861	0862	0863
36	0864	0865	0866	0867	0868	0869	0870	0871	0872	0873	0874	0875	0876	0877	0878	0879
37	0880	0881	0882	0883	0884	0885	0886	0887	0888	0889	0890	0891	0892	0893	0894	0895
38	0896	0897	0898	0899	0900	0901	0902	0903	0904	0905	0906	0907	0908	0909	0910	0911
39	0912	0913	0914	0915	0916	0917	0918	0919	0920	0921	0922	0923	0924	0925	0926	0927
3A	0928	0929	0930	0931	0932	0933	0934	0935	0936	0937	0938	0939	0940	0941	0942	0943
3B	0944	0945	0946	0947	0948	0949	0950	0951	0952	0953	0954	0955	0956	0957	0958	0959
3C	0960	0961	0962	0963	0964	0965	0966	0967	0968	0969	0970	0971	0972	0973	0974	0975
3D	0976	0977	0978	0979	0980	0981	0982	0983	0984	0985	0986	0987	0988	0989	0990	0991
3E	0992	0993	0994	0995	0996	0997	0998	0999	1000	1001	1002	1003	1004	1005	1006	1007
3F	1008	1009	1010	1011	1012	1013	1014	1015	1016	1017	1018	1019	1020	1021	1022	1023
40	1024	1025	1026	1027	1028	1029	1030	1031	1032	1033	1034	1035	1036	1037	1038	1039
41	1040	1041	1042	1043	1044	1045	1046	1047	1048	1049	1050	1051	1052	1053	1054	1055
42	1056	1057	1058	1059	1060	1061	1062	1063	1064	1065	1066	1067	1068	1069	1070	1071
43	1072	1073	1074	1075	1076	1077	1078	1079	1080	1081	1082	1083	1084	1085	1086	1087
44	1088	1089	1090	1091	1092	1093	1094	1095	1096	1097	1098	1099	1100	1101	1102	1103
45	1104	1105	1106	1107	1108	1109	1110	1111	1112	1113	1114	1115	1116	1117	1118	1119
46	1120	1121	1122	1123	1124	1125	1126	1127	1128	1129	1130	1131	1132	1133	1134	1135
47	1136	1137	1138	1139	1140	1141	1142	1143	1144	1145	1146	1147	1148	1149	1150	1151
48	1152	1153	1154	1155	1156	1157	1158	1159	1160	1161	1162	1163	1164	1165	1166	1167
49	1168	1169	1170	1171	1172	1173	1174	1175	1176	1177	1178	1179	1180	1181	1182	1183
4A	1184	1185	1186	1187	1188	1189	1190	1191	1192	1193	1194	1195	1196	1197	1198	1199
4B	1200	1201	1202	1203	1204	1205	1206	1207	1208	1209	1210	1211	1212	1213	1214	1215
4C	1216	1217	1218	1219	1220	1221	1222	1223	1224	1225	1226	1227	1228	1229	1230	1231
4D	1232	1233	1234	1235	1236	1237	1238	1239	1240	1241	1242	1243	1244	1245	1246	1247
4E	1248	1249	1250	1251	1252	1253	1254	1255	1256	1257	1258	1259	1260	1261	1262	1263
4F	1264	1265	1266	1267	1268	1269	1270	1271	1272	1273	1274	1275	1276	1277	1278	1279
50	1280	1281	1282	1283	1284	1285	1286	1287	1288	1289	1290	1291	1292	1293	1294	1295
51	1296	1297	1298	1299	1300	1301	1302	1303	1304	1305	1306	1307	1308	1309	1310	1311
52	1312	1313	1314	1315	1316	1317	1318	1319	1320	1321	1322	1323	1324	1325	1326	1327
53	1328	1329	1330	1331	1332	1333	1334	1335	1336	1337	1338	1339	1340	1341	1342	1343
54	1344	1345	1346	1347	1348	1349	1350	1351	1352	1353	1354	1355	1356	1357	1358	1359
55	1360	1361	1362	1363	1364	1365	1366	1367	1368	1369	1370	1371	1372	1373	1374	1375
56	1376	1377	1378	1379	1380	1381	1382	1383	1384	1385	1386	1387	1388	1389	1390	1391
57	1392	1393	1394	1395	1396	1397	1398	1399	1400	1401	1402	1403	1404	1405	1406	1407
58	1408	1409	1410	1411	1412	1413	1414	1415	1416	1417	1418	1419	1420	1421	1422	1423
59	1424	1425	1426	1427	1428	1429	1430	1431	1432	1433	1434	1435	1436	1437	1438	1439
5A	1440	1441	1442	1443	1444	1445	1446	1447	1448	1449	1450	1451	1452	1453	1454	1455
5B	1456	1457	1458	1459	1460	1461	1462	1463	1464	1465	1466	1467	1468	1469	1470	1471
5C	1472	1473	1474	1475	1476	1477	1478	1479	1480	1481	1482	1483	1484	1485	1486	1487
5D	1488	1489	1490	1491	1492	1493	1494	1495	1496	1497	1498	1499	1500	1501	1502	1503
5E	1504	1505	1506	1507	1508	1509	1510	1511	1512	1513	1514	1515	1516	1517	1518	1519
5F	1520	1521	1522	1523	1524	1525	1526	1527	1528	1529	1530	1531	1532	1533	1534	1535

Table H-2. Hexadecimal-Decimal Conversion Table (*continued*)

	0	1	2	3	4	5	6	7	8	9	A	B	C	D	E	F
60	1536	1537	1538	1539	1540	1541	1542	1543	1544	1545	1546	1547	1548	1549	1550	1551
61	1552	1553	1554	1555	1556	1557	1558	1559	1560	1561	1562	1563	1564	1565	1566	1567
62	1568	1569	1570	1571	1572	1573	1574	1575	1576	1577	1578	1579	1580	1581	1582	1583
63	1584	1585	1586	1587	1588	1589	1590	1591	1592	1593	1594	1595	1596	1597	1598	1599
64	1600	1601	1602	1603	1604	1605	1606	1607	1608	1609	1610	1611	1612	1613	1614	1615
65	1616	1617	1618	1619	1620	1621	1622	1623	1624	1625	1626	1627	1628	1629	1630	1631
66	1632	1633	1634	1635	1636	1637	1638	1639	1640	1641	1642	1643	1644	1645	1646	1647
67	1648	1649	1650	1651	1652	1653	1654	1655	1656	1657	1658	1659	1660	1661	1562	1663
68	1664	1665	1666	1667	1668	1669	1670	1671	1672	1673	1674	1675	1676	1677	1678	1679
69	1680	1681	1682	1683	1684	1685	1686	1687	1688	1689	1690	1691	1692	1693	1694	1695
6A	1696	1697	1698	1699	1700	1701	1702	1703	1704	1705	1706	1707	1708	1709	1710	1711
6B	1712	1713	1714	1715	1716	1717	1718	1719	1720	1721	1722	1723	1724	1725	1726	1727
6C	1728	1729	1730	1731	1732	1733	1734	1735	1736	1737	1738	1739	1740	1741	1742	1743
6D	1744	1745	1746	1747	1748	1749	1750	1751	1752	1753	1754	1755	1756	1757	1758	1759
6E	1760	1761	1762	1763	1764	1765	1766	1767	1768	1769	1770	1771	1772	1773	1774	1775
6F	1776	1777	1778	1779	1780	1781	1782	1783	1784	1785	1786	1787	1788	1789	1790	1791
70	1792	1793	1794	1795	1796	1797	1798	1799	1800	1801	1802	1803	1804	1805	1806	1807
71	1808	1809	1810	1811	1812	1813	1814	1815	1816	1817	1818	1819	1820	1821	1822	1823
72	1824	1825	1826	1827	1828	1829	1830	1831	1832	1833	1834	1835	1836	1837	1838	1839
73	1840	1841	1842	1843	1844	1845	1846	1847	1848	1849	1850	1851	1852	1853	1854	1855
74	1856	1857	1858	1859	1860	1861	1862	1863	1864	1865	1866	1867	1868	1869	1870	1871
75	1872	1873	1874	1875	1876	1877	1878	1879	1880	1881	1882	1883	1884	1885	1886	1887
76	1888	1889	1890	1891	1892	1893	1894	1895	1896	1897	1898	1899	1900	1901	1902	1903
77	1904	1905	1906	1907	1908	1909	1910	1911	1912	1913	1914	1915	1916	1917	1918	1919
78	1920	1921	1922	1923	1924	1925	1926	1927	1928	1929	1930	1931	1932	1933	1934	1935
79	1936	1937	1938	1939	1940	1941	1942	1943	1944	1945	1946	1947	1948	1949	1950	1951
7A	1952	1953	1954	1955	1956	1957	1958	1959	1960	1961	1962	1963	1964	1965	1966	1967
7B	1968	1969	1970	1971	1972	1973	1974	1975	1976	1977	1978	1979	1980	1981	1982	1983
7C	1984	1985	1986	1987	1988	1989	1990	1991	1992	1993	1994	1995	1996	1997	1998	1999
7D	2000	2001	2002	2003	2004	2005	2006	2007	2008	2009	2010	2011	2012	2013	2014	2015
7E	2016	2017	2018	2019	2020	2021	2022	2023	2024	2025	2026	2027	2028	2029	2030	2031
7F	2032	2033	2034	2035	2036	2037	2038	2039	2040	2041	2042	2043	2044	2045	2046	2047
80	2048	2049	2050	2051	2052	2053	2054	2055	2056	2057	2058	2059	2060	2061	2062	2063
81	2064	2065	2066	2067	2068	2069	2070	2071	2072	2073	2074	2075	2076	2077	2078	2079
82	2080	2081	2082	2083	2084	2085	2086	2087	2088	2089	2090	2091	2092	2093	2094	2095
83	2096	2097	2098	2099	2100	2101	2102	2103	2104	2105	2106	2107	2108	2109	2110	2111
84	2112	2113	2114	2115	2116	2117	2118	2119	2120	2121	2122	2123	2124	2125	2126	2127
85	2128	2129	2130	2131	2132	2133	2134	2135	2136	2137	2138	2139	2140	2141	2142	2143
86	2144	2145	2146	2147	2148	2149	2150	2151	2152	2153	2154	2155	2156	2157	2158	2159
87	2160	2161	2162	2163	2164	2165	2166	2167	2168	2169	2170	2171	2172	2173	2174	2175
88	2176	2177	2178	2179	2180	2181	2182	2183	2184	2185	2186	2187	2188	2189	2190	2191
89	2192	2193	2194	2195	2196	2197	2198	2199	2200	2201	2202	2203	2204	2205	2206	2207
8A	2208	2209	2210	2211	2212	2213	2214	2215	2216	2217	2218	2219	2220	2221	2222	2223
8B	2224	2225	2226	2227	2228	2229	2230	2231	2232	2233	2234	2235	2236	2237	2238	2239
8C	2240	2241	2242	2243	2244	2245	2246	2247	2248	2249	2250	2251	2252	2253	2254	2255
8D	2256	2257	2258	2259	2260	2261	2262	2263	2264	2265	2266	2267	2268	2269	2270	2271
8E	2272	2273	2274	2275	2276	2277	2278	2279	2280	2281	2282	2283	2284	2285	2286	2287
8F	2288	2289	2290	2291	2292	2293	2294	2295	2296	2297	2298	2299	2300	2301	2302	2303

Table H-2. Hexadecimal-Decimal Conversion Table (*continued*)

	0	1	2	3	4	5	6	7	8	9	A	B	C	D	E	F
90	2304	2305	2306	2307	2308	2309	2310	2311	2312	2313	2314	2315	2316	2317	2318	2319
91	2320	2321	2322	2323	2324	2325	2326	2327	2328	2329	2330	2331	2332	2333	2334	2335
92	2336	2337	2338	2339	2340	2341	2342	2343	2344	2345	2346	2347	2348	2349	2350	2351
93	2352	2353	2354	2355	2356	2357	2358	2359	2360	2361	2362	2363	2364	2365	2366	2367
94	2368	2369	2370	2371	2372	2373	2374	2375	2376	2377	2378	2379	2380	2381	2382	2383
95	2384	2385	2386	2387	2388	2389	2390	2391	2392	2393	2394	2395	2396	2397	2398	2399
96	2400	2401	2402	2403	2404	2405	2406	2407	2408	2409	2410	2411	2412	2413	2414	2415
97	2416	2417	2418	2419	2420	2421	2422	2423	2424	2425	2426	2427	2428	2429	2430	2431
98	2432	2433	2434	2435	2436	2437	2438	2439	2440	2441	2442	2443	2444	2445	2446	2447
99	2448	2449	2450	2451	2452	2453	2454	2455	2456	2457	2458	2459	2460	2461	2462	2463
9A	2464	2465	2466	2467	2468	2469	2470	2471	2472	2473	2474	2475	2476	2477	2478	2479
9B	2480	2481	2482	2483	2484	2485	2486	2487	2488	2489	2490	2491	2492	2493	2494	2495
9C	2496	2497	2498	2499	2500	2501	2502	2503	2504	2505	2506	2507	2508	2509	2510	2511
9D	2512	2513	2514	2515	2516	2517	2518	2519	2520	2521	2522	2523	2524	2525	2526	2527
9E	2528	2529	2530	2531	2532	2533	2534	2535	2536	2537	2538	2539	2540	2541	2542	2543
9F	2544	2545	2546	2547	2548	2549	2550	2551	2552	2553	2554	2555	2556	2557	2558	2559
A0	2560	2561	2562	2563	2564	2565	2566	2567	2568	2569	2570	2571	2572	2573	2574	2575
A1	2576	2577	2578	2579	2580	2581	2582	2583	2584	2585	2586	2587	2588	2589	2590	2591
A2	2592	2593	2594	2595	2596	2597	2598	2599	2600	2601	2602	2603	2604	2605	2606	2607
A3	2608	2609	2610	2611	2612	2613	2614	2615	2616	2617	2618	2619	2620	2621	2622	2623
A4	2624	2625	2626	2627	2628	2629	2630	2631	2632	2633	2634	2635	2636	2637	2638	2639
A5	2640	2641	2642	2643	2644	2645	2646	2647	2648	2649	2650	2651	2652	2653	2654	2655
A6	2656	2657	2658	2659	2660	2661	2662	2663	2664	2665	2666	2667	2668	2669	2670	2671
A7	2672	2673	2674	2675	2676	2677	2678	2679	2680	2681	2682	2683	2684	2685	2686	2687
A8	2688	2689	2690	2691	2692	2693	2694	2695	2696	2697	2698	2699	2700	2701	2702	2703
A9	2704	2705	2706	2707	2708	2709	2710	2711	2712	2713	2714	2715	2716	2717	2718	2719
AA	2720	2721	2722	2723	2724	2725	2726	2727	2728	2729	2730	2731	2732	2733	2734	2735
AB	2736	2737	2738	2739	2740	2741	2742	2743	2744	2745	2746	2747	2748	2749	2750	2751
AC	2752	2753	2754	2755	2756	2757	2758	2759	2760	2761	2762	2763	2764	2765	2766	2767
AD	2768	2769	2770	2771	2772	2773	2774	2775	2776	2777	2778	2779	2780	2781	2782	2783
AE	2784	2785	2786	2787	2788	2789	2790	2791	2792	2793	2794	2795	2796	2797	2798	2799
AF	2800	2801	2802	2803	2804	2805	2806	2807	2808	2809	2810	2811	2812	2813	2814	2815
B0	2816	2817	2818	2819	2820	2821	2822	2823	2824	2825	2826	2827	2828	2829	2830	2831
B1	2832	2833	2834	2835	2836	2837	2838	2839	2840	2841	2842	2843	2844	2845	2846	2847
B2	2848	2849	2850	2851	2852	2853	2854	2855	2856	2857	2858	2859	2860	2861	2862	2863
B3	2864	2865	2866	2867	2868	2869	2870	2871	2872	2873	2874	2875	2876	2877	2878	2879
B4	2880	2881	2882	2883	2884	2885	2886	2887	2888	2889	2890	2891	2892	2893	2894	2895
B5	2896	2897	2898	2899	2900	2901	2902	2903	2904	2905	2906	2907	2908	2909	2910	2911
B6	2912	2913	2914	2915	2916	2917	2918	2919	2920	2921	2922	2923	2924	2925	2926	2927
B7	2928	2929	2930	2931	2932	2933	2934	2935	2936	2937	2938	2939	2940	2941	2942	2943
B8	2944	2945	2946	2947	2948	2949	2950	2951	2952	2953	2954	2955	2956	2957	2958	2959
B9	2960	2961	2962	2963	2964	2965	2966	2967	2968	2969	2970	2971	2972	2973	2974	2975
BA	2976	2977	2978	2979	2980	2981	2982	2983	2984	2985	2986	2987	2988	2989	2990	2991
BB	2992	2993	2994	2995	2996	2997	2998	2999	3000	3001	3002	3003	3004	3005	3006	3007
BC	3008	3009	3010	3011	3012	3013	3014	3015	3016	3017	3018	3019	3020	3021	3022	3023
BD	3024	3025	3026	3027	3028	3029	3030	3031	3032	3033	3034	3035	3036	3037	3038	3039
BE	3040	3041	3042	3043	3044	3045	3046	3047	3048	3049	3050	3051	3052	3053	3054	3055
BF	3056	3057	3058	3059	3060	3061	3062	3063	3064	3065	3066	3067	3068	3069	3070	3071

Table H-2. Hexadecimal-Decimal Conversion Table (*continued*)

	0	1	2	3	4	5	6	7	8	9	A	B	C	D	E	F
C0	3072	3073	3074	3075	3076	3077	3078	3079	3080	3081	3082	3083	3084	3085	3086	3087
C1	3088	3089	3090	3091	3092	3093	3094	3095	3096	3097	3098	3099	3100	3101	3102	3103
C2	3104	3105	3106	3107	3108	3109	3110	3111	3112	3113	3114	3115	3116	3117	3118	3119
C3	3120	3121	3122	3123	3124	3125	3126	3127	3128	3129	3130	3131	3132	3133	3134	3135
C4	3136	3137	3138	3139	3140	3141	3142	3143	3144	3145	3146	3147	3148	3149	3150	3151
C5	3152	3153	3154	3155	3156	3157	3158	3159	3160	3161	3162	3163	3164	3165	3166	3167
C6	3168	3169	3170	3171	3172	3173	3174	3175	3176	3177	3178	3179	3180	3181	3182	3183
C7	3184	3185	3186	3187	3188	3189	3190	3191	3192	3193	3194	3195	3196	3197	3198	3199
C8	3200	3201	3202	3203	3204	3205	3206	3207	3208	3209	3210	3211	3212	3213	3214	3215
C9	3216	3217	3218	3219	3220	3221	3222	3223	3224	3225	3226	3227	3228	3229	3230	3231
CA	3232	3233	3234	3235	3236	3237	3238	3239	3240	3241	3242	3243	3244	3245	3246	3247
CB	3248	3249	3250	3251	3252	3253	3254	3255	3256	3257	3258	3259	3260	3261	3262	3263
CC	3264	3265	3266	3267	3268	3269	3270	3271	3272	3273	3274	3275	3276	3277	3278	3279
CD	3280	3281	3282	3283	3284	3285	3286	3287	3288	3289	3290	3291	3292	3293	3294	3295
CE	3296	3297	3298	3299	3300	3301	3302	3303	3304	3305	3306	3307	3308	3309	3310	3311
CF	3312	3313	3314	3315	3316	3317	3318	3319	3320	3321	3322	3323	3324	3325	3326	3327
D0	3328	3329	3330	3331	3332	3333	3334	3335	3336	3337	3338	3339	3340	3341	3342	3343
D1	3344	3345	3346	3347	3348	3349	3350	3351	3352	3353	3354	3355	3356	3357	3358	3359
D2	3360	3361	3362	3363	3364	3365	3366	3367	3368	3369	3370	3371	3372	3373	3374	3375
D3	3376	3377	3378	3379	3380	3381	3382	3383	3384	3385	3386	3387	3388	3389	3390	3391
D4	3392	3393	3394	3395	3396	3397	3398	3399	3400	3401	3402	3403	3404	3405	3406	3407
D5	3408	3409	3410	3411	3412	3413	3414	3415	3416	3417	3418	3419	3420	3421	3422	3423
D6	3424	3425	3426	3427	3428	3429	3430	3431	3432	3433	3434	3435	3436	3437	3438	3439
D7	3440	3441	3442	3443	3444	3445	3446	3447	3448	3449	3450	3451	3452	3453	3454	3455
D8	3456	3457	3458	3459	3460	3461	3462	3463	3464	3465	3466	3467	3468	3469	3470	3471
D9	3472	3473	3474	3475	3476	3477	3478	3479	3480	3481	3482	3483	3484	3485	3486	3487
DA	3488	3489	3490	3491	3492	3493	3494	3495	3496	3497	3498	3499	3500	3501	3502	3503
DB	3504	3505	3506	3507	3508	3509	3510	3511	3512	3513	3514	3515	3516	3517	3518	3519
DC	3520	3521	3522	3523	3524	3525	3526	3527	3528	3529	3530	3531	3532	3533	3534	3535
DD	3536	3537	3538	3539	3540	3541	3542	3543	3544	3545	3546	3547	3548	3549	3550	3551
DE	3552	3553	3554	3555	3556	3557	3558	3559	3560	3561	3562	3563	3564	3565	3566	3567
DF	3568	3569	3570	3571	3572	3573	3574	3575	3576	3577	3578	3579	3580	3581	3582	3583
E0	3584	3585	3586	3587	3588	3589	3590	3591	3592	3593	3594	3595	3596	3597	3598	3599
E1	3600	3601	3602	3603	3604	3605	3606	3607	3608	3609	3610	3611	3612	3613	3614	3615
E2	3616	3617	3618	3619	3620	3621	3622	3623	3624	3625	3626	3627	3628	3629	3630	3631
E3	3632	3633	3634	3635	3636	3637	3638	3639	3640	3641	3642	3643	3644	3645	3646	3647
E4	3648	3649	3650	3651	3652	3653	3654	3655	3656	3657	3658	3659	3660	3661	3662	3663
E5	3664	3665	3666	3667	3668	3669	3670	3671	3672	3673	3674	3675	3676	3677	3678	3679
E6	3680	3681	3682	3683	3684	3685	3686	3687	3688	3689	3690	3691	3692	3693	3694	3695
E7	3696	3697	3698	3699	3700	3701	3702	3703	3704	3705	3706	3707	3708	3709	3710	3711
E8	3712	3713	3714	3715	3716	3717	3718	3719	3720	3721	3722	3723	3724	3725	3726	3727
E9	3728	3729	3730	3731	3732	3733	3734	3735	3736	3737	3738	3739	3740	3741	3742	3743
EA	3744	3745	3746	3747	3748	3749	3750	3751	3752	3753	3754	3755	3756	3757	3758	3759
EB	3760	3761	3762	3763	3764	3765	3766	3767	3768	3769	3770	3771	3772	3773	3774	3775
EC	3776	3777	3778	3779	3780	3781	3782	3783	3784	3785	3786	3787	3788	3789	3790	3791
ED	3792	3793	3794	3795	3796	3797	3798	3799	3800	3801	3802	3803	3804	3805	3806	3807
EE	3808	3809	3810	3811	3812	3813	3814	3815	3816	3817	3818	3819	3820	3821	3822	3823
EF	3824	3825	3826	3827	3828	3829	3830	3831	3832	3833	3834	3835	3836	3837	3838	3839

Table H-2. Hexadecimal-Decimal Conversion Table (*continued*)

	0	1	2	3	4	5	6	7	8	9	A	B	C	D	E	F
F0	3840	3841	3842	3843	3844	3845	3846	3847	3848	3849	3850	3851	3852	3853	3854	3855
F1	3856	3857	3858	3859	3860	3861	3862	3863	3864	3865	3866	3867	3868	3869	3870	3871
F2	3872	3873	3874	3875	3876	3877	3878	3879	3880	3881	3882	3883	3884	3885	3886	3887
F3	3888	3889	3890	3891	3892	3893	3894	3895	3896	3897	3898	3899	3900	3901	3902	3903
F4	3904	3905	3906	3907	3908	3909	3910	3911	3912	3913	3914	3915	3916	3917	3918	3919
F5	3920	3921	3922	3923	3924	3925	3926	3927	3928	3929	3930	3931	3932	3933	3934	3935
F6	3936	3937	3938	3939	3940	3941	3942	3943	3944	3945	3946	3947	3948	3949	3950	3951
F7	3952	3953	3954	3955	3956	3957	3958	3959	3960	3961	3962	3963	3964	3965	3966	3967
F8	3968	3969	3970	3971	3972	3973	3974	3975	3976	3977	3978	3979	3980	3981	3982	3983
F9	3984	3985	3986	3987	3988	3989	3990	3991	3992	3993	3994	3995	3996	3997	3998	3999
FA	4000	4001	4002	4003	4004	4005	4006	4007	4008	4009	4010	4011	4012	4013	4014	4015
FB	4016	4017	4018	4019	4020	4021	4022	4023	4024	4025	4026	4027	4028	4029	4030	4031
FC	4032	4033	4034	4035	4036	4037	4038	4039	4040	4041	4042	4043	4044	4045	4046	4047
FD	4048	4049	4050	4051	4052	4053	4054	4055	4056	4057	4058	4059	4060	4061	4062	4063
FE	4064	4065	4066	4067	4068	4069	4070	4071	4072	4073	4074	4075	4076	4077	4078	4079
FF	4080	4081	4082	4083	4084	4085	4086	4087	4088	4089	4090	4091	4092	4093	4094	4095

Screen Display Forms I

Use photocopies of the forms in this appendix to plan the appearance of the display screen. On the text screen form (Figure I-1), row and column numbers start with 1, which is appropriate for text work. On the low-resolution graphics screen form (Figure I-2), row and column numbers start with 0, as do low-resolution graphics commands. For 80-column text screen planning, use graph paper with eight squares to the inch. For high-resolution graphics design, use graph paper with 20 squares to the inch.

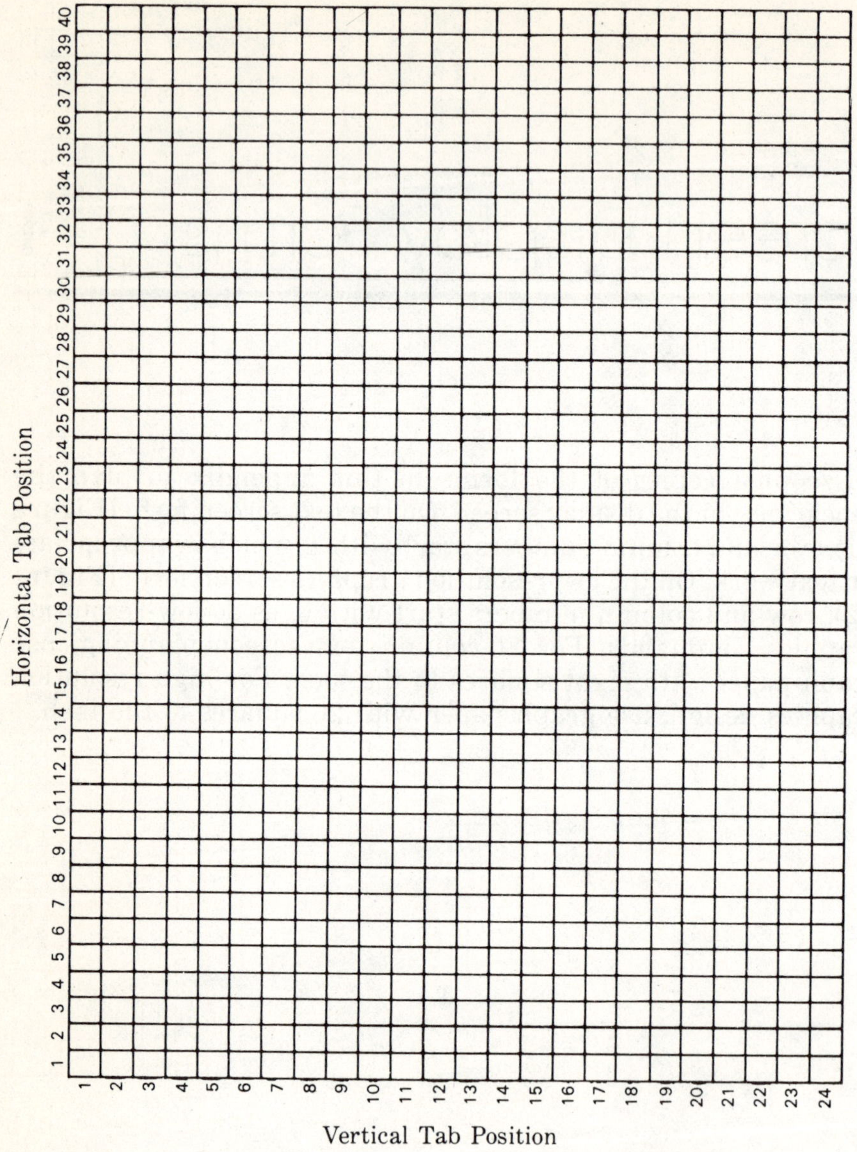

Figure I-1. Text Screen

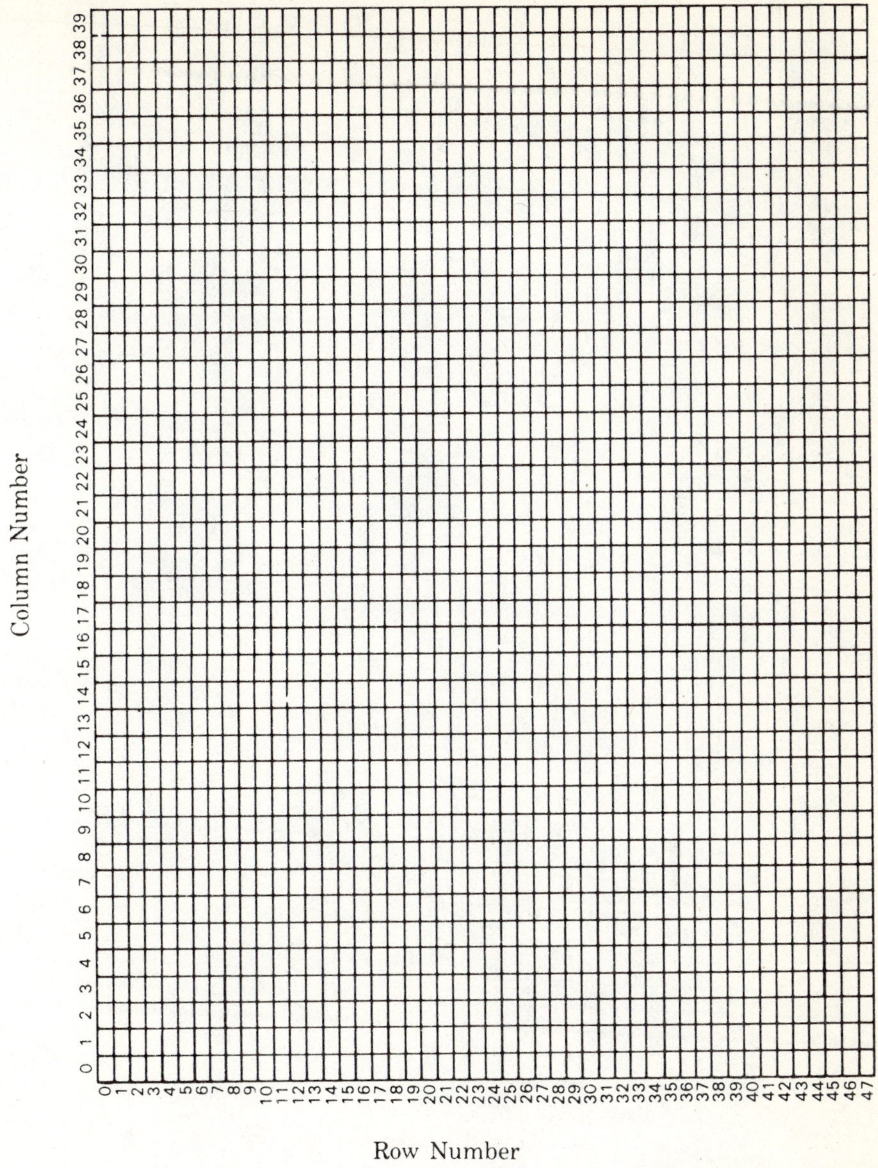

Figure I-2. Low-resolution graphics screen

Index